THE SPORTSMAN'S ANTHOLOGY

The Sportsman's Anthology

EDITED BY

ROBERT F. KELLEY

New York

HOWELL, SOSKIN, PUBLISHERS

THE CONTENTS

THE SPORTSMAN'S ANTHOLOGY

Foreword

This book encompasses the writing in the field of sports which has interested and amused the editor and most of his friends who have spent a good part of their lives with sports. The collection does not pretend to be based on any standard of immortality; the selections have been made because the material has provided enjoyment for people who know the particular sport it covers; know that sport from the standpoint of participant and devotee. Some of the authors are known to most of those who read books of any kind; some are known only to those who happen to care for the particular sport concerned; some few are not known to either of these groups, but they know their material and they have an intelligent affection for their sport.

In so far as possible, the effort has been made to steer clear of the obvious and the purely sentimental. The selections include fiction and articles, not at all confined to the United States. The articles move all the way from Surtees and Frank Forester, perhaps the greatest of American sports writers.

The editor has spent some twenty years in sports, as a newspaperman and an official. He hopes to stay with sports to the end of his thinning allotment of days. This book, then, represents his effort to bring together things which have given pleasure. If they afford entertainment and interest to some who may have missed them, the purpose of the publication will have been served.

Tale of the Gypsy Horse

By DONN BYRNE

I THOUGHT first of the old lady's face, in the candlelight of the dinner table at Destiny Bay, as some fine precious coin, a spade guinea perhaps, well and truly minted. How old she was I could not venture to guess, but I knew well that when she was young men's heads must have turned as she passed. Age had boldened the features much, the proud nose and definite chin. Her hair was grey, like a grey wave curling in to crash on the sands of Destiny. And I knew that in another woman that hair would be white as scutched flax. When she spoke, the thought of the spade guinea came to me again, so rich and golden was her voice.

"Lady Clontarf," said my uncle Valentine, "this is Kerry, Hector's boy."

"May I call you Kerry? I am so old a woman and you are so much a boy. Also I knew your father. He was of that great line of soldiers who read their Bibles in their tents, and go into battle with a prayer in their hearts. I always seem to have known," she said, "that he would fondle no grey beard."

"Madame," I said, "what should I be but Kerry to my father's friends!"

It seemed to me that I must know her because of her proud high face, and her eyes of a great lady, but the title of Clontarf made little impress on my brain. Our Irish titles have become so hawked and shopworn that the most hallowed names in Ireland may be borne by a porter brewer or former soap boiler. O'Conor Don and MacCarthy More mean so much more to us than the Duke of This or the Marquis of There, now the politics have so muddled chivalry. We may resent the presentation of this title or that to a foreigner, but what can you do? The loyalty of the

---

From "Destiny Bay," Little, Brown and Company.

Northern Irishman to the Crown is a loyalty of head and not of heart. Out of our Northern country came the United Men, if you remember. But for whom should our hearts beat faster? The Stuarts were never fond of us, and the Prince of Orange came over to us, talked a deal about liberty, was with us at a few battles, and went off to grow asparagus in England. It is so long since O'Neill and O'Donnell sailed for Spain!

Who Lady Clontarf was I did not know. My uncle Valentine is so offhand in his presentations. Were you to come on him closeted with a heavenly visitant he would just say: "Kerry, the Angel Gabriel." Though as to what his Angelicness was doing with my uncle Valentine, you would be left to surmise. My uncle Valentine will tell you just as much as he feels you ought to know and no more—a quality that stood my uncle in good stead in the days when he raced and bred horses for racing. I did know one thing: Lady Clontarf was not Irish. There is a feeling of kindness between all us Irish that we recognise without speaking. One felt courtesy, gravity, dignity in her, but not that quality that makes your troubles another Irish person's troubles, if only for the instant. Nor was she English. One felt her spiritual roots went too deep for that. Nor had she that brilliant armour of the Latin. Her speech was the ordinary speech of a gentlewoman, unaccented. Yet that remark about knowing my father would never fondle a grey beard!

Who she was and all about her I knew I would find out later from my dear aunt Jenepher. But about the old drawing-room of Destiny there was a strange air of formality. My uncle Valentine is most courteous, but to-night he was courtly. He was like some Hungarian or Russian noble welcoming an empress. There was an air of deference about my dear aunt Jenepher that informed me that Lady Clontarf was very great indeed. Whom my aunt Jenepher likes is lovable, and whom she respects is clean and great. But the most extraordinary part of the setting was our butler James Carabine. He looked as if royalty were present, and I began to say to myself: "By damn, but royalty is! Lady Clontarf is only a racing name. I know that there's a queen or princess in Germany who's held by the Jacobites to be Queen of England. Can it be herself that's in it? It sounds impossible, but sure there's nothing impossible where my uncle Valentine's concerned."

At dinner the talk turned on racing, and my uncle Valentine inveighed bitterly against the new innovations on the track; the starting gate, and the new seat introduced by certain American jockeys, the crouch now recognised as orthodox in flat-racing. As to the value of the starting gate my uncle was open to conviction. He recognised how unfairly the apprentice was treated by the crack jockey with the old method of the flag, but he dilated on his favourite theme: that machinery was the curse of man. All these innovations—

"But it isn't an innovation, sir. The Romans used it."

"You're a liar!" said my uncle Valentine.

My uncle Valentine, or any other Irishman for the matter of that, only means that he doesn't believe you. There is a wide difference.

"I think I'm right, sir. The Romans used it for their chariot races. They dropped the barrier instead of raising it." A tag of my classics came back to me, as tags will. "Repagula submittuntur, Pausanias writes."

"Pausanias, begob!" My uncle was visibly impressed.

But as to the new seat he was adamant. I told him competent judges had placed it about seven pounds' advantage to the horse.

"There is only one place on a horse's back for a saddle," said my uncle Valentine. "The shorter your leathers, Kerry, the less you know about your mount. You are only aware whether or not he is winning. With the ordinary seat, you know whether he is lazy, and can make proper use of your spur. You can stick to his head and help him."

"Races are won with that seat, sir."

"Be damned to that!" said my uncle Valentine. "If the horse is good enough, he'll win with the rider facing his tail."

"But we are boring you, Madame," I said, "with our country talk of horses."

"There are three things that are never boring to see: a swift swimmer swimming, a young girl dancing, and a young horse running. And three things that are never tiring to speak of: God, and love, and the racing of horses."

"Akushto jukel is also rinkeno, mi pen," suddenly spoke our butler, James Carabine.

"Dabla, James Carabine, you roker like a didakai. A jukel to catch kanangre!" And Lady Clontarf laughed. "What in all the tem is as dinkeno as a kushti-dikin grai?"

"A tatsheno jukel, mi pen, like Rory Bosville's," James Carabine evidently stood his ground, "that noshered the Waterloo Cup through wafro bok!"

"Avali! You are right, James Carabine." And then she must have seen my astonished face, for she laughed, that small golden laughter that was like the ringing of an acolyte's bell. "Are you surprised to hear me speak the tawlo tshib, the black language, Kerry? I am a gypsy woman."

"Lady Clontarf, Mister Kerry," said James Carabine, "is saying there is nothing in the world like a fine horse. I told her a fine greyhound is a good thing too. Like Rory Bosville's, that should have won the Waterloo Cup in Princess Dagmar's year."

"Lady Clontarf wants to talk to you about a horse, Kerry," said my uncle Valentine. "So if you would like to go into the gunroom, Jenepher, instead of the withdrawing room while you play—"

"May I not hear about the horse too?" asked my aunt Jenepher.

"My very, very dear," said the gypsy lady to my blind aunt Jenepher, "I would wish you to, for where you are sitting, there a blessing will be."

My uncle Valentine had given up race horses for as long as I can remember. Except with Limerick Pride, he had never had any luck, and so he had quitted racing as an owner, and gone in for harness ponies, of which, it is admitted, he bred and showed the finest of their class. My own two chasers, while winning many good Irish races, were not quite up to Aintree form, but in the last year I happened to buy, for a couple of hundred guineas, a handicap horse that had failed signally as a three-year-old in classic races, and of which a fashionable stable wanted to get rid. It was Ducks and Drakes, by Drake's Drum out of Little Duck, a beautifully shaped, dark grey horse, rather short in the neck, but the English stable was convinced he was a hack. However, as often happens, with a change of trainers and jockeys, Ducks and Drakes became a different horse and won five good races, giving me so much in hand that I was able to purchase for a matter of nine hundred guineas a colt I was optimistic about, a son of Saint Simon's. Both horses were in training with Robinson at the

Curragh. And now it occurred to me that the gypsy lady wanted to buy one or the other of them. I decided beforehand that it would be across my dead body.

"Would you be surprised," asked my uncle Valentine, "to hear that Lady Clontarf has a horse she expects to win the Derby with?"

"I should be delighted, sir, if she did," I answered warily. There were a hundred people who had hopes of their nominations in the greatest of races.

"Kerry," the gypsy lady said quietly, "I think I will win." She had a way of clearing the air with her voice, with her eyes. What was a vague hope now became an issue.

"What is the horse, Madame?"

"It is as yet unnamed, and has never run as a two-year-old. It is a son of Irlandais, who has sired many winners on the Continent, and who broke down sixteen years ago in preparation for the Derby and was sold to one of the Festetics. Its dam is Iseult III, who won the Prix de Diane four years ago."

"I know so little about Continental horses," I explained.

"The strain is great-hearted, and with the dam, strong as an oak tree. I am a gypsy woman, and I know a horse, and I am an old, studious woman," she said, and she looked at her beautiful, unringed golden hands, as if she were embarrassed, speaking of something we, not Romanies, could hardly understand, "and I think I know propitious hours and days."

"Where is he now, Madame?"

"He is at Dax, in the Basse-Pyrenees, with Romany folk."

"Here's the whole thing in a nutshell, Kerry: Lady Clontarf wants her colt trained in Ireland. Do you think the old stables of your grandfather are still good?"

"The best in Ireland, sir, but sure there't no horse been trained there for forty years, barring jumpers."

"Are the gallops good?"

"Sure, you know yourself, sir, how good they are. But you couldn't train without a trainer, and stable boys—"

"We'll come to that," said my uncle Valentine. "Tell me, what odds will you get against an unknown, untried horse in the winter books?"

I thought for an instant. It had been an exceptionally good year for two-year-olds, the big English breeders' stakes having been bitterly contested. Lord Shire had a good horse; Mr. Paris a dangerous colt. I should say there were fifteen good colts, if they wintered well, two with outstanding chances.

"I should say you could really write your own ticket. The ring will be only too glad to get money. There's so much up on Sir James and Toison d'Or."

"To win a quarter-million pounds?" asked my uncle Valentine.

"It would have to be done very carefully, sir, here and there, in ponies and fifties and hundreds, but I think between four and five thousand pounds would do it."

"Now if this horse of Lady Clontarf's wins the Two Thousand and the Derby, and the Saint Leger—"

Something in my face must have shown a lively distaste for the company of lunatics, for James Carabine spoke quietly from the door by which he was standing.

"Will your young Honour be easy, and listen to your uncle and my lady."

My uncle Valentine is most grandiose, and though he has lived in epic times, a giant among giants, his schemes are too big for practical business days. And I was beginning to think that the gypsy lady, for all her beauty and dignity, was but an old woman crazed by gambling and tarot cards, but James Carabine is so wise, so beautifully sane, facing all events, spiritual and material, foursquare to the wind.

"—what would he command in stud fees?" continued quietly my uncle Valentine. "I merely wish to know if the ordinary brain arrives at these conclusions of mine; if they are, to use a word of Mr. Thackeray's, apparent."

"I quite understand, sir," I said politely.

"And now," said my uncle Valentine, "whom would you suggest to come to Destiny Bay as trainer?"

"None of the big trainers will leave their stables to come here, sir. And the small ones I don't know sufficiently. If Sir Arthur Pollexfen were still training, and not so old—"

"Sir Arthur Pollexfen is not old," said my uncle Valentine. "He cannot be more than seventy-two or seventy-three."

"But at that age you cannot expect a man to turn out at five in the morning and oversee gallops."

"How little you know Mayo men," said my uncle Valentine. "And Sir Arthur with all his triumphs never won a Derby. He will come."

"Even at that, sir, how are you going to get a crack jockey? Most big owners have first or second call on them. And the great free lances, you cannot engage one of those and ensure secrecy."

"That," said my uncle Valentine, "is already arranged. Lady Clontarf has a Gitano, or Spanish gypsy in whom her confidence is boundless. And now," said my uncle Valentine, "we come to the really diplomatic part of the proceeding. Trial horses are needed, so that I am commissioned to approach you with delicacy and ask you if you will bring up your two excellent horses Ducks and Drakes and the Saint Simon colt and help train Lady Clontarf's horse. I don't see why you should object."

To bring up the two darlings of my heart, and put them under the care of a trainer who had won the Gold Cup at Ascot fifty years before, and hadn't run a horse for twelve years, and have them ridden by this Gitano or Spanish gypsy, as my uncle called him; to have them used as trial horses to this colt which might not be good enough for a starter's hack. Oh, no! Not damned likely. I hardened my heart against the pleading gaze of James Carabine.

"Will you or won't you?" roared my uncle diplomatically.

My aunt Jenepher laid down the lace she was making, and reaching across, her fingers caught my sleeve and ran down to my hand, and her hand caught mine.

"Kerry will," she said.

So that was decided.

"Kerry," said my uncle Valentine, "will you see Lady Clontarf home?"

I was rather surprised. I had thought she was staying with us. And I was a bit bothered, for it is not hospitality to allow the visitor to Destiny to put up at the local pub. But James Carabine whispered: " 'Tis on the downs she's staying, Master Kerry, in her own great van with four horses." It was difficult to believe that the tall graceful lady in the golden and red Spanish shawl, with the quiet speech of our own people, was a roaming gypsy, with the whole world as her home.

"Good night, Jenepher. Good night, Valentine. Boshto dok, good luck, James Carabine!"

"Boshto dok, mi pen. Good luck, sister."

We went out into the October night of the full moon—the hunter's moon—and away from the great fire of turf and dogwood in our drawing-room the night was vital with an electric cold. One could sense the film of ice in the bogs, and the drumming of snipes' wings, disturbed by some roving dog, came to our ears. So bright was the moon that each whitewashed apple tree stood out clear in the orchard, and as we took the road toward Grey River, we could see a barkentine offshore, with sails of polished silver—some boat from Bilbao probably, making for the Clyde, in the daytime a scrubby ore carrier but to-night a ship out of some old sea story, as of Magellan, or our own Saint Brendan:

"Feach air muir lionadh gealach buidhe mar or," she quoted in Gaelic; "see on the filling sea the full moon yellow as gold. . . . It is full moon and full tide, Kerry; if you make a wish, it will come true."

"I wish you success in the Derby, Madame."

Ahead of us down the road moved a little group to the sound of fiddle and mouth organ. It was the Romany body-guard ready to protect their chieftainess on her way home.

"You mean that, I know, but you dislike the idea. Why?"

"Madame," I said, "if you can read my thoughts as easily as that, it's no more impertinent to speak than think. I have heard a lot about a great colt to-night, and of his chance for the greatest race in the world, and that warms my heart. But I have heard more about money, and that chills me."

"I am so old, Kerry, that the glory of winning the Derby means little to me. Do you know how old I am? I am six years short of an hundred old."

"Then the less—" I began, and stopped short, and could have chucked myself over the cliff for my unpardonable discourtesy.

"Then the less reason for my wanting money," the old lady said. "Is not that so?"

"Exactly, Madame."

"Kerry," she said, "does my name mean anything to you?"

"It has bothered me all evening. Lady Clontarf, I am so sorry my father's son should appear to you so rude and ignorant a lout."

"Mifanwy, Countess Clontarf and Kincora."

I gaped like an idiot. "The line of great Brian Boru. But I thought—"

"Did you really ever think of it, Kerry?"

"Not really, Madame," I said. "It's so long ago, so wonderful. It's like the old city they speak of in the country tales, under Ownaglass, the grey river, with its spires and great squares. It seems to me to have vanished like that, in rolling clouds of thunder."

"The last O'Neill has vanished, and the last Plantagenet. But great Brian's strain remains. When I married my lord," she said quietly, "it was in a troubled time. Our ears had not forgotten the musketry of Waterloo, and England was still shaken by fear of the Emperor, and poor Ireland was hurt and wounded. As you know, Kerry, no peer of the older faith sat in College Green. It is no new thing to ennoble, and steal an ancient name. Pitt and Napoleon passed their leisure hours at it. So that of O'Briens, Kerry, sirred and lorded, there are a score, but my lord was Earl of Clontarf and Kincora since before the English came.

"If my lord was one of the great blood of Kincora, myself was not lacking in blood. We Romanies are old, Kerry, so old that no man knows our beginning, but that we came from the uplands of India centuries before history. We are a strong, vital race, and we remain with our language, our own customs, our own laws until this day. And to certain families of us, the Romanies all over the world do reverence, as to our own, the old Lovells. There are three Lovells, Kerry, the dinelo or foolish Lovells, the gozvero or cunning Lovells, and the puro Lovells, the old Lovells. I am of the old Lovells. My father was the great Mairik Lovell. So you see I am of great stock too."

"Dear Madame, one has only to see you to know that."

"My lord had a small place left him near the Village of Swords, and it was near there I met him. He wished to buy a horse from my father Mairik, a stallion my father had brought all the way from the Nejd in Arabia. My lord could not buy that horse. But when I married my lord, it was part of my dowry, that and two handfuls of uncut Russian emeralds, and a chest of gold coins, Russian and Indian and Turkish coins, all gold. So I did not come empty-handed to my lord."

"Madame, do you wish to tell me this?"

"I wish to tell it to you, Kerry, because I want you for a friend to my little people, the sons of my son's son. You must know everything about friends to understand them.

"My lord was rich only in himself and in his ancestry. But with the great Arab stallion and the emeralds and the gold coins we were well. We did a foolish thing, Kerry; we went to London. My lord wished it, and his wishes were my wishes, although something told me we should not have gone. In London I made my lord sell the great Arab. He did not wish to, because it came with me, nor did I wish to, because my father had loved it, but I made him sell it. All the Selim horses of to-day are descended from him, Sheykh Selim.

"My lord loved horses, Kerry. He knew horses, but he had no luck. Newmarket Heath is a bad spot for those out of luck. And my lord grew worried. When one is worried, Kerry, the heart contracts a little—is it not so? Or don't you know yet? Also another thing bothered my lord. He was with English people, and English people have their codes and ordinances. They are good people, Kerry, very honest. They go to churches, and like sad songs, but whether they believe in God, or whether they have hearts or have no hearts, I do not know. Each thing they do by rote and custom, and they are curious in this: they will make excuses for a man who has done a great crime, but no excuses for a man who neglects a trivial thing. An eccentricity of dress is not forgiven. An eccentric is an outsider. So that English are not good for Irish folk.

"My own people," she said proudly, "are simple people, kindly and loyal as your family know. A marriage to them is a deep thing, not the selfish love of one person for another, but involving many factors. A man will say: Mifanwy Lovell's father saved my honour once. What can I do for Mifanwy Lovell and Mifanwy Lovell's man? And the Lovells said when we were married: Brothers, the gawjo rai, the foreign gentleman, may not understand the gypsy way, that our sorrows are his sorrows, and our joys his, but we understand that his fights are our fights, and his interests the interests of the Lovell Clan.

"My people were always about my lord, and my lord hated it. In our London house in the morning, there were always gypsies waiting to tell my lord of a great fight coming off quietly on Epsom Downs, which it might interest him to see, or of a good horse to be bought cheaply, or some news of a dog soon to run in a coursing match for a great stake, and of the dog's excellences or his defects. They wanted no money. They only wished to do him a kindness. But my lord was embarrassed, until he began to loathe the sight of a gypsy neckerchief. Also, in the race courses, in the betting ring where my lord would be, a gypsy would pay hard-earned entrance money to tell my lord quietly of something they had noticed that morning in the gallops, or horses to be avoided in betting, or of neglected horses which would win. All kindnesses to my lord. But my lord was with fashionable English folk, who do not understand one's having a strange friend. Their uplifted eyebrows made my lord ashamed of the poor Romanies. These things are things you might laugh at, with laughter like sunshine, but there would be clouds in your heart.

"The end came at Ascot, Kerry, where the young queen was, and the Belgian King, and the great nobles of the court. Into the paddock came one of the greatest of gypsies, Tyso Herne, who had gone before my marriage with a great draft of Norman trotting horses to Mexico, and came back with a squadron of ponies, suitable for polo. Tyso was a vast man, a pawni Romany, a fair gypsy. His hair was red, and his moustache was long and curling, like a Hungarian pandour's. He had a flaunting diklo of fine yellow silk about his neck, and the buttons on his coat were gold Indian mohurs, and on his bell-shaped trousers were braids of silver bells, and the spurs on his Wellingtons were fine silver, and his hands were covered with rings, Kerry, with stones in them such as even the young queen did not have. It was not vulgar ostentation. It was just that Tyso felt rich and merry, and no stone on his hand was as fine as his heart.

"When he saw me he let a roar out of him that was like the roar of the ring when the horses are coming in to the stretch.

" 'Before God,' he shouted, 'it's Mifanwy Lovell.' And, though I am not a small woman, Kerry, he tossed me in the air, and caught me in the air. And he laughed and kissed me, and I laughed and kissed him, so happy was I to see great Tyso once more, safe from over the sea.

" 'Go get your rom, mi tshai, your husband, my lass, and we'll go to the kitshima and have a jeraboam of Champagne wine.'

"But I saw my lord walk off with thunder in his face, and all the English folk staring and some women laughing. So I said: 'I will go with you alone, Tyso.' For Tyso Herne had been my father's best friend and my mother's cousin, and had held me as a baby, and no matter how he looked, or who laughed, he was well come for me.

"Of what my lord said, and of what I said in rebuttal, we will not speak. One says foolish things in anger, but, foolish or not, they leave scars. For out of the mouth come things forgotten, things one thinks dead. But before the end of the meeting, I went to Tyso Herne's van. He was braiding a whip with fingers light as a woman's, and when he saw me he spoke quietly.

" 'Is all well with thee, Mifanwy?'

" 'Nothing is well with me, father's friend.'

"And so I went back to my people, and I never saw my lord any more."

We had gone along until in the distance I could see the gypsy fire, and turning the headland we saw the light on Farewell Point. A white flash; a second's rest; a red flash; three seconds occultation; then white and red again. There is something heartening and brave in Farewell Light. Ireland keeps watch over her share of the Atlantic sea.

"When I left my lord, I was with child, and when I was delivered of him, and the child weaned and strong, I sent him to my lord, for every man wants his man child, and every family its heir. But when he was four and twenty he came back to me, for the roving gypsy blood and the fighting Irish blood were too much for him. He was never Earl of Clontarf. He died while my lord still lived. He married a Herne, a grandchild of Tyso, a brave golden girl. And he got killed charging in the Balkan Wars.

"Niall's wife—my son's name was Niall—understood, and when young Niall was old enough, we sent him to my lord. My lord was old at this time, older than his years, and very poor. But of my share of money he would have nothing. My lord died when Niall's Niall was at school, so the little lad became Earl of Clontarf and Kincora. I saw to it he had sufficient money, but he married no rich woman. He married a poor Irish girl, and by her had two children, Niall and Alick. He was interested in horses, and rode well, my English friends tell me. But mounted on a brute in the Punchestown races, he made a mistake at the stone wall. He did not know the horse very well. So he let it have its head at the stone wall. It threw its head up, took the jump by the roots, and so Niall's Niall was killed. His wife, the little Irish girl, turned her face away from life and died.

"The boys are fifteen and thirteen now, and soon they will go into the world. I want them to have a fair chance, and it is for this reason I wish them to have money. I have been rich and then poor, and then very rich and again poor, and rich again and now poor. But if this venture succeeds, the boys will be all right."

"Ye-s," I said.

"You don't seem very enthusiastic, Kerry."

"We have a saying," I told her, "that money won from a book-maker is only lent."

"If you were down on a race meeting and on the last race of the day you won a little, what would you say?"

"I'd say I only got a little of my own back."

"Then we only get a little of our own back over the losses of a thousand years."

We had come now to the encampment. Around the great fire were tall swarthy men with coloured neckerchiefs, who seemed more reserved, cleaner than the English gypsy. Dalmation dogs rose too. In the half light the picketed horses could be seen, quiet as trees.

"This is the Younger of Destiny Bay," said the old lady, "who is kind enough to be our friend."

"Sa shan, rai!" they spoke with quiet courtesy. "How are you, sir?"

Lady Clontarf's maid hurried forward with a wrap, scolding, and speaking English with beautiful courtesy. "You are dreadful, sister. You go walking the roads at night like a courting girl in spring. Gentleman, you are wrong to keep the rawnee out, and she an old woman and not well."

"Supplistia," Lady Clontarf chided, "you have no more manners than a growling dog."

"I am the rawnee's watchdog," the girl answered.

"Madame, your maid is right. I will go now."

"Kerry," she stopped me, "will you be friends with my little people?"

"I will be their true friend," I promised, and I kissed her hand.

"God bless you!" she said. And "kushto bok, rai!" the gypsies wished me. "Good luck, sir!" And I left the camp for my people's house. The hunter's moon was dropping toward the edge of the world, and the light on Farewell Point flashed seaward its white and red, and as I walked along, I noticed that a wind from Ireland had sprung up, and the Bilbao boat was bowling along nor'east on the starboard tack. It seemed to me an augury.

In those days, before my aunt Jenepher's marriage to Patrick Herne, the work of Destiny Bay was divided in the manner: my dear aunt Jenepher was, as was right, supreme in the house. My uncle Valentine planned and superintended the breeding of the harness ponies, and sheep, and black Dexter cattle which made Destiny Bay so feared at the Dublin Horse Show and at the Bath and West. My own work was the farms. To me fell the task of preparing the stables and training grounds for Lady Clontarf's and my own horses. It was a relief and an adventure to give up thinking of turnips, wheat, barley, and seeds, and to examine the downs for training ground. In my great grandfather's time, in pre-Union days, many a winner at the Curragh had been bred and trained at Destiny Bay. The soil of the downs is chalky, and the matted roots of the woven herbage have a certain give in them in the driest of weather. I found out my great-grandfather's mile and a half, and two miles and a half with a turn and shorter gallops of various gradients. My grandfather had used them as a young man, but mainly for hunters, horses which he sold for the great Spanish and Austrian regiments. But to my delight the stables were as good as ever. Covered with reed thatch, they required few repairs. The floors were of chalk, and the boxes beautifully ventilated. There were also great tanks for rainwater, which is of all water the best for horses in training. There were also a few stalls for restless horses. I was worried a little about lighting, but my uncle Valentine told me that Sir Arthur Pollexfen allowed no artificial lights where he trained. Horses went to bed with the fowls and got up at cockcrow.

My own horses I got from Robinson without hurting his feelings. "It's this way, Robinson," I told him. "We're trying to do a crazy thing at Destiny, and I'm not bringing them to another trainer. I'm bringing another trainer there. I can tell you no more."

"Not another word, Mr. Kerry. Bring them back when you want to. I'm sorry to say good-bye to the wee colt. But I wish you luck."

We bought three more horses, and a horse for Ann-Dolly. So that with the six we had a rattling good little stable. When I saw Sir Arthur Pollexfen, my heart sank a little, for he seemed so much out of a former century. Small, ruddy-cheeked, with the white hair of a bishop, and a bishop's courtesy, I never thought he could run a stable. I thought, perhaps, he had grown too old and had been thinking for a long time now of the Place whither he was going, and that we had brought him back from his thoughts and he had left his vitality behind. His own servant came with him to Destiny Bay, and though we wished to have him in the house with us, yet he preferred to stay in a cottage by the stables. I don't know what there was about his clothes, but they were all of an antique though a beautiful cut. He never wore riding breeches but trousers of a bluish cloth and strapped beneath his varnished boots. A flowered waistcoat with a satin stock, a short covert coat, a grey bowler hat and gloves. Always there was a freshly cut flower in his buttonhole, which his servant got every evening from the greenhouses at Destiny Bay, and kept overnight in a glass of water into which the least drop of whiskey had been poured. I mention this as extraordinary, as most racing men will not wear flowers. They believe flowers bring bad luck, though how the superstition arose I cannot tell. His evening trousers also buckled under his shoes, or rather half Wellingtons, such as army men wear, and though there was never a crease in them there was never a wrinkle. He would never drink port after dinner when the ladies had left, but a little whiskey punch which James Carabine would compose for him. Compared to the hard shrewd-eyed trainers I knew, this bland, soft-spoken old gentleman filled me with misgiving.

I got a different idea of the old man the first morning I went out to the gallops. The sun had hardly risen when the old gentleman appeared, as beautifully turned out as though he were entering the Show Ring at Ballsbridge. His servant held his horse, a big grey, while he swung into the saddle as light as a boy. His hack was feeling good that morning, and he and I went off toward the training ground at a swinging canter, the old gentleman half

standing in his stirrups, with a light firm grip of his knees, riding
as Cossacks do, his red terrier galloping behind him. When we
settled down to walk he told me the pedigree of his horse, descended through Matchem and Whalebone from Oliver Cromwell's great charger The White Turk, or Place's White Turk, as
it was called from the Lord Protector's stud manager. To hear
him follow the intricacies of breeding was a revelation. Then I
understood what a great horseman he was. On the training ground
he was like a marshal commanding an army, such respect did
every one accord him. The lads perched on the horses' withers,
his head man, the grooms, all watched the apple-ruddy face, while
he said little or nothing. He must have had eyes in the back of
his head, though. For when a colt we had brought from Mr.
Gubbins, a son of Galtee More's, started lashing out and the lad
up seemed like taking a toss, the old man's voice came low and
sharp: "Don't fall off, boy." And the boy did not fall off. The red
terrier watched the trials with a keen eye, and I believe honestly
that he knew as much about horses as any one of us and certainly
more than any of us about his owner. When my lovely Ducks
and Drakes went out at the lad's call to beat the field by two
lengths over five furlongs, the dog looked up at Sir Arthur and
Sir Arthur looked back at the dog, and what they thought toward
each other, God knoweth.

I expected when we rode away that the old gentleman would
have some word to say about my horses, but coming home, his
remarks were of the country. "Your Derry is a beautiful country,
young Mister Kerry," he said, "though it would be treason to say
that in my own country of Mayo." Of my horses not a syllable.

He could be the most silent man I have ever known, though
giving the illusion of keeping up a conversation. You could talk
to him, and he would smile, and nod at the proper times, as
though he were devouring every word you said. In the end you
thought you had a very interesting conversation. But as to whether
he had even heard you, you were never sure. On the other hand
when he wished to speak, he spoke to the point and beautifully.
Our bishop, on one of his pastoral visitations, if that be the term,
stayed at Destiny Bay, and because my uncle Cosimo is a bishop
too, and because he felt he ought to do something for our souls
he remonstrated with us for starting our stable. My uncle Valen-

tine was livid, but said nothing, for no guest must be contradicted in Destiny Bay.

"For surely, Sir Valentine, no man of breeding can mingle with the rogues, cutpurses and their womenfolk who infest race courses, drunkards, bawds and common gamblers, without lowering himself to some extent to their level," his Lordship purred. "Yourself, one of the wardens of Irish chivalry, must give an example to the common people."

"Your Lordship," broke in old Sir Arthur Pollexfen, "is egregiously misinformed. In all periods of the world's history, eminent personages have concerned themselves with the racing of horses. We read of Philip of Macedon, that while campaigning in Asia Minor, a courier brought him news of two events, of the birth of his son Alexander and of the winning, by his favourite horse, of the chief race of Athens, and we may reasonably infer that his joy over the winning of the race was equal to if not greater than that over the birth of Alexander. In the life of Charles the Second, the traits which do most credit to that careless monarch are his notable and gentlemanly death and his affection for his great race horse Old Rowley. Your Lordship is, I am sure," said Sir Arthur, more blandly than any ecclesiastic could, "too sound a Greek scholar not to remember the epigrams of Maecius and Philodemus, which show what interest these antique poets took in the racing of horses. And coming to present times, your Lordship must have heard that his Majesty (whom God preserve!) has won two Derbies, once with the leased horse Minoru, and again with his own great Persimmon. The premier peer of Scotland, the Duke of Hamilton, Duke of Chastellerault in France, Duke of Brandon in England, hereditary prince of Baden, is prouder of his fine mare Eau de Vie than of all his titles. As to the Irish families, the Persses of Galways, the Dawsons of Dublin, and my own, the Pollexfens of Mayo, have always been interested in the breeding and racing of horses. And none of these—my punch, if you please, James Carabine!—are, as your Lordship puts it, drunkards, bawds, and common gamblers. I fear your Lordship has been reading—" and he cocked his eye, bright as a wren's, at the bishop, "religious publications of the sensational and morbid type."

It was all I could do to keep from leaping on the table and giving three loud cheers for the County of Mayo.

Now, on those occasions, none too rare, when my uncle Valentine and I differed on questions of agricultural economy, or of national policy, or of mere faith and morals, he poured torrents of invective over my head, which mattered little. But when he was really aroused to bitterness he called me "modern." And by modern my uncle Valentine meant the quality inherent in brown buttoned boots, in white waistcoats worn with dinner jackets, in nasty little motor cars—in fine, those things before which the angels of God recoil in horror. While I am not modern in that sense, I am modern in this, that I like to see folk getting on with things. Of Lady Clontarf and of Irlandais colt, I heard no more. On the morning after seeing her home I called over to the caravan but it was no longer there. There was hardly a trace of it. I found a broken fern and a slip of oaktree, the gypsy pattern. But what it betokened or whither it pointed I could not tell. I had gone to no end of trouble in getting the stables and training grounds ready, and Sir Arthur Pollexfen had been brought out of his retirement in the County of Mayo. But still no word of the horse. I could see my uncle Valentine and Sir Arthur taking their disappointment bravely, if it never arrived, and murmuring some courteous platitude, out of the reign of good Queen Victoria, that it was a lady's privilege to change her mind. That might console them in their philosophy, but it would only make me hot with rage. For to me there is no sex in people of standards. They do not let one another down.

Then one evening the horse arrived.

It arrived at sundown in a large van drawn by four horses, a van belonging evidently to some circus. It was yellow and covered with paintings of nymphs being wooed by swains, in clothes hardly fitted to agricultural pursuits: of lions of terrifying aspect being put through their paces by a trainer of an aspect still more terrifying: of an Indian gentleman with a vast turban and a small loincloth playing a penny whistle to a snake that would have put the heart crosswise in Saint Patrick himself; of a most adipose lady in tights swinging from a ring while the husband and seven sons hung on to her like bees in a swarm. Floridly painted over the van was "Arsene Bombaudiac, Prop., Bayonne." The whole added no dignity to Destiny Bay, and if some sorceress had disclosed to Mr. Bombaudiac of Bayonne that he was about to lose a van by fire at low tide on the beach of Destiny in Ireland within forty-eight hours— The driver was a burly gypsy, while two of the most utter scoundrels I have ever laid eyes on sat beside him on the wide seat.

"Do you speak English?" I asked the driver.

"Yes, sir," he answered, "I am a Petulengro."

"Which of these two beauties beside you is the jockey?"

"Neither sir, These two are just gypsy fighting men. The jockey is inside with the horse."

My uncle Valentine came down stroking his great red beard. He seemed fascinated by the pictures on the van. "What your poor aunt Jenepher, Kerry," he said, "misses by being blind!"

"What she is spared, sir! Boy," I called one of the servants, "go get Sir Arthur Pollexfen. Where do you come from?" I asked the driver.

"From Dax, sir, in the South of France."

"You're a liar," I said. "Your horses are half-bred Clydesdale. There's no team like that in the South of France."

"We came to Dieppe with an attelage basque, six yoked oxen. But I was told they would not be allowed in England, so I telegraphed our chief, Piramus Petulengro, to have a team at Newhaven. So I am not a liar, sir."

"I am sorry."

"Sir, that is all right."

Sir Arthur Pollexfen came down from where he had been speaking to my aunt Jenepher. I could see he was tremendously excited, because he walked more slowly than was usual, spoke with more deliberation. He winced a little as he saw the van. But he was of the old heroic school. He said nothing.

"I think, Sir Valentine," he said, "we might have the horse out."

"Ay, we might as well know the worst," said my uncle Valentine.

A man jumped from the box, and swung the crossbar up. The door opened and into the road stepped a small man in dark clothes. Never on this green earth of God's have I seen such dignity. He was dressed in dark clothes with a wide dark hat, and his face was brown as soil. White starched cuffs covered half of his hands. He took off his hat and bowed first to my uncle Valentine, then to Sir Arthur, and to myself last. His hair was plastered

a sort of sub-trainer for the colt, allowing none else to attend to its feeding. The small donkey was its invariable stable companion, and had to be led out to exercise with it. The donkey belonged to Joselito. Don Frasco rode many trials on the other horses. He might appear small standing, but on horseback he seemed a large man, so straight did he sit in the saddle. The little boys rode with a fairly short stirrup, but the gitano scorned anything but the traditional seat. He never seemed to move on a horse. Yet he could do what he liked with it.

The Irlandais colt was at last named Romany Baw, or "gypsy friend" in English, as James Carabine explained to us, and Lady Clontarf's colours registered, quartered red and gold. When the winter lists came out, we saw the horse quoted at a hundred to one, and later at the call over of the Victoria Club, saw that price offered but not taken. My uncle Valentine made a journey to Dublin, to arrange for Lady Clontarf's commission being placed, putting it in the hands of a Derry man who had become big in the affairs of Tattersall's. What he himself and Sir Arthur Pollexfen and the jockey had on I do not know, but he arranged to place an hundred pounds of mine, and fifty of Ann-Dolly's. As the months went by, the odds crept down gradually to thirty-three to one, stood there for a while and went out to fifty. Meanwhile Sir James became a sensational favourite at fives, and Toison d'Or varied between tens and one hundred to eight. Some news of a great trial of Lord Shire's horse had leaked out which accounted for the ridiculously short price. But no word did or could get out about Lady Clontarf's colt. The two gypsy fighters from Dax patrolled Destiny Bay, and God help any poor tipster or wretched newspaper tout who tried to plumb the mysteries of training. I honestly believe a bar of iron and a bog hole would have been his end.

The most fascinating figure in this crazy world was the gypsy jockey. To see him talk to Sir Arthur Pollexfen was a phenomenon. Sir Arthur would speak in English and the gypsy answer in Spanish, neither knowing a word of the other's language, yet each perfectly understanding the other. I must say that this only referred to how a horse ran, or how Romany Baw was feeding and feeling. As to more complicated problems, Ann-Dolly was called in, to translate his Spanish.

"Ask him," said Sir Arthur, "has he ever ridden in France?"

"Oiga, Frasco," and Ann-Dolly would burst into a torrent of gutturals.

"Si, si, Dona Anna."

"Ask him has he got his clearance from the Jockey Club of France?"

"Seguro, Don Arturo!" And out of his capacious pocket he extracted the French Jockey Club's "character." They made a picture I will never forget, the old horseman ageing so gently, the vivid boyish beauty of Ann-Dolly, and the overpowering dignity and manliness of the jockey. Always, except when he was riding or working at his anvil,—for he was our smith too—he wore the dark clothes, which evidently some village tailor of the Pyrenees made for him—the very short coat, the trousers tubed like cig-arettes, his stiff shirt with the vast cuffs. He never wore a collar, nor a neckerchief. Always his back was flat as the side of a house.

When he worked at the anvil, with his young ruffian of a brother at the bellows, he sang. He had shakes and grace notes enough to make a thrush quit. Ann-Dolly translated one of his songs for us.

> No tengo padre ni madre . . .
> Que desgraciado soy yo!
> Soy como el arbol solo
> Que echas frutas y no echa flor . . .

"He sings he has no father or mother. How out of luck he is! He is like a lonely tree, which bears the fruit and not the flower."

"God bless my soul, Kerry," my uncle was shocked. "The little man is homesick."

"No, no!" Ann-Dolly protested. "He is very happy. That is why he sings a sad song."

One of the reasons of the little man's happiness was the discovery of our national game of handball. He strolled over to the Irish Village and discovered the court back of the Inniskillen Dragoon, that most notable of rural pubs. He was tremendously excited, and getting some gypsy to translate for him, challenged the local champion for the stake of a barrel of porter. He made

the local champion look like a carthorse in the Grand National.
When it was told to me I couldn't believe it.

"But don't they play pelota with a basket?"

"Real pelota is a mains neus, 'with the hands naked.' "

"You mean Irish handball," I told her.

I regret that the population of Destiny made rather a good
thing out of Don Frasco's prowess on the court, going from village
to village, and betting on a certain win. The end was a match
between Mick Tierney, the Portrush Jarvey and the jockey. The
match was billed for the champion of Ulster, and Don Frasco was
put down on the card, to explain his lack of English, as Danny
Frask, the Glenties Miracle, the Glenties being a district of Donegal where Erse is the native speech. The match was poor, the
Portrush Jarvey, after the first game, standing and watching the
ball hiss past him with his eyes on his cheek bones. All Donegal
seemed to have turned out for the fray. When the contest was
over, a big Glenties man pushed his way toward the jockey.

"Dublin and London and New York are prime cities," he
chanted, "but Glenties is truly magnificent. Kir do lauv anshin,
a railt na hooee, 'Put your hand there, Star of the North.' "

"No entiendo, senor," said Don Frasco. And with that the
fight began.

James Carabine was quick enough to get the jockey out of the
court before he was lynched. But Destiny Bay men, gypsies,
fishers, citizens of Derry, bookmakers and their clerks and the
fighting tribes of Donegal went to it with a vengeance. Indeed,
according to experts, nothing like it, for spirit or results, had
been seen since or before the Prentice Boys had chased King
James (to whom God give his deserts!) from Derry Walls. The
removal of the stunned and wounded from the courts drew the
attention of the police, for the fight was continued in grim silence. But on the entrance of half a dozen peelers commanded by
a huge sergeant, Joselito, the jockey's young brother, covered
himself with glory. Leaping on the reserved seats, he brought his
right hand over hard and true to the sergeant's jaw, and the sergeant was out for half an hour. Joselito was arrested, but the case
was laughed out of court. The idea of a minuscule jockey who
could ride at ninety pounds knocking out six foot three of Royal
Irish Constabulary was too much. Nothing was found on him but

his bare hands, a packet of cigarettes and thirty sovereigns he had won over the match. But I knew better. I decided to prove him with hard questions.

"Ask him in Romany, James Carabine, what he had wrapped around that horseshoe he threw away."

"He says: 'Tow, Mister Kerry.'"

"Get me my riding crop," I said; "I'll take him behind the stables." And the training camp lost its best lightweight jockey for ten days, the saddle suddenly becoming repulsive to him. I believe he slept on his face.

But the one who was really wild about the affair was Ann-Dolly. She came across from Spanish Men's Rest flaming with anger.

"Because a Spanish wins, there is fighting, there is anger. If an Irish wins, there is joy, there is drinking. Oh, shame of sportsmanship!"

"Oh, shut your gab, Ann-Dolly," I told her. "They didn't know he was a Spanish, as you call it."

"What did they think he was if not a Spanish? Tell me. I demand it of you."

"They thought he was Welsh."

"Oh, in that case . . ." said Ann-Dolly, completely mollified. Ipsa hibernis hiberniora!

I wouldn't have you think that all was beer and skittles, as the English say, in training Romany Baw for the Derby. As spring came closer, the face of the old trainer showed signs of strain. The Lincoln Handicap was run and the Grand National passed, and suddenly flat-racing was on us. And now not the Kohinoor was watched more carefully than the Derby horse. We had a spanking trial on a course as nearly approaching the Two Thousand Guineas route as Destiny Downs would allow, and when Romany Baw flew past us, beating Ducks and Drakes who had picked him up at the mile for the uphill dash, and Sir Arthur clicked his watch, I saw his tense face relax.

"He ran well," said the old man.

"He'll walk it," said my uncle Valentine.

My uncle Valentine and Jenico and Ann-Dolly were going across to Newmarket Heath for the big race, but the spring of the year is the time that the farmer must stay by his land, and nurse it like a child. All farewells, even for a week, are sad, and I was loath to see the horses go into the races. Romany Baw had a regular summer bloom on him and his companion, the donkey, was corpulent as an alderman. Ducks and Drakes looked rough and backward, but that didn't matter.

"You've got the best-looking horse in the United Kingdom," I told Sir Arthur.

"Thank you, Kerry," the old man was pleased. "And as to Ducks and Drakes, looks aren't everything."

"Sure, I know that," I told him.

"I wouldn't be rash," he told me, "but I'd have a little on both. That is, if they go to the post fit and well."

I put in the days as well as I could, getting ready for the Spring Show at Dublin. But my heart and my thoughts were with my people and the horses at Newmarket. I could see my uncle Valentine's deep bow with his hat in his hand as they passed the Roman ditch at Newmarket, giving that squat wall the reverence that racing men have accorded it since races were run there, though why, none knew. A letter from Ann-Dolly apprised me that the horses had made a good crossing and that Romany Baw was well —"and you mustn't think, my dear, that your colt is not as much and more to us than the Derby horse, no, Kerry, not for one moment. Lady Clontarf is here, in her caravan, and oh, Kerry, she looks ill. Only her burning spirit keeps her frail body alive. Jenico and I are going down to Eastbourne to see the little Earl and his brother . . . You will get this letter, cousin, on the morning of the race. . . ."

At noon that day I could stand it no longer so I had James Carabine put the trotter in the dogcart. "There are some things I want in Derry," I told myself, "and I may as well get them to-day as to-morrow." And we went spinning toward Derry Walls. Ducks and Drakes' race was the two-thirty. And after lunch I looked at reapers I might be wanting in July until the time of the race. I went along to the club, and had hardly entered it when I saw the boy putting up the telegram on the notice board.

1, Ducks and Drakes, an hundred to eight; 2, Geneva, four to six; 3, Ally Sloper, three to one. "That's that!" I said. Another telegram gave the betting for the Two Thousand: Threes, Sir James; seven to two, Toison d'Or; eights, Ca' Canny, Greek

Singer, Germanicus; tens, six or seven horses; twenty to one any other. No word in the betting of the gypsy horse, and I wondered had anything happened. Surely a horse looking as well as he did must have attracted backers' attention. And as I was worrying the result came in, Romany Baw, first; Sir James, second, Toison d'Or, third.

"Kerry," somebody called.

"I haven't a minute," I shouted. Neither I had, for James Carabine was outside, waiting to hear the result. When I told him he said: "There's a lot due to you, Mister Kerry, in laying out those gallops." "Be damned to that," I said, but I was pleased all the same.

I was on tenterhooks until I got the papers describing the race. Ducks and Drakes' win was dismissed summarily, as that of an Irish outsider, and the jockey, Flory Cantillon (Frasco could not manage the weight), was credited with a clever win of two lengths. But the account of Romany Baw's race filled me with indignation. According to it, the winner got away well, but the favourites were hampered at the start and either could have beaten the Irish trained horse, only that they just didn't. The race was won by half a length, a head separating second and third, and most of the account was given to how the favourites chased the lucky outsider, and in a few more strides would have caught him. There were a few dirty backhanders given at Romany's jockey, who, they said, would be more at home in a circus than on a modern race track. He sat like the rider of a century back, they described it, more like an exponent of the old manege than a modern jockey, and even while the others were thundering at his horse's hindquarters he never moved his seat or used his whip. The experts' judgment of the race was that the Irish colt was forward in a backward field, and that Romany would be lost on Epsom Downs, especially with its "postillion rider."

But the newspaper criticisms of the jockey and his mount did not seem to bother my uncle Valentine or the trainer or the jockey's self. They came back elated; even the round white donkey had a humorous happy look in his full Latin eye.

"Did he go well?" I asked.

"He trotted it," said my uncle Valentine.

"But the accounts read, sir," I protested, "that the favourites would have caught him in another couple of strides."

"Of course they would," said my uncle Valentine, "at the pace he was going," he added.

"I see," said I.

"You see nothing," said my uncle Valentine. "But if you had seen the race you might talk. The horse is a picture. It goes so sweetly that you wouldn't think it was going at all. And as for the gypsy jockey—"

"The papers say he's antiquated."

"He's seven pounds better than Flory Cantillon," said my uncle Valentine.

I whistled. Cantillon is our best Irish jockey, and his retaining fees are enormous, and justified. "They said he was nearly caught napping—"

"Napping be damned!" exploded my uncle Valentine. "This Spanish gypsy is the finest judge of pace I ever saw. He knew he had the race won, and he never bothered."

"If the horse is as good as that, and you have as high an opinion of the rider, well, sir, I won a hatful over the Newmarket meeting, and as the price hasn't gone below twenties for the Derby, I'm going after the Ring. There's many a bookmaker will wish he'd stuck to his father's old-clothes business."

"I wouldn't, Kerry," said my uncle Valentine. "I'm not sure I wouldn't hedge a bit of what I have on, if I were you."

I was still with amazement.

"I saw Mifanwy Clontarf," said my uncle Valentine, "and only God and herself and myself and you, know how ill that woman is."

"But ill or not ill, she won't scratch the horse."

"She won't," said my uncle Valentine, and his emphasis on 'she' chilled me to the heart. "You're forgettng, Kerry," he said very quietly, "the Derby Rule."

Of the Derby itself on Epsom Downs, everybody knows. It is supposed to be the greatest test of a three-year-old in the world, though old William Day used to hold it was easy. The course may have been easy for Lord George Bentinck's famous and unbeaten mare Crucifix, when she won the Oaks in 1840, but most winners over the full course justify their victory in other races. The course starts up a heartbreaking hill, and swinging around the top, comes down again toward Tattenham Corner. If a horse waits to steady itself coming down it is beaten. The famous Fred Archer (whose tortured soul God rest!) used to take Tattenham Corner with one leg over the rails. The straight is uphill. A mile and a half of the trickiest, most heartbreaking ground in the world. Such is Epsom. Its turf has been consecrated by the hoofs of great horses since James I established there a race for the Silver Bell: by Cromwell's great Coffin Mare; by the Arabs, Godolphin and Darby; by the great bay, Malton; by the prodigious Eclipse; by Diamed, son of Florizel, who went to America. . . .

Over the Derby what sums are wagered no man knows. On it is won the Calcutta Sweepstake, a prize of which makes a man rich for life, and the Stock Exchange sweep, and other sweeps innumerable. Some one has ventured the belief that on it annually are five million pounds of sterling, and whether he is millions short, or millions over none knows. Because betting is illegal.

There are curious customs in regard to it, as this: that when the result is sent over the ticker to clubs, in case of a dead heat, the word "dead heat" must come first, because within recent years a trusted lawyer, wagering trust funds on a certain horse, was waiting by the tape to read the result, and seeing another horse's name come up, went away forthwith and blew his brains out. Had he been less volatile he would have seen his own fancy's name follow that, with "dead heat" after it and been to this day rich and respected. So now, for the protection of such, "dead heat" comes first. A dead heat in the Derby is as rare a thing as there is in the world, but still you can't be too cautious. But the quaintest rule of the Derby is this: that if the nominator of a horse for the Derby Stakes dies, his horse is automatically scratched. There is a legend to the effect that an heir-at-law purposed to kill the owner of an entry, and to run a prime favourite crookedly, and that on hearing this the Stewards of the Jockey Club made the rule. Perhaps it has a more prosaic reason. The Jockey Club may have considered that when a man died, in the trouble of fixing his estates, forfeits would not be paid, and that it was best for all concerned to have the entry scratched. How it came about does not matter, it exists. Whether it is good in law is not certain. Racing folk will quarrel with His Majesty's Lord Justices of Appeal, with the Privy Council, but they will not quarrel with the Jockey Club. Whether it is good in fact is indisputable, for certain owners can tell stories of narrow escapes from racing gangs, in those old days before the Turf was cleaner than the Church, when attempts were made to nobble favourites, when jockeys had not the wings of angels under their silken jackets, when harsh words were spoken about trainers—very, very long ago. There it is, good or bad, the Derby Rule!

As to our bets on the race, they didn't matter. It was just bad luck. But to see the old lady's quarter million of pounds and more go down the pike was a tragedy. We had seen so much of shabby great names that I trembled for young Clontarf and his brother. Armenian and Greek families of doubtful antecedents were always on the lookout for a title for their daughters, and crooked businesses always needed directors of title to catch gulls, so much in the United Kingdom do the poor trust their peers. The boys would not be exactly poor, because the horse, whether or not it ran in the Derby, would be worth a good round sum. If it were as good as my uncle Valentine said, it would win the Leger and the Gold Cup at Ascot. But even with these triumphs it wouldn't be a Derby winner. And the Derby means so much. There are so many people in England who remember dates by the Derby winners' names, as "I was married in Bend Or's year," or "the Achilles was lost in the China seas, let me see when,— that was in Sainfoin's year." Also I wasn't sure that the Spanish gypsy would stay to ride him at Doncaster, or return for Ascot. I found him one day standing on the cliffs of Destiny and looking long at the sea, and I knew what that meant. And perhaps Romany Baw would not run for another jockey as he ran for him.

I could not think that Death could be so cruel as to come between us and triumph. In Destiny we have a friendliness for the Change which most folk dread. One of our songs says:

"When Mother Death in her warm arms shall embrace me,
Low lull me to sleep with sweet Erin-go-bragh—"

We look upon it as a kind friend who comes when one is tired and twisted with pain, and says: "Listen, avourneen, soon the dawn will come, and the tide is on the ebb. We must be going." And we trust him to take us, by a short road or a long road to a place of birds and bees, of which even lovely Destiny is but a clumsy seeming. He could not be such a poor sportsman as to come before the aged gallant lady had won her last gamble. And poor Sir Arthur, who had come out of his old age in Mayo to win a Derby! It would break his heart. And the great horse, it would be so hard on him. Nothing will convince me that a thoroughbred does not know a great race when he runs one. The streaming competitors, the crackle of silk, the roar as they come into the straight, and the sense of the jockey calling on the great heart that the writer of Job knew so well. "The glory of his nostril is terrible," says the greatest of poets. "He pauseth in the valley and rejoiceth in his strength: he goeth on to meet the armed men." Your intellectual will claim that the thoroughbred is an artificial brainless animal evolved by men for their amusement. Your intellectual, here again, is a liar.

Spring came in blue and gold. Blue of sea and fields and trees; gold of sun and sand and buttercup. Blue of wild hyacinth and bluebell; gold of primrose and laburnum tree. The old gypsy lady was with her caravan near Bordeaux, and from the occasional letter my uncle Valentine got, and from the few words he dropped to me, she was just holding her own. May drowsed by with the cheeping of the little life in the hedgerows. The laburnum floated in a cloud of gold and each day Romany Baw grew stronger. When his blankets were stripped from him he looked a mass of fighting muscle under a covering of satin, and his eye showed that his heart was fighting too. Old Sir Arthur looked at him a few days before we were to go to England, and he turned to me.

"Kerry," he said very quietly.

"Yes, Sir Arthur."

"All my life I have been breeding and training horses, and it just goes to show," he told me, "that goodness of God that he let me handle this great horse before I died."

The morning before we left my uncle Valentine received a letter which I could see moved him. He swore a little as he does when moved and stroked his vast red beard and looked fiercely at nothing at all.

"Is it bad news, sir?" I asked.

He didn't answer me directly. "Lady Clontarf is coming to the Derby," he told me.

Then it was my turn to swear a little. It seemed to me to be but little short of maniacal to risk a Channel crossing and the treacherous English climate in her stage of health. If she should die on the way or on the downs, then all her planning and our work was for nothing. Why could she not have remained in the soft French air, husbanding her share of life until the event was past!

"She comes of ancient, violent blood," thundered my uncle Valentine, "and where should she be but present when her people or her horses go forth to battle?"

"You are right, sir," I said.

The epithet of "flaming" which the English apply to their June was in this year of grace well deserved. The rhododendrons were bursting into great fountains of scarlet, and near the swans the cygnets paddled, unbelievably small. The larks fluttered in the air above the downs, singing so gallantly that when you heard the trill of the nightingale in the thicket giving his noontime song, you felt inclined to say: "Be damned to that Italian bird; my money's on the wee fellow!" All through Surrey the green walls of spring rose high and thick, and then suddenly coming, as we came, through Leatherhead and topping the hill, in the distance the black colony of the downs showed like a thundercloud. At a quarter mile away, the clamour came to you, like the vibration when great bells have been struck.

The stands and enclosure were packed so thickly that one wondered how movement was possible, how people could enjoy themselves, close as herrings. My uncle Valentine had brought his beautiful harness ponies across from Ireland, "to encourage English interest in the Irish horse" he explained it, but with his beautifully cut clothes, his grey high hat, it seemed to me that more people looked at him as we spun along the road than looked at the horses. Behind us sat James Carabine, with his face brown as autumn and the gold rings in his thickened ears. We got out near the paddock and Carabine took the ribbons. My uncle Valentine said quietly to him: "Find out how things are, James Carabine." And I knew he was referring to the gypsy lady. Her caravan was somewhere on the Downs guarded by her gypsies, but my uncle had been there the first day of the meeting, and on Monday night, at the National Sporting, some of the gypsies had waited for him coming out and given him news. I asked him how she was, but all his answer was: "It's in the hands of God."

Along the track toward the grand stand we made our way. On the railings across the track the bookmakers were proclaiming their market: "I'll give fives the field. I'll give nine to one bar two. I'll give twenty to one bar five. Outsiders! Outsiders! Fives Sir James. Seven to one Toison d'Or. Nines Honey Bee. Nines Welsh Melody. Ten to one the gypsy horse."

"It runs all right," said my uncle Valentine, "up to now."

"Twenty to one Maureen Roe! Twenties Asclepiades! Twenty-five Rifle Ranger. Here thirty-three to one Rifle Ranger, Monk of Sussex, or Presumptuous—"

"Gentlemen, I am here to plead with you not to back the favourite. In this small envelope you will find the number of the winner. For the contemptible sum of two shillings or half a dollar, you may amass a fortune. Who gave the winner of last year's Derby?" a tipster was calling. "Who gave the winner of the Oaks? Who gave the winner of the Steward's Cup?"

"All right, guv'nor, I'll bite. 'Oo the 'ell did?"

Opposite the grand stand the band of the Salvation Army was blaring the music of "Work, for the Night is Coming." Gypsy girls were going around dukkering or telling fortune. "Ah, gentleman, you've a lucky face. Cross the poor gypsy's hand with silver—"

"You better cut along and see your horse saddled," said my uncle Valentine. Ducks and Drakes was in the Ranmore Plate and with the penalty he received after Newmarket, Frasco could ride him. As I went toward the paddock I saw the numbers go up, and I saw we were drawn third, which I think is best of all on the tricky Epsom five-furlong dash. I got there in time to see the gypsy swing into the saddle in the green silk jacket and orange cap, and Sir Arthur giving him his orders. "Keep back of the Fusilier," he pointed to the horse, "and then come out. Hit him once if you have to, and no more."

"Si, si, Don Arturo!" And he grinned at me.

"Kerry, read this," said the old trainer, and he gave me a newspaper, "and tell me before the race," his voice was trembling a little, "if there's truth in it."

I pushed the paper into my pocket and went back to the box where my uncle Valentine and Jenico and Ann-Dolly were. "What price my horse," I asked in Tattersall's. "Sixes, Mister

MacFarlane." "I'll take six hundred to an hundred twice." As I moved away there was a rush to back it. It tumbled in five minutes to five to two.

"And I thought I'd get tens," I said to my uncle Valentine, "with the Fusilier and Bonny Hortense in the race. I wonder who's been backing it."

"I have," said Ann-Dolly. "I got twelves."

"You might have the decency to wait until the owner gets on," I said bitterly. And as I watched the tapes went up. It was a beautiful start. Everything except those on the outside seemed to have a chance as they raced for the rails. I could distinguish the green jacket but vaguely until they came to Tattenham Corner, when I could see Fusilier pull out, and Bonny Hortense follow. But back of Fusilier, racing quietly beside the filly, was the jacket green.

"I wish he'd go up," I said.

"The favourite wins," they were shouting. And a woman in the box next us began to clap her hands calling: "Fusilier's won. Fusilier wins it!"

"You're a damn fool, woman," said Ann-Dolly. "Ducks and Drakes has it." And as she spoke, I could see Frasco hunch forward slightly and dust his mount's neck with his whip. He crept past the hard-pressed Fusilier to win by half a length.

In my joy I nearly forgot the newspaper, and I glanced at it rapidly. My heart sank. "Gypsy Owner Dying as Horse runs in Derby," I read, and reading down it I felt furious. Where the man got his information from I don't know, but he drew a picturesque account of the old gypsy lady on her deathbed on the downs as Romany Baw was waiting in his stall. The account was written the evening before, and "it is improbable she will last the night," it ended. I gave it to my uncle Valentine, who had been strangely silent over my win.

"What shall I say to Sir Arthur Pollexfen?"

"Say she's ill, but it's all rot she's dying."

I noticed as I went to the paddock a murmur among the race-goers. The attention of all had been drawn to the gypsy horse by its jockey having won the Ranmore Plate. Everywhere I heard questions being asked as to whether she were dead. Sir James had hardened to fours. And on the heath I heard a woman proffer a sovereign to a bookmaker on Romany Baw, and he said, "That horse don't run, lady." I forgot my own little triumph in the tragedy of the scratching of the great horse.

In the paddock Sir Arthur was standing watching the lads leading the horses around. Twenty-seven entries, glossy as silk, muscled like athletes of old Greece, ready to run for the Derby stakes. The jockeys, with their hard wizened faces, stood talking to trainers and owners, saying nothing about the race, all already having been said, but just putting in the time until the order came to go to the gate. I moved across to the old Irish trainer and the gypsy jockey. Sir Arthur was saying nothing, but his hand trembled as he took a pinch of snuff from his old-fashioned silver horn. The gypsy jockey stood erect, with his overcoat over his silk. It was a heart-rending five minutes standing there beside them, waiting for the message that they were not to go.

My uncle Valentine was standing with a couple of the Stewards. A small race official was explaining something to them. They nodded him away. There was another minute's conversation and my uncle came toward us. The old trainer was fumbling pitifully with his silver snuff horn, trying to find the pocket in which to put it.

"It's queer," said my uncle Valentine, "but nobody seems to know where Lady Clontarf is. She's not in her caravan."

"So—" questioned the old trainer.

"So you run," said my uncle Valentine. "The horse comes under starter's orders. You may have an objection, Arthur, but you run."

The old man put on youth and grandeur before my eyes. He stood erect. With an eye like an eagle's he looked around the paddock.

"Leg up, boy!" he snapped at Frasco.

"Here, give me your coat." I helped throw the golden-and-red shirted figure into the saddle. Then the head lad led the horse out.

We moved down the track and into the stand, and the parade began. Lord Shire's great horse, and the French hope Toison d'Or; the brown colt owned by the richest merchant in the world, and the little horse owned by the Leicester butcher, who served in his own shop; the horse owned by the peer of last year's making; and the bay filly owned by the first baroness in England. They went down past the stand, and turning breezed off at a gallop back, to cross the downs toward the starting gate, and as they went with each went some one's heart. All eyes seemed turned on the gypsy horse, with his rider erect as a Life Guardsman. As Frasco raised his whip to his cap in the direction of our box, I heard in one of the neighbouring boxes a man say: "But that horse's owner is dead!"

"Is that so, Uncle Valentine?" asked Ann-Dolly. There were tears in her eyes. "Is that true?"

"Nothing is true until you see it yourself," parried my uncle Valentine. And as she seemed to be about to cry openly,—"Don't you see the horse running?" he said. "Don't you know the rule?" But his eyes were riveted through his glasses on the starting gate. I could see deep furrows of anxiety on his bronze brow. In the distance, over the crowd's heads, over the bookmakers' banners, over the tents, we could see the dancing horses at the tape, the gay colours of the riders moving here and there in an intricate pattern, the massed hundreds of black figures at the start. Near us, across the rails, some religious zealots let fly little balloons carrying banners reminding us that doom was waiting. Their band broke into a lugubrious hymn, while nasal voices took it up. In the silence of the crowded downs, breathless for the start, the religious demonstration seemed startlingly trivial. The line of horses, formed for the gate, broke, and wheeled. My uncle snapped his fingers in vexation.

"Why can't the fool get them away?"

Then out of a seemingly inextricable maze, the line formed suddenly and advanced on the tapes. And the heavy silence exploded into a low roar like growing thunder. Each man shouted: "They're off!" The Derby had started.

It seemed like a river of satin, with iridescent foam, pouring, against all nature, uphill. And for one instant you could distinguish nothing. You looked to see if your horse had got away well, had not been kicked or cut into at the start, and as you were disentangling them, the banks of gorse shut them from your view, and when you saw them again they were racing for the turn of the hill. The erect figure of the jockey caught my eye before his colours did.

"He's lying fifth," I told my uncle Valentine.

"He's running well," my uncle remarked quietly.

"They swung around the top of the hill, appearing above the rails and gorse, like something tremendously artificial, like some theatrical illusion, as of a boat going across the stage. There were three horses grouped together, then a black horse—Esterhazy's fine colt—then Romany Baw, after that a stretching line of horses. Something came out of the pack at the top of the hill, and passed the gypsy horse and the fourth.

"Toison d'Or is going up," Jenico told me.

But the gallant French colt's bolt was flown. He fell back, and now one of the leaders dropped back. And Romany was fourth as they started downhill for Tattenham Corner. "How slow they go!" I thought.

"What a pace!" said Jenico, his watch in his hand.

At Tattenham Corner the butcher's lovely little horse was beaten, and a sort of moan came from the rails where the poor people stood. Above the religious band's outrageous nasal tones, the ring began roaring: "Sir James! Sir James has it. Twenty to one bar Sir James!"

As they came flying up the stretch I could see the favourite going along, like some bird flying low, his jockey hunched like an ape on his withers. Beside him raced an outsider, a French-bred horse owned by Kazoutlian, an Armenian banker. Close to his heels came the gypsy horse on the inside, Frasco sitting as though the horse were standing still. Before him raced the favourite and the rank outsider.

"It's all over," I said. "He can't get through. And he can't pull around. Luck of the game!"

And then the rider on the Armenian's horse tried his last effort. He brought the whip high in the air. My uncle Valentine thundered a great oath.

"Look, Kerry!" His fingers gripped my shoulder.

I knew, when I saw the French horse throw his head up, that he was going to swerve at the whip, but I never expected Frasco's mad rush. He seemed to jump the opening, and land the horse past Sir James.

"The favourite's beat!" went up the cry of dismay.

Romany Baw, with Frasco forward on his neck, passed the winning post first by a clear length.

Then a sort of stunned silence fell on the Derby crowd. Nobody knew what would happen. If, as the rumour went around, the owner was dead, then the second automatically won. All eyes were on the horse as the trainer led him into the paddock, followed by second and third. All eyes turned from the horse toward the notice board as the numbers went up: 17, 1, 26. All folk were waiting for the red objection signal. The owner of the second led his horse in, the burling Yorkshire peer. An old gnarled man, with a face like a walnut, Kazoutlian's self, led in the third.

"I say, Kerry," Jenico called quietly, "something's up near the paddock."

I turned and noticed a milling mob down the course on our right. The mounted policemen set off at a trot toward the commotion. Then cheering went into the air like a peal of bells.

Down the course came all the gypsies, all the gypsies in the world, it seemed to me. Big-striding, black men with gold earrings and coloured neckerchiefs, and staves in their hands. And gypsy women, a-jingle with coins, dancing. Their tambourines jangled, as they danced forward in a strange East Indian rhythm. There was a loud order barked by the police officer, and the men stood by to let them pass. And the stolid English police began cheering too. It seemed to me that even the little trees of the downs were cheering, and in an instant I cheered too.

For back of an escort of mounted gypsies, big foreign men with moustaches, saddleless on their shaggy mounts, came a gypsy cart with its cover down, drawn by four prancing horses. A wild-looking gypsy man was holding the reins. On the cart, for all to see, seated in a great arm-chair, propped up by cushions, was Lady Clontarf. Her head was laid back on a pillow, and her eyes were closed, as if the strain of appearing had been too much for her. Her little maid was crouched at her feet.

For an instant we saw her, and noticed the aged beauty of her face, noticed the peace like twilight on it. There was an order from a big Roumanian gypsy and the Romany people made a lane. The driver stood up on his perch and maneuvring his long snakelike whip in the air, made it crack like a musket. The horses broke into a gallop, and the gypsy cart went over the turfed course toward Tattenham Corner, passed it, and went up the hill and disappeared over the Surrey downs. All the world was cheering.

"Come in here," said my uncle Valentine, and he took me into the cool beauty of our little church of Saint Columba's-in-Paganry. "Now what do you think of that?" And he pointed out a brass tablet on the wall.

"In Memory of Mifanwy, Countess of Clontarf and Kincora," I read. Then came the dates of her birth and death, "and who is buried after the Romany manner, no man knows where." And then came the strange text, "In death she was not divided."

"But surely," I objected, "the quotation is: 'In death they were not divided.' "

"It may be," said my uncle Valentine, "or it may not be. But as the living of Saint Columba's-in-Paganry is in my gift, surely to God!" he broke out, "a man can have a text the way he wants it in his own Church."

This was arguable, but something more serious caught my eye.

"See, sir," I said, "the date of her death is wrong. She died on the evening of Derby Day, June the second. And here it is given as June the first."

"She did not die on the evening of Derby Day. She died on the First."

"Then," I said, "when she rode down the course on her gypsy cart," and a little chill came over me, "she was—"

"As a herring, Kerry, as a gutted herring," my uncle Valentine said.

"Then the rule was really infringed, and the horse should not have won."

"Wasn't he the best horse there?"

"Undoubtedly, sir, but as to the betting."

"The bookmakers lost less than they would have lost on the favourite."

"But the backers of the favourite."

"The small backer in the silver ring is paid on the first past the post, so they'd have lost, anyway. At any rate, they all should have lost. They backed their opinion as to which was the best horse, and it wasn't."

"But damn it all, sir! and God forgive me for swearing in this holy place—there's the Derby Rule."

" 'The letter killeth,' Kerry," quoted my uncle gravely, even piously. " 'The letter killeth.' "

A Second Out of Eternity

By MAJOR F. YEATS-BROWN

AND NOW the scene changes to Naini Tal, a hill station near Bareilly, where I am playing in the final match of a polo tournament. The time is a summer afternoon of the late Edwardian age.

My ponies are Daim, Tot, Crediton, with Ur of the Chaldees as a reserve. I'll give Crediton his breather first. The white ball bounds before us; Crediton follows it without touch of rein or spur. Tap—tap—tap I've dribbled it the length of the field and through the goal at full gallop. That is easier to do on this little Naini Tal polo ground than on a field of regulation size.

Crediton has stopped, for he has seen the crowd, and guesses that this is the final. He is sweating in front of his saddle and dancing from side to side; and now his muzzle's on the ground. He's bowing and scraping. . . . He's hysterical.

Now for Daim. You'll see the band from the middle of the ground, Daim, without standing on your hind legs. The noise puzzles you? You shouldn't think so much: It's bad for ponies. And why, oh why, do you have to twist your tongue over the bit? Rubber can't hurt you.

Still five minutes to go. Joey is hitting the length of the small ground in a single stroke. I wish I could do that. Billy—our captain—is talking with the umpire. They're not nervous. They're both natural athletes, and both destined, as a matter of fact, to play for England against America—Joey three times.

Nothing has happened to my lunch. Soup, meat, trifle have undergone no diminution or digestion. Sick? Yes, it's curious how Nature can make a violent effort of rejection when it would have

From "The Lives of a Bengal Lancer," The Viking Press.

been so much less trouble to deal with the meal in the usual way. And all this fuss is only about a game.

I'm sleepy now, with funk. Why don't we begin? Flags and sun and people. I'm thick in the head.

I'll play Crediton first. None of your circus tricks: this is serious. If I catch you bending. . . . Rough looking fellow, my opposing No. 1. Red head to match his jersey, and native made breeches and boots too low. The umpire is holding up his hand. Beyond him I see parasols, white dresses, glitter. The ball's the thing.

"Ride him, Y.B.!"

Isn't that what I'm doing? Crediton is leaning across the opposing No. 1. We bear down towards the umpire, tussling; he has only to put the ball at my feet and the game will begin. But he whistles, and turns, and sends us back. All to do again. I rein around in a daze. Shall I ever see the ball through this infernal sleep? Now we are galloping towards the umpire—now—now—and now! The ball has flown past us in the air.

Joey has it. He turns, hits down the ground.

"Ride, Y.B.!"

"Get out of my way, damn you!"

I am still entangled with No. 1. No hope of catching the back, who slashes at the ball on his near side, returning it amongst us. Billy meets it and dribbles it again toward the enemy's goal.

"Ride, Y.B.!"

This time Crediton and I overtake the back so that he misses his return. With a clean crack Billy drives the ball forward, past us, toward goal. There is a thunder and a crying. The back and I are neck and neck. He is a big man, but his pony is out of hand, snatching at the bridle. Crediton leans on him, jerking his wise old head. His grip is loosening and I am forcing him off his saddle.

Billy is on the line of the ball, but he's being ridden off. Joey, unmarked, bears down. The ball is six yards from goal, in its centre. Can he miss? Not Joey. He taps it through with a flick of the wrist; the whistle blows: we raise our sticks and yell for joy. First goal.

Cheers and fluttered handkerchiefs. Crediton faces the grandstand and begins to kneel down again.

"Hurry up, Y.B.!"

"All right, all right!"

The umpire won't throw the ball straight. It has gone to their No. 2, who is off like a streak. The crowd cheers. The ball bounces off Joey's helmet, so that he can't hit a backhander. Bad luck, that, for No. 2 is on it, and is tapping it round. He'll never do it at that pace. God, he has. He—has—! It's a goal!

Whistle. Yells. One all. We must begin again. No, Crediton! That was a goal against us and that's what you get in the mouth for being an idiot.

Where's the ball? Under my feet?

"Get out!"

"Go to hell!"

"Get off it!"

It's mine, out of the scrimmage. Hit or dribble?

"Ride, Y.B.!"

Must I leave it? God, that's hard.

Joey hits a glorious ball, clean and straight. Back and I are having a great fight. He curses me, for he is a portly man of nearly sixty, while I am bony and ruthless.

"Damn it, can't you hear the whistle?"

Already? I thought we had only just begun.

What's the matter? I swing my leg over Crediton's neck. It's his off fore. Lifting his gaiter, I feel his nobbly fetlock wet with blood.

"Well played, Y.B.," said Billy. I hardly touched the ball, but praise is sweet.

Daim is standing on his hind legs, again. I wish I didn't have temperamental ponies. Will Crediton be fit for another? Khushal is wrapping his legs in hot bandages.

We line up where we stopped play. Daim is on his hind legs when the ball is thrown in, so that I can't reach it. Then he jumps six feet into space. But I have it, somehow. A tap now. We're off. We have the legs of the field. Just now I dribbled the ball the length of the field: I must do it again. Hell's foundations quiver! As my stick came down, the ball bounced, or Daim did. Daim, you brute, we must bump the back.

Back won't be bumped. He's on a crafty Arab, which turns on a sixpence and leaves Daim cavorting about alone. Wait till we race for the ball!

Is this chukker never going to end? The last passed in a flash, now we seem to have been playing half an hour. My throat's dry. The reins have rubbed my fingers raw.

"For God's sake, mark your man, Y.B.!"

I can't hold Daim, that's the truth. He needs two hands to stop him. There's the ball. I'll let the swine loose!

"Hi! Hi! God Almighty!"

Whistle. Foul against us.

"Man alive," says Billy, "you can't cross like that."

A dangerous foul. That means a goal to them. In silence we ride back behind our goal. All my fault.

Our opponents take their positions fifty yards opposite us. The back has only to hit the ball through our undefended flags. Two whistles, the end of the second chukker.

"We're holding them," says Billy during the brief interval. "It can't be helped about the foul. Ride at him as soon as he begins to hit. You never know."

Tot feels like a battleship under me. I have had a sip of champagne. The band is playing "Bonnie Dundee."

Ride! Can I hit a ball in mid-air? I've missed, but why is Joey yelling "Played, Y.B.?" I've hit it. Well, Tot has, with her hoof. Billy is on the ball now, and I'm marking my man as I should.

Up and down we race. I'm clinging desperately to the back, using him as a cushion. That's useful, anyway. Time. That period was quickly over. One all, and half time.

Can I ride Crediton again? He's better on three legs than Daim on four. But Billy says that I must keep Crediton for the last chukker. So my choice is between Ur of the Chaldees or that India rubber son of a gun, Daim, who's cut my hands to ribbons. I'll give him a trial. Yes, Brownstone; it's one all. Can't you read the numbers? Water on the back of my neck: how good it feels, dripping.

I think we'll win, if I don't disgrace myself.

The opposing one trots out lame, goes back. We wait. He has reappeared on a black carthorse.

I've got the ball this time at last, and have tapped it forward to Billy under Daim's neck. Up and down, up and down. Will the ball never come back to me? I'm enjoying myself, though, bump-

ing the back over the sidelines, and turning under the carthorse's
nose. Here's a backhander for me to hit—and I've hit it too, for
once in a blue moon. Joey has the ball. Will he? No, his shot goes
wide. My stick's broken. A stick—quick! They have hit it out from
behind, and No. 2 swoops down to our goal.

Goal to them, almost before I knew what was happening.
Time. The score's 2-1 against us.

"I wish to God you'd keep on the ground and try to hit the
ball," says Joey.

Yes, I know his censure is deserved.

Billy slices to the sidewall as soon as we begin again; Joey
takes the rebound with a near-side shot. Two inches more to the
right, it would have been a goal.

"Meet it, can't you?"

I can't. Tot is slow on her helm. My stick weighs a ton. These
seven minutes are seven hours.

The last period. It is only forty minutes since I began this
living . . . Crediton, poor, sweet good angel! If you die, it will be
in a good cause. Steady. We've met it, by God!

I wish everyone would stop shouting. I know I've got to hit
that spot of white. The goal flags are a little to my left. Now is
our chance, Crediton. You are smooth and steady and fast; no
one can catch us.

I am alone in the world with an open goal in front. A steady
shot: a calm shot amidst the hoof-beats and cheers. I can't bring
my stick down. It's stuck. My stick has been hooked. I'm helpless.
The ball bobs by; but Billy, bless him, is behind. And following
him, trying to hook, comes the red headed No. 1. His hat's fallen
off. Will the umpire stop the game? I can't look or listen. Back
and I surge through the goal-flags, scattering a group of spectators
who shout even as they run, for Billy has sent the ball true and
straight, whizzing past my face.

We're level. Two all and six minutes to play. The crowd is a
wild beast, roaring for its food.

Quick back to the line up. Crediton is lame at the trot, but
can forget his pain. I must get the ball again. Yes, no, yes. I pass
it to Billy, who shoots, but the wind carries it wide.

The game is becoming sticky with tension.

"Don't stand on the ball!"

"Get to hell out of it!"

Crediton could creep under these scrums. Yes, we've nosed in among the sticks, and are out with the ball.

But a bugle sounds, and I hesitate. The umpire is shouting to me to play on (the rule is that when we are level we continue until the ball goes out) but I have missed my stroke and the ball trickles over the backline. That ends the period.

After a minute's interval, we shall continue until one of us scores. I'll ride Daim again, my fastest pony, chastened now by hard work.

"Stick to the back, Y.B.!" says Billy, "I'll meet the ball." So be it.

When the umpire throws in, I hurl myself at my opponent. Billy has it. No, it is Joey, and he is taking it to the center of the ground. Why, he's standing still! For an instant that seems spun out to years, Joey stands there, a tower of blue and ivory, supremely sure of himself, glancing now at goal and now at two opponents who are turning on him. He taps the ball tenderly in front of his pony's forelegs, he aims, he brings his stick down with a crack that echoes yet in memory.

The driven balls sails low and swift. I've reined up to stare at Victory as she steals inch by inch over my senses.

Daim shies away toward the back whom he has been so cheerfully bumping, for he understands riding off, but not this voice of a raging beast that is coming from all round us. How did Joey carve that second out of eternity? How has he conquered time? The ball is still in the air: As it reaches the goal-posts it rises and soars between them. The goal umpire is gripping his signal flag. He's waved it.

Finish!

People are running all over the ground. We've won! That's all, Daim. Bran mash for you. Baksheesh for the servants. The syces will get drunk, I suppose.

The Matterhorn

By A. F. MUMMERY

AT THE AGE of fifteen the crags of the Via Mala and the snows of the Theodule roused a passion within me that has grown with years, and has to no small extent moulded my life and thought. It has led me into regions of such fairy beauty that the fabled wonders of Xanadu seem commonplace beside them; it has brought me friends who may be relied on in fair weather and in foul; and it has stored my mind with memories that are treasures, corruptible neither by moth nor rust, sickness nor old age. My boyish delight in the great white peaks towering above the gloom of pines is still awakened when the lumbering diligence rolls through the gorge of the Diosaz or when the Matterhorn rises from out the foliage of the Val Tournanche. I remember, as if it were yesterday, my first sight of the great mountain. It was shining in all the calm majesty of a September moon, and, in the stillness of an autumn night, it seemed the very embodiment of mystery and a fitting dwelling-place for the spirits with which old legends people its stone-swept slopes. From that moment I have been one of the great peak's most reverent worshippers, and whenever the mighty rock appears above the distant horizon, I hail its advent with devoutest joy. Even the vulgarisation of Zermatt, the cheap trippers and their trumpery fashions, cannot wholly drive me from the lower slopes, and I still love to gaze at it from amongst the pines of the Riffelberg, or to watch its huge mass soaring above the flowery meadows of the Staffelalp. In those distant days (1871), however, it was still

From "My Climb in the Alps and Caucasus," Loring and Mussey.

shrouded with a halo of but half-banished inaccessibility, and, as I looked at it through the tangle of the pines or from the breezy alps, I scarcely dared to hope that one day I might be numbered among the glorious few who had scaled its frozen cliffs. Three years later, however, the ascent had become fashionable, the deluge had begun, and with its earlier waves I was swept on to the long desired summit.

I am aware that from that moment my interest in the peak should have ceased, that the well-conducted climber never repeats an ascent; that his object is to reach the summit, and, that object once attained, his work is over and he should rest in ignoble ease. The true faith on this subject is crystallized and resplendent in a remark made to me last year by a bandbox inmate of the Monte Rosa Hotel: "I had to go to Grindelwald to ascend the Eiger; it was a beastly nuisance, but I wanted to finish off the Oberland: shall never go there again!"

For myself, I am fain to confess a deplorable weakness in my character. No sooner have I ascended a peak than it becomes a friend, and delightful as it may be to seek "fresh woods and pastures new," in my heart of hearts I long for the slopes of which I know every wrinkle, and on which each crag awakens memories of mirth and laughter and of the friends of long ago. As a consequence of this terrible weakness, I have been no less than seven times on the top of the Matterhorn. I have sat on the summit with my wife when a lighted match would not flicker in the windless air, and I have been chased from its shattered crest and down the Italian ridge by the mad fury of thunder, lightning, and whirling snow. Yet each memory has its own peculiar charm, and the wild music of the hurricane is hardly a less delight than the glories of a perfect day. The idea which cleaves unto the orthodox mountaineer that a single ascent, on one day, in one year, enables that same mountaineer to know and realise how that peak looks on all other days, in all other years, suggests that he is still wallowing in the lowest bogs of Philistinism. It is true the crags and pinnacles are the same, but their charm and beauty lies in the ever changing light and shade, in the mists which wreath around them, in the huge cornices and pendent icicles, in all the varying circumstances of weather, season, and hour. Moreover, it is not merely that the actual vision impressed on the retina reflects every mood and change of summer storm and sunshine; but the observer himself is hardly less inconstant. On one day he is dominated by the tingling horror of the precipice, the gaunt bareness of the stupendous cliffs, or the deadly rush of the rocks when some huge block breaks from its moorings and hurtles through the air—a fit emblem of resistless wrath. On yet another day he notices none of these things; lulled by the delicate tints of opal and azure, he revels in the vaporous softness of the Italian valleys, in the graceful sweep of the wind-drifted snow, or even in the tiny flowers wedged in the joints of the granite. While the mountain may sometimes impress its mood on the spectator, as often the spectator only sees that which harmonises with his own. A man may doubtless be so constructed that

> *"A primrose by the river's brim*
> *A yellow primrose is to him"*

and in no conceivable circumstance or time could it ever be aught else; but others more happily constituted, who can rejoice in the beauty of the external world, are scarcely likely to feel the "taint of staleness," no matter how thoroughly they may know the substantial basis of rock and ice on which the sun and cloud, mist, air, and sky are ever weaving the glory of the view.

It was, then, with an interest in the great mountain only intensified by my first ascent, that I crossed the Tiefenmattenjoch in 1879. Whilst descending the glacier, I gazed long and earnestly at the great Z'Mutt ridge towering above the long slopes of rock and stone-swept couloirs of the western face. I was by no means the first who had so gazed; amongst others, Mr. Whymper with his guides Michel Croz and Christian Almer, had studied it carefully from the crags of the Dent Blanche. The conclusions they came to may be gathered from the following paragraph: "My old enemy—the Matterhorn—seen across the basin of the Z'Muttgletscher, looked totally unassailable. 'Do you think,' the men asked, 'that you, or anyone else, will ever get up that mountain?' And when, undismayed by their ridicule, I stoutly answered, 'Yes, but not upon that side,' they burst into derisive chuckles. I must confess that my hopes sank; for nothing can look, or be, more completely inaccessible than the Matterhorn on its northern and

north-west sides." It did not appear, however, that this judgment
was wholly warranted. The snow ridge and the jagged rocks by
which it is continued for some distance further, offered an obtru-
sively easy route to a height of about 13,000 feet, and on the final
ridge, from about 14,000 feet to the summit, the climber had
little to fear. Serious difficulty was limited to the short section of
the route by which these two highways would have to be connected. From observations on this and previous occasions, it was
evident that where the Z'Mutt ridge first steepens, till it verges
on the perpendicular, it would be necessary to bear to the left
into a deeply cut couloir, which falls in appalling precipices to
the Matterhorn Glacier. The upper part of this couloir, where
alone we should have to deal with it, did not, however, look altogether hopeless, and, provided it could be ascended, the ridge
would be regained above the first inaccessible step. A short distance further, where it again becomes perpendicular, or rather
actually overhangs, it was apparently possible to swerve to the
right on to the long slopes of the western face, and, after a considerable ascent, to regain the Z'Mutt ridge above all serious
difficulty. Having decided upon this somewhat ambitious pro-
gramme I went down to Zermatt to find a suitable guide to carry
it out.

In front of the Monte Rosa Hotel I met an old companion,
Alois Burgener, who gave me the joyful news that his brother
Alexander might possibly be able to join me for a few days. The
broad-shouldered Alexander, his face half hidden in beard, was
then interviewed; he bluntly expressed his opinion that to go
on such an expedition with a Herr of whom he knew nothing
would be a verfluchte Dummheit. I was much taken by this bold
expression of opinion, which appeared to me not merely indica-
tive of a wise distrust of an untried climber, but also of a determination to drive home the attack, when once begun, to the
utmost limits of possibility. My previous experience had been
chiefly, if not exclusively, with men who were eager to start on
any attempt, no matter how desperate, and who were far too
polite to inquire whether their employer knew anything about the
art of climbing. At an early stage in the proceedings, however,
these men had invariably developed a most touching, but none
the less most inconvenient, affection for their wives and families,

and were compelled by these most commendable feelings to discontinue the ascent. The confident carriage of Alexander, and the honest out-spokenness of his language, seemed to show that he was not of this sort, and to presage well for our future acquaintance. I gladly accepted his suggestions, and agreed that we should make a few preliminary expeditions together.

We accordingly crossed to the Laquintal by the Mischabel and Laquin passes, forcing our way back over the Fletschhorn by a new and remarkably difficult route. We then ascended the Portjenhorn, and on the fifth day returned to Zermatt by the Ried pass and St. Niklaus. Our campaign having been thus successfully inaugurated, we were ready to turn our attention to the Z'Mutt ridge. We felt, however, that we had fairly earned a day's rest, so we spent the last of August lying among the haymakers of the lower slopes. Towards evening we heard that Mr. Penhall, with Ferdinand Imseng and L. Zurbrucken, had started that very day to sleep on the mountain and assault the Z'Mutt ridge the next morning. We had little doubt about their success. The weather looked perfect, the mountain was in exceptionally good condition and the party was of most unusual skill and strength. We determined in consequence to vary our plans and cross the Col Durand. This would enable us to watch their progress and obtain useful information for the future, and we hoped that possibly the east ridge or north-east face of the Dent Blanche would afford us consolation for the loss of the Z'Mutt ridge.

The next morning, on our way to the Staffelalp we found that so fierce a wind was raging on the higher peaks that it seemed hardly possible any serious ascent could be effected. Our thoughts and aspirations consequently veered back to the Z'Mutt ridge, and when we met Penhall's party returning, and heard that they had definitely abandoned the ridge route, we determined to spend the day at the Stockje and see whether the wind and clouds really meant mischief. On our arrival there the men soon came to the conclusion that the weather was hopeless. I was, however, much too young and too eager to dream of returning, and being wholly ignorant of all meteorological lore, I was able to prophesy fair things with such an appearance of well-founded knowledge that Burgener was half convinced. A second difficulty then arose. Our provisions were calculated on the basis of a ten hours' walk, and were obviously insufficient for a two days' campaign. Gentinetta's feelings, stimulated doubtless by the contemplation of these limited supplies, at length overcame his usual taciturnity and, unabashed by "the dignity that doth hedge" a Herr, he expressed his opinion of my prophecies. He backed this up by stating that at no period since the creation of the world, nor for that matter anterior to it, had such wind and such clouds resulted in aught but the most desperate and lasting bad weather. We felt that exercise would be good for his spirits, and that in any case his company would be depressing, so he was sent back to Zermatt for extra supplies and the best man he could find to help carry them. We pointed out the place where we should camp, and undertook to intercept him on his way back should the weather appear to us too evil for sleeping out.

Ever darkening clouds rolled over the Col Tournanche, and the roar of the wind through the crags of the Matterhorn became distinctly audible, telling of the furious hurricane that was raging round its mighty ridges. Burgener's confidence began to waver, and he again suggested retiring to the Capuan luxuries of the Monte Rosa Hotel. I felt more than a tremor of doubt myself, but the die was cast, so I trusted to luck, kept a cheerful countenance and declared that, come what might, we should have fair play from the weather. Burgener was impressed. The constant blotting out of the distant ridges, the ever gathering mass of cloud round the Matterhorn, and more than a suspicion of dampness in the fierce squalls of wind that smote us at short intervals, were signs so distinct and unmistakable that he thought even a Herr must recognise them. My persistence, therefore, suggested occult knowledge. I was, perhaps, a Mahatma (or its Saastal equivalent), and he settled himself in a sheltered corner, and charmed by the caresses of my Lady Nicotine, told me weird tales of the ghosts and goblins which still haunt the great circle of cliffs towering above the Val Anzasca. As the day wore on, the burden of a cheerful countenance became too much for me, so I sought to drown my anxieties in sleep. Late in the afternoon Burgener awoke me with a great thump and bid me look at the weather. My first impression was that he had come to upbraid me as an impostor, and hold up my prophecies to scorn and derision. His jubilant air and a look of thinness about the lingering clouds, however, negatived these painful thoughts, and I found that the thump was intended to convey devout appreciation of my astounding wisdom! I shook myself free from the damp rugs, and a gleam of sunshine breaking through the mists, we welcomed the returning orb of day with ear-splitting yells and a "break down" as vigorous as hobnailed boots would permit. Our conduct would doubtless have suggested to competent critics that we were pious followers of Zoroaster (or escaped lunatics?). These ebullitions of joy having exhausted themselves and us, we packed the knapsacks and, appropriating the store of rugs belonging to the hut, made for the rendezvous appointed with Gentinetta.

At the extreme north-western corner of the great buttress or shelf on which rests the Matterhorn Glacier, is a stony plateau from which the ice has long since retreated. We hoped to discover a sheltered hollow amongst the debris with which it is strewn, and thitherward we slowly wended our way. On our arrival we found a total absence of convenient hollows, and we were fain to content ourselves with such protection as the side of a big rock affords. Above us frowned the great ice cliffs of the glacier, cutting off nearly all view of the mountain. To the right, and out of reach of any fragments that might fall from them, was a long ridge of rock leading to the foot of the snow arete. Having lit our fire and set the pot to boil, we sat down at the edge of the cliff overlooking the Z'Mutt Glacier, and soon discovered Gentinetta and another man making their way rapidly through the crevasses. Meanwhile the sun had set, and with the gathering darkness the last lingering clouds dispersed as by magic. About eight o'clock the men arrived, and we found that our new recruit was Johann Petrus. We were both delighted, for no bolder climber or more resolute man has ever delighted the heart of an eager Herr.

Gentinetta's commissariat arrangements had taken a very fluid form. Our dinner consisted chiefly of the remains of our original provisions and a heterogeneous mixture of red wine and marsala, bottled beer and cognac. During the continuance of this festivity, Burgener and Gentinetta vied with each other in extolling the weather wisdom of their Herr. Petrus was called upon to bear witness to its utterly uncompromising appearance in the morning, and, not content with his testimony, the absent Imseng was added to my triumph: for had he not also given it up as hopeless? "Yet their Herr never faltered in his confidence"—little did they guess my feelings during the afternoon—"and had consistently borne true witness in the face of an adverse host." Subsequent experience has been quite thrown away on Burgener; he still regards me as of transcendent merit in this branch of the climber's craft. When, as usually happens, facts do not agree with my forecast, he, like the celebrated French scientist, is inclined to exclaim: Tant pis pour les faits.

The night proved intensely cold. The clouds had prevented any sunshine reaching the plateau, and the small pools of water and patches of snow, even when we first reached it, were still hard frozen and a keen north wind above seemed to freeze us to the very marrow, and we shivered with the pain of cold under our scanty rugs. We were all glad when it was time to be moving, and at the first hint of dawn (4.15 a.m.) we began to scramble up the rocks and along the ridge leading towards the snow arete. At 5.20 a.m. we reached its foot, and on a sheltered ledge found the debris of Penhall's camp. Here we halted for breakfast and deposited the blankets, which, thinking it just possible we might have to spend another night on the mountain, we had brought with us to this point. After half an hour's halt we put on the rope and began to ascend the snow ridge. Reaching the rocky teeth, which, when seen from Zermatt, stand out conspicuously against the sky, we scrambled over the rickety piles of frost-riven rock. Beyond the third tooth we were pulled up by a deep cleft. Burgener and Petrus soon scrambled down the face of the rocks to our right and succeeded in getting into it. Further direct progress was, however, impossible, as the ridge rose perpendicularly above them, and a great rib supporting it bulged out in front and precluded all chance of traversing. Of itself this would not have stopped either of the men, as a narrow gully between this rib and the fangs of the tooth on which Gentinetta and I were sitting offered an obvious means of descending below the obstruction; further in front and to the left, however, rose a slope with the unpleasant look that tells of a basis of rotten rock, glazed with ice and masked with powdery snow. Higher up it steepened till it seemed almost perpendicular. Up this slope we knew we must go or abandon the ascent, and, startled by its appearance, the men recoiled to the rocks where I was still posted.

For another three-quarters of an hour we examined it without being able to see a satisfactory way across, and unpleasant doubts were being freely expressed when a distant jodel attracted our attention. Far away down the mountain we spied three dots, whom we at once and rightly guessed to be Penhall and his guides. We wasted the next half-hour in alternately watching their progress and studying our slope. At length they disappeared behind a projecting buttress, and this excuse for delay having disappeared, it was decided that we should pass the cleft in front and examine the slope more nearly. We descended into the gap. Burgener and Petrus then scrambled down the gully and soon found a way on to the face. On reaching this point a few minutes later I found Burgener and Petrus already working upwards, and in a few minutes we were again on the arete. After following it a short distance, we reached the point at which it was necessary to take to the evil slope, and the discussion was once more renewed. Burgener was distinctly averse to attempting it, but as there was no other way, Petrus went forward to explore.

I have not the slightest doubt that Burgener's objection to this slope was exclusively due to the fact that we had never previously been together on this sort of work. It was obviously practicable, but it was equally obvious that the slip of one meant the destruction of all who were roped to him. Subsequent experience enables me to sympathise with his feelings. The knowledge that you can do nothing to arrest a slip, combined with a lively fear that one may occur, creates as unpleasant a situation as it is easy to imagine. The fear of slipping oneself is almost a delight when compared with the trap-like feeling induced by the rope with an "unknown quantity" at the end of it.

Our halts at this point and on the third tooth had exceeded two hours, and we had no more time to lose. Petrus seemed to be getting on all right, so Burgener made ready for the traverse. Though by no means a big man in the valley, on an ice-glazed slope he seems to visibly dilate, and looks like a veritable giant when wielding his resistless axe. For some reason, probably to get a decent excuse for unroping Gentinetta and saving him from the risk of the "unknown quantity," Burgener told us to pay him out till he should be ganz fest. We paid out a hundred feet of rope, and as there was no immediate prospect of his being ganz fest, and

as in the event of a slip it was tolerably certain that it would make
no difference whether he were or no, I cautiously followed his
track; Gentinetta bringing up the rear, free from the dangerous
entanglement of the rope. Having traversed in all about a hundred and fifty feet we were able to turn up the slope, and soon
reached firm rock, which, though very steep, offered good hold
and plenty of it. Burgener dashed up at a furious pace. Suddenly
a splinter of rock caught his coat, and an agonised yell told us
that his pipe, his faithful companion in many a hard-fought climb,
and the gift of his most trusted Herr, had been jerked out of his
pocket and had plunged down to the Matterhorn Glacier.

Soon afterwards we regained the ridge, and, without halting,
followed it to the point where it not merely becomes perpendicular, but actually overhangs. We had now to traverse to our right
on to the great western face of the mountain. Burgener anxiously
scanned the huge cliff and then gripped my hand and exclaimed,
"The pipe is avenged, we are on the summit," which I took to
mean that we should be there sometime.

The men began the construction of a stone man, whilst I
utilised the halt in a diligent search for a diminute chicken
which Burgener averred was concealed in the knapsack. We then
prepared one of our numerous bottles for the due reception of
our names, and it was subsequently carefully built into the cairn.
These duties having been performed, and Burgener having borrowed Gentinetta's pipe—which, by the way, he did not return till
we got back to Zermatt—we began the ascent of the western face.
We traversed a short distance and then turned straight up over
slabby, icy, and somewhat loose rocks. They were not, however,
difficult, and we made rapid progress. Probably we should have
done better still further to the right, but Burgener was very
properly averse to this course, as he thought it might bring us
too directly above the other party. Even where we were, he insisted on the utmost care to avoid upsetting stones. I subsequently
learned from Penhall that his party was too far to the right to be
affected by anything we sent down, and the one or two fragments
we did dislodge never came within sight or hearing.

After some steady climbing, we reached a point from which
it appeared possible to work back on to the Z'Mutt ridge, but
Burgener was not quite certain, and on hearing that Carrel had

traversed by a ledge higher up, he preferred to take that course. We soon gained this ledge—the well-known "corridor" of the early Breuil ascents—and found no difficulty in following it to the fault that bars access to the ridge. Petrus was promptly swung over to see if the last man could get down unaided. This being pronounced impossible, our second rope was got out. A good deal of time was spent before it could be fixed, the only available knob of rock being too round to admit of its being easily attached. Meanwhile, I had time to look along the ledge which winds like a pathway, round all the irregularities of the mountain, to the southern ridge. It was quite free from ice and snow, and in its then condition could have been traversed with ease. I also came upon a deeply rusted hook driven into the rock, a relic, I suppose, of Mr. Grove's ascent in 1867. Having slid down the rope, we found the remainder of the ledge was very different. Instead of offering firm foothold on the rock, it was loaded with incoherent snow, and the few knobs which protruded through this were glazed with ice, and, for the most part, rotten. It was, however, of no great extent, and we were soon able to plunge through the snow on to the ridge (12.50 p.m.) Petrus, who had been more or less erratic in his movements all day, had disappeared. We followed his traces, occasionally on the arete, but more often on the steep slope to the left, and in three-quarters of an hour found him on the summit (1.45 p.m.)

The day was perfectly calm and the view cloudless. Time fled swiftly, and when Burgener came up to me with the rope at 2.30 p.m. I could hardly believe we had been three-quarters of an hour on the summit.

Then we descended the chain-clad north-eastern arete to the elbow, where we waited a few minutes to watch Penhall's party, which had just come in sight on the Z'Mutt ridge. With a parting jodel to our friends we plunged down the slopes to the cabane. Great care, however, was required to avoid the broken glass and sardine boxes which had accumulated in large quantities. After a short halt we ran down to the Furggen Glacier, and at 5.30 p.m. were unbuckling our gaiters on the moraine under the Hornli. An hour and a half later we tramped down the high street of Zermatt, and were soon enjoying the rewards of the faithful.

A year later, at Couttet's Hotel, I was dreaming peacefully of

my bien aimee the Aiguille des Charmoz—whom we had successfully wooed the previous day—when Burgener broke in upon my
slumbers and ejected me, ruthlessly, from the soft comfort of my
bed.

Protests were vain. The huge Furggen ridge of the Matterhorn
had long tempted his desires, and what are such things as sleep,
rest, or blissful ease, when weighed in the balance with the wild
joy of gripping grey-brown ledges, and hacking and beating the
long gullies of ice into submission? All the ingrained fighting
instinct was aroused in him. He wished to hurl himself once more
at the cliffs and ridges, matching his skill against their dumb,
passionless resistance, and forcing them now, as ever, to yield to
his reckless onslaught. Time, however, pressed, and if this attempt
was to be made, without prejudicing other long-cherished hopes,
it was necessary to reach Stalden that very night.

We hurried along to Argentiere, and then the driver, thinking
he had fairly got us in his power, coolly told us that it was quite
impossible to the catch the mid-day train at Martigny; at all
events, neither his horses nor anyone else's could do it. We were
not, however, to be beaten. Seizing our axes and knapsacks, we
left the voiture disconsolate on the road, and trudged manfully
up the paths toward the Col de Balme. The driver, who saw the
piled up wealth of the Martigny tariff dwindling into a mere ten
francs, protested with all the vigour of a Chamoniard.

We were buoyed up, during the ascent, by the hope that a
voiture would be procurable at the Forclaz inn. But when we
arrived there, we found that luck had abandoned us, and we must
face the grim terrors of the road down to Martigny. Half choked
by dust, and more than half baked by the blazing sun, we reached
the railway station with just twenty minutes to spare. Burgener
quickly recognised the necessities of the situation—borrowing a
franc, he dashed into the town, and, before we could realise the
nature of his quest, he returned with a great stoneware jar full
of foaming beer. Jolly John Barleycorn quickly appeased our
miseries, and by the time the lumbering train had arrived happiness was once more enshrined in the party.

We reached Stalden about 4 p.m., and halted for the night.
By so doing, Burgener and Venetz were enabled to make those
ecclesiastical arrangements which the peculiar enormities of the

Furggen ridge seemed to render desirable. Such elaborate and careful preparations appeared to me a trifle uncanny, and subsequent events showed very clearly the evil effects which this sort of indulgence in religious festivities has upon the nerves. However, both Burgener and Venetz appeared to be in excellent spirits when they returned, and we whiled away the summer evening with stories of chamois hunting and the great deeds wrought amongst the winter snow.

The next day we strolled up to St. Niklaus, and drove merrily on to Zermatt, starting about half-past ten the same evening for our ridge. Near the last chalets, the guides, allured by the pleasing appearance of a small hollow, curled themselves up and went fast to sleep. I soon found that the grass was damp, not to say wet, and the wind bitterly cold. The contemplation of these discomforts gradually exhausted my patience, and, as there were no signs of waking, I gently stirred the sleepers with an ice-axe. The knapsacks were picked up, and we went slowly on our way. From this point our pace became steadily worse, until, at last, Burgener confessed to being very unwell. In consequence, I took his load, and we struggled onwards till we came to a great stone, close to the Schwarzsee. It was quite obvious by this time that the ascent must be abandoned, and, after an hour's halt, we tramped wearily back to Zermatt, where we arrived too early for breakfast and too late for bed.

After a bathe in the Triftbach, I returned to a sad and solitary meal in the Monte Rose Hotel, and, from a secluded corner, heard my chances of success discussed on all sides; the more eager folk even neglecting their breakfasts in favour of the painful attitudes requisite to watch the Furggen ridge through the big telescope.

A well-known climber has expressed a doubt whether the Christian virtue of good temper is binding on a man before 9.30 a.m. I sincerely trust it may not be, or Venetz and I most certainly have a mauvais quart d'heure before us. Burgener, with much wisdom, went to bed, and was thus free from the wrangles with which Venetz and I sought to pass the dragging hours. As the day wore on, things began to take a more hopeful turn. Burgener was reported better, and, towards evening, even in favour of a renewed attempt. Two other parties were leaving for the Hornli route at 11 p.m., so, to avoid the bustle and discomfort of an innumerable host, we determined not to start before midnight.

Owing to the usual delays, we did not actually get off till 12.45 a.m., and, once more, tramped up the slopes to our last night's halting place. Whilst the men were consuming a sort of preparatory breakfast, I watched the curious movements of a light, far below on the Gorner Glacier. The light, obviously, proceeded from a lantern, but its movements were most extraordinary and undecided. At one moment it would make good progress up the glacier, then it would halt, wobble up and down, in and out, dodge behind intervening rocks or ice, again reappear, and finally redescend to the original point of departure. These proceedings were then repeated, and there seemed to be no possible aim or object to its vagaries. However, my mind was chiefly occupied with the Furggen ridge, and, so soon as we again got under way, I thought no more of its strange behaviour. The men were evidently determined to make up for our slow progress on the preceding night by the rapidity of their movements on this, and it was with no small delight that I hailed our arrival on the level stretch of boggy ground, under the Schwarzsee.

A few minutes later we were surrounded by the weird, unearthly flicker of innumerable will-o'-the-wisps. At every step they floated away on either hand, yet, seemingly, no sooner had we passed, than they crept up stealthily behind, dogging our footsteps with a cruel vindictiveness from which there appeared no hope of escape or flight.

The men were horror-struck. Burgener gripped my arm and hoarsely whispered—Sehen Sie, Herr, die toten Leute!

We were marked out for the vengeance of the immortal gods. The fiends who haunt the crags of the Matterhorn were already gloating over their prey! Such was the purport of the agonised whispers of the men. I am fain to confess, the crawling, bluish flames, the utter silence, and the contagion of my companions' superstitious fear, thrilled me with instinctive horror. I perceived, however, that if we were not to return to Zermatt, baffled and beaten a second time, the delights of a spiritualistic seance must be abandoned in favour of a matter-of-fact explanation. My efforts in this direction led Burgener and Venetz to the somewhat erroneous belief that every square yard of England, Scotland, and Wales is illuminated, nightly, by similar, but far more brilliant and nerve-shattering displays. Despite the unfortunate way in which my German would give out just as I was making a really effective point, the men were evidently inclined to think that these Geister were, perhaps, impostors; but, alas! this was not all.

"Ach lieber Herr, did you not see the wandering light on the Gorner Glacier? There is no boggy ground there. That was a Geist."

In vain I protested that it was a lantern. "A lantern! What could anyone want there? It was on the road to nowhere; besides, it did not move forwards like a lantern, but kept wandering to and fro, twinkling and dodging, precisely as a disembodied spirit, with no particular business on hand, might be expected to do."

The position was serious enough in all conscience. It is a well-ascertained fact (attested by all the ecclesiastical authorities of the Saas, Zermatt, and Anzasca valleys) that anyone seeing a Geist is certain to be killed within twenty-four hours! I pointed out to Burgener that this being so, there could be no advantage in turning back, for, either they were ghosts, in which case we must be killed, or they were not ghosts, in which case we might as well go on. The men admitted the dilemma, but suggested that even so, climbing up a peak for the purpose of being chucked off it by mischievous Geister is not pure and unalloyed joy. I readily assented to this proposition, but pointed out the inconvenience and discomfort, both mental and bodily, of being haled from the Monte Rosa Hotel, perhaps from the very table d'hote itself, by the foul fiend and his myrmidons. I asked him to consider the scorn and contempt with which the Zermatt priesthood, ever jealous of their Saastal brethren, would witness his flight, as, clutched by the huge talons, the black wings bore him to the underworld. Burgener, who, like Luther and the early Christian fathers, had had personal acquaintance with his Satanic Majesty, agreed that this would be altogether too grievous, and, taking everything into consideration, that the balance of advantage lay with an advance. Being the most sceptical of the party, I was allotted the post of leader.

Suddenly, in the distance, appeared two lights. "The other parties!" I exclaimed, thinking the men's fears would be somewhat allayed by company. But Burgener and Venetz had Geister on the brain, and vowed that these also were undoubted specimens of that genus. I urged them to force the pace and find out. "What!" cried they, "do you know so little of Geister as to attempt such a thing as that?" Burgener, after much persuasion, consented to jodel, a proceeding attended with very grave danger—Geister don't like being jodelled at—and only to be effected in doubtful and tremulous sort. To our delight, however, back came a cheery yell, that the men recognised as belonging to Peter Taugwalder.

The sceptics in the party being much strengthened by this most opportune support, we pushed onwards more cheerily. When, lo! a great luminous figure with out-stretched arm sprang across our path, and, as instantly, melted into the blackness of night. I will freely admit that the inveterate sceptic was startled at this apparition, and stood motionless with horror and super-stitious fear. The men, however, were actuated by other feelings. They knew that only a few yards off were the consecrated walls of the Schwarzsee chapel, and, dashing past me, they rushed, wild with panic fear, towards this tiny oasis of safety.

A second time the apparition stood before us, but now we could see that our mysterious foe was naught else than the door-post of the sacred edifice itself. A candle left in the chapel by Taugwalder throwing a fitful light on the limbered porch, as the unlatched door swung to and fro in the light breeze.

The men entered for devotional purposes, whilst I proceeded slowly on my way. Reaching the Furggen Glacier, I sat down on a stone and waited. Half an hour passed, and I began to wonder whether a fresh troop of ghosts had driven them incontinently back to Zermatt. Happily, just as the first grey light of dawn began to show in the east, my shouts were answered, and, once more united, we tramped rapidly up the glacier. As the sun rose, its earliest beams fell on long wisps of snow torn from the crest of the Matterhorn, and though of fairy-like beauty, suggestive of more wind than we quite cared for.

We had by now reached the base of the steep glacier that clings to the eastern face of the Matterhorn, and as our ghostly adventures had most unduly delayed us, we determined to try a short cut and ascend traversely over the distorted ice to a rock couloir that obviously gave access to the broken cliff immediately under the Furggen ridge. The adoption of this line of ascent illustrates very clearly the errors to which even the best ice-men are occasionally subject. I have no hesitation in saying, that Burgener is second to no one living, in the skill with which he can steer his party through an icefall, and the instinctive art of taking the best route. But on this occasion he was hopelessly astray. An easy route to the foot of our couloir can be found, either by keeping close under the north-eastern ridge till the upper level of the glacier is reached, and thence traversing across slightly inclined snow; or the climber may push over the flat glacier to the foot of the Furggengrat, and find an equally easy way to the upper snows, close to its base.

We, however, took neither of these courses, and were soon involved in ice work of the most sensational kind. At one point it appeared as if we should be forced to retreat. The upper lip of a huge crevasse towered forty feet or more above us, and it was only by the most brilliant skill that Burgener and Venetz succeeded in forcing their way up in a small transverse crevasse that, luckily, intersected it. Above this obstruction we halted a few minutes, to examine our line of attack.

From the Breuiljoch to the great snow slopes of the eastern face, a steep cliff guards all approach to the upper part of the mountain, and the rock couloir, referred to above, seemed to be the only point at which we could break through these defences. The main objections to it were the obvious frequency of stone avalanches, and the impossibility of conveniently gaining its base, save by the ascent of the deep groove cut by these same stones in the ice slope below. However, we all agreed that well-behaved stones in the nineteenth century were scarcely likely to be on the move at 5 a.m., so we turned a couple of bergschrunds, scrambled into the avalanche groove, and dashed up at a furious pace; an occasional rattle overhead stimulating our movements to the utmost. The rock couloir proved to be ice-glazed, and not free from difficulty; moreover, we could only ascend exactly in the line of fire. It was, therefore, with feelings of great delight that we perceived a flaw in the cliff on our left, and were able to find a way through to the easy slopes of the face.

Here we halted to take breath, for our desperate exertions had been more than even the most active amongst us quite appreciated. A little stream, which the sun had just woke from its icy sleep, then suggested breakfast, and we unpacked the knapsacks and settled ourselves for half an hour's rest. Far below, a party bound for the Furggenjoch spied us on our lofty seats, and roused the echoes of the mountain with their jodels.

Bearing to our left we soon reached the ridge, and ascended without difficult of any sort, till at 9 a.m. we reached the great tower, seen from Zermatt on the left sky line just beneath the final peak. Standing in the gap between this tower and the mass of the mountain, we looked down a couloir of most appalling steepness. Far beneath us, amongst its lower crags and ridges, mists were curling and seething, seeming in their restless activity to be the half awakened Geister hungering for their victims. So strange and mysterious did that deep chasm seem, that I half expected to see the writhing vapour take form and substance, and sweep to their doom those rash mortals who had surprised the dead amid their nightly revels.

Far above, the great ridges, armed with fantastic icicles, at one moment would stand out hard and sharp against a blue-black sky, and the next be lost in a blurred cloud of driving snow, the roar of each furious gust being followed by the ominous clatter of broken icicles, and the crash of great stones torn from the summit rocks.

The final peak looked very formidable, and, in such weather, could not have been assailed with any reasonable approach to safety. We resolved, in consequence, to traverse on to the ordinary Hornli route. Scrambling up to a second tower, just above that already mentioned (also visible from Zermatt), we halted for a few minutes and made ready for a rapid traverse. So far, we had not been in the line of fire, but we were now compelled to break cover, and run the gauntlet of the hail of broken ice and stones that the gale was stripping from the top-most crags. The process of avoiding these missiles was rendered exceptionally difficult, by the way in which the furious wind would deflect them from their course, and bring those which seemed to be falling well in front of the party, right into its very midst. After more than one extremely narrow escape, we reached a point somewhat sheltered by a projecting crag above. Burgener turned straight up the slope towards it, and, at racing speed, led us to a secure ledge at its foot.

Immediately in front, the long, pitiless slabs, ceaselessly swept by whizzing, shrieking fragments of all sorts and sizes, suggested to Burgener—who has a most proper and prudent objection to every form of waste—that it would be well to drink our Bouvier, and consume our other provisions, before any less fitting fate should overtake them. The knapsack was accordingly unpacked, and, in the grave and serious mood befitting the solemnity of the occasion, we proceeded to demolish these good things with which the thoughtful Seiler had stored our bags. Under these various benign influences our spirits rose rapidly, and Burgener's face resumed its wonted look of confidence; he once more shook his beard with defiance at the falling stones, and called Der Teufel to witness that we had been in quite as bad places before. Looking back on that distant lunch, I have little doubt that Burgener fully realised that a rollicking, self-confident party can dodge falling stones and dance across steep slabs, in a manner, and at a pace, which is impossible to anxious and disheartened men. His object was fully attained; by the time we had tied on our hats with sundry handkerchiefs, seen to the lacing of our boots, and otherwise pulled ourselves together, we felt quite satisfied that the stones and ice would exhibit their usual skill in missing the faithful climber.

We were soon springing across the slabs like a herd of frightened chamois. At one or two places, where the whole party was simultaneously on extremely insecure ground, we were forced to moderate the pace a little; but even then our leader would brook no hesitation, whether we liked it or whether we did not, his Schnell nur schnell hurried us ever forwards. An occasional rap on the head by a splinter of ice, or the hurtle of a great stone, as it spun playfully between the various members of the party, most thoroughly accentuated Burgener's admonitions.

It is needless to say, a very few minutes of this sort of progress took us out of range, and we were able to rest in safety. A short distance further was the well-known "shoulder." Scattered up and down it, were the two parties ascending by the ordinary route. To reach them, however, was not easy. Bare rock, destitute of hold and extremely steep, intervened. Burgener made an effort to creep across, but one of the guides on the "shoulder" scrambled towards us, and after inspecting the cliff shouted that it was ganz unmoglich. Our leader retreated on hearing this, and we tried to traverse on a line some thirty feet below. This proved wholly impracticable, and the guides on the ridge kindly recommended us to go back by the way we had come. The advice was doubtless well meant, but it raised our ire, and we turned once again to Burgener's original line of effort. After considerable difficulty we succeeded in working our way across and refuting our timorous advisers. We reached the "shoulder" just at the point where the ridge abuts against the final summit.

The other parties, having seen our success was assured, were already ascending, so we tucked ourselves under a great rock, and expressed heartfelt regrets for the Bouvier that was no more, and the good things that we had devoured. Subsequently we scrambled to the top, rattled back to the "shoulder," and should have been in Zermatt by 5 p.m. had I not made an unlucky remark concerning Geister and toten Leute. These good (or bad?) people had been forgotten amidst the excitement of the climb, but my unlucky remark awakened Burgener to the imminence of the catastrophe that must necessarily overtake us. For some reason which he could not make very clear, he considered it certain that the Geister would either push us off the mountain or drop something hard and heavy on our heads before we reached the point where the new hut now stands. It was in vain I pointed out to him that the various supernatural powers would able to effect our destruction as easily in Zermatt as on the mountain. Burgener, whilst admitting the theoretic excellence of my doctrine, evidently did not accord it any actual acceptance. His position on this subject appeared to be as illogical as his views on Sunday mountaineering. On this latter great question, he holds that difficult expeditions are an obvious and distinct "tempting of Providence." Easy expeditions, on the other hand, he considers may be undertaken, for, says he, on such and such mountains you can hang on no matter what happens, and he proceeds to back up this opinion with arguments of a painfully materialistic type. In the present instance he clearly thought that the natural advantages of the ground would give us a good chance of defeating the lurking enemy. We descended with the utmost elaboration of care, only one moved at a time, and constant entreaties were even then required before rope enough was paid out to enable anybody to move. These elaborate precautions were backed up by a great profusion of pious (and sometimes the reverse) ejaculations, and we each vowed a candle of peculiar splendour and size to a saint of Burgener's acquaintance, subject, of course, to the provision that the said saint enabled us to baffle the malignant Geister. When we had duly arrived on the Furggen Glacier, Venetz suggested a doubt as to whether the saint had really earned the candles. He showed us a small necklet he was wearing, which contained the tooth or thumb-nail, or other decaying debris, of an exceptionally holy saint, and which, he averred, was, as cricketers would say, "Quite able to lick all the Zermatt Geister off its own bat." However, Burgener assured me that, in bargains of this sort, it is always the better plan to pay, "especially," he added, "when a few francs are alone at issue." So we subsequently duly discharged our debts. We got back to Zermatt just in time for table d'hote, after a day of the most varied interest and excitement.

The next day we walked, railed, and drove back to Chamonix. Our minds were chiefly occupied with the various apparitions we had encountered. Burgener, after a protracted talk with the priest at Stalden, had come to the conclusion that the candles and Venetz's amulet would have been wholly ineffective against toten Leute, and that, consequently, the apparitions we had seen could not have been real, bona fide specimens. My explanation of the will-o'-the-wisps was accepted, and they were dismissed as mere natural phenomena. But it was less easy to dispose of the light on the Gorner Glacier. Burgener and Venetz thought that probably a big lump of gold had seen fit to wachsen on or near the glacier, and they supported this theory by much ingenious argument. Was there not gold in the Macugnaga valley? And if there was gold on one side of Monte Rosa, why not on the other? Now it is evident that the only way in which gold could get there would be by a "wachsening" (if that is the right derivative) process, and if this happened at Macugnaga, why not in Zermatt? It was further obvious that during the growing stage, gold would be likely to shine with just such a light as we had seen. I was prepared to accept all these propositions, but I could not agree that gold in its infantile stages would be likely to take such idiotic and senseless walks on the glacier. On the other hand, I pointed out that the place was well suited to be the home of a dragon, and the movements we had seen appeared exactly appropriate to what is known as the reptile's habits. The men, however, were deplorably sceptical on this point, and even with the well authenticated instances related by Scheuchzer to back me, they would not admit the existence of this most interesting animal.

On our arrival at Chamonix, a friend joined our councils and threw fresh and startling light on the problem. A girls' school, with mistresses and all the paraphernalia of learning and wisdom, had been staying in Zermatt. Wishing to acquire close and intimate acquaintance with a glacier, they had walked up to the Gorner and scattered themselves about the ice. One of the girls, with the instincts of a born mountaineer, fearing to be late for the table d'hote, had tracked back by herself. Accordingly, when her companions were once more assembled and ranged under the stern eye of the "genius tutelary," her absence excited alarm, and the whole school once more distributed itself over the glacier, seeking for some traces of the lost demoiselle. The sun meanwhile set, and both teachers and taught found themselves unable to escape from their entanglements. Monsieur Seiler ultimately became alarmed, and sent a guide with a lantern to look for them; and this guide spent the rest of the night in rescuing the disconsolate maidens from the various holes and chasms into which they had fallen.

Thus Burgener's hopes of fortune, and mine of discovering a real nineteenth-century dragon, were rudely shattered. Still, as Burgener said, Geister or no Geister we had had a splendid day, and stored up memories that would last us through many a winter evening. He added, "It was a pity we were in such a hurry about those candles."

Behind the Footlights

By BARRY WOOD

THE QUIET BUSTLE of ordinary traffic was interrupted by the insistent wail of a distant police siren. Rising from a low moan to a high-pitched shriek, falling, and rising again, it grew louder and louder as the police car approached. The frantic waving of a State trooper warned cars to pull over to the side of the road, and two motorcycle policemen sped into sight, followed by a line of long, low busses. Traffic lights were flashed to green, and at every crossing the policemen held up long lines of machines to let the procession pass. Pedestrians, alarmed by the screech of the siren, stopped to watch the busses go by. A group of small boys recognized a football team on its way to a game, and ran along the sidewalk, pointing and yelling in great excitement.

In the first bus one man sat alone near the front. This was his senior year; he had played for three seasons, yet he still wondered what the people thought who watched the busses pass with their police escort. They seemed to have an astonished expression on their faces as they stopped and peered at the rather formidable procession. No wonder they expected a great deal from football players—most ordinary people do not require a police escort. It was hard to get used to, well aware as he was in his own mind that he was only going to play in a college game.

An hour before, he had tried to eat a light lunch, but he hadn't been hungry. Hot tea tasted good, but the rest was hard to get down, especially the meat. He had eaten only half a piece of toast, a little potato, and lemon sherbet. It was always like that; even the coaches didn't eat much. He had learned that it was only because

From "What Price Football?", Houghton Mifflin Company.

he was keyed-up, and that he felt better if he ate very little. He always put a few lumps of sugar in his pocket to eat on the bus; that seemed to help, for someone had told him that suger served as a 'quick source of energy.'

His hands felt moist in the pockets of his overcoat, his head throbbed a little, and he seemed to perspire, even though he had not moved for almost half an hour. It was like having a very slight fever. A feeling of laziness stole over him as he lolled back in the soft seat of the bus, and something made his stomach feel weak. He had been trying to forget the game, trying to think of something that would take his mind from it, but always his thoughts led him back to football. Almost unconsciously, he had been going over play after play, checking up on his assignments and remembering what the scouts had reported during the week about the opponents' formations and weaknesses. The pictures of certain 'key' plays from the movies taken by one of the scouts of the opponents' last game flashed at intervals across his mind. Last night he had played the whole game through several times before going to sleep. He knew that sleep would have done him more good than thinking about the game, but Friday nights somehow were always like that. Why couldn't he forget football until he went onto the field? Why did he always experience that same weak feeling before a game? By this time he should have grown used to it all.

The busses stopped in front of the field-house, and he piled out with the rest of the players and went to the visiting-team room. Five or six assistant managers had been there hours before, unpacking huge trunks and arranging equipment. A separate locker had been assigned to each player, bearing his name, and containing his own uniform, including a pair of mud-cleats to be used if the field were soggy. He found an illustrated program in the top of his locker and sat down to read it, or rather to look at the pictures. The team was not scheduled to go onto the field for another hour.

At one end of the room stood three long rubbing-tables, and the wall at the head of each was covered with broad strips of adhesive tape. They had been cut by the managers and were to be used as ankle-straps, for every man's ankles had to be taped before the game by one of the doctors or trainers.

After browsing through the program, he undressed slowly and took his place in the line waiting to be 'taped.' Most of the men did not seem to be in a hurry, for there was plenty of time, but he noticed that a few sophomores were almost all dressed when he started. Sophomores often did that; he remembered that he had done it himself two years ago. They would only have longer to wait now, and somehow waiting was not easy. As he stood in line, he watched the doctor tape a lineman's shoulder and then his knee; covered with adhesive tape, the player looked more like a wounded veteran than an aggressive tackle. At the next table one of the trainers was rubbing out a stiff 'Charlie-horse.'

With his own ankles taped and one wrist strapped, he returned to his locker and pulled on the rest of his uniform. Before putting on his shoes, however, he obtained a pair of white lacings from the manager and sat down to replace the black ones which had been given to him. He was superstitious about shoe-laces—white ones always seemed to bring him luck. The shoes were made of light kangaroo leather and had just been oiled to protect them from the moisture. They were beautifully made. As he laced the right one, he examined the square kicking-toe attached to its sole; it was a great help to his place-kicking.

Coaches moved about the room, most of them smoking nervously. From time to time, one would take a player aside and give him a few final instructions. The doctors and trainers were now taping up the last few men. Although everything moved rather slowly and quietly, there was a distinct tenseness in the atmosphere.

Pulling on a heavy hood over his uniform, he ambled into the next room, where mattresses and blankets had been spread on the floor, and the players, fully dressed, lay stretched out, quietly resting. He found a vacant space and lay down. The strange weak feeling in his stomach was worse than ever. He wondered if everyone in the starting line-up felt that way before a big game; he always had. If the coach had told him that someone else was to start in his place, it would have been a relief. He didn't know just why, for there was nothing about a football game that he disliked; in fact, the actual playing was more fun than almost anything else he knew. It wasn't that howling mob in the stands, either; they made a lot of noise, but no one minded that. Was it the responsibility of playing in a game that interested so many people which seemed to weigh heavily on his shoulders? It would be so much easier to be a substitute, a spectator, or a newspaper reporter; they had nothing to worry about. Yet he knew that if he had not been chosen to start the game, he would have been keenly disappointed. The same thought recurred before every game, and he was hardly proud of it. As soon as the kick-off was over, this would all go, and he would be playing football, his whole mind intent upon the game; but now, half an hour before the opening whistle, he had time to think about what was coming, and merely thinking about it brought on the weak feeling in his stomach, arms, and legs, the clammy perspiration, and the strange laziness that pervaded his whole body. Why couldn't he forget it all until two o'clock? It never worked that way, and he knew that he would not play as well if he were not nervous before the game.

The voice of the head manager informed the players that it was time to leave for the field. Crowding into the locker room, they filed slowly out through the narrow door. Outside, the coaches were waiting in a group, and walked along with the squad, following the captain and the head manager to the stadium entrance. The crowds moving toward the near-by portals were held up by policemen, and watched them curiously as they passed. When they reached the end of the long low tunnel under the stadium, the manager stopped to allow the squad to bunch up then, with the captain in the lead, they jogged out onto the field.

He was vaguely conscious of the cheering as he trotted across the gridiron with the squad. A manager tossed him a ball, and peeling off his heavy hood, he followed the place-kickers to the far end of the field. Feeling a little shaky, he flubbed his first two tries, then settled down and kicked six goals without a miss. The day before, the squad had had a short work-out in the stadium, and its vast emptiness had given it a quiet, deserted appearance. Now there were spectators jamming their way in through every portal; each section was being rapidly filled, and only a few scattered patches of empty gray remained. Everything seemed to be in motion—people crowding into their seats, ushers running up and down the narrow aisles. There was a dull murmur from the thousands of voices; the quiet of the deserted stadium was gone.

After the place-kicking he did some punting, with and against the wind, trying especially to get his kicks away fast. He had had one blocked two weeks ago and he had not forgotten it. The wind was not strong enough to be of much advantage either way. He caught a few forward passes from the quarterback, and then went off with the rest of the squad, as the opponents' gaudy sixty-piece band paraded pompously up the center of the field amid wild applause from the stands.

It was warm inside the small team-room under the stadium. Only the eleven men starting the game, the coaches, and two managers had come in; the rest of the squad waited outside. The atmosphere was even more tense than it had been in the locker room. The players sat silently in a row on the narrow wooden benches along the wall. One of the managers, with a small can containing a mixture of shoe-blacking and water, was smearing the faces of the ends and backs just under the eyes to keep off the glare of the sun. The backfield coach had taken the quarterback aside and was speaking to him in a low voice. The other assistant coaches stood in a group by the door, and the head coach, after nervously lighting a cigarette, walked back and forth across the room. He stopped, pulled out his watch and looked at it closely, thrust it back into his pocket, and nodded to the coaches and managers. They went out, the last one closing the door quietly behind him, leaving the head coach alone with his players.

That nod from the coach, he knew, meant 'three minutes more!' His head throbbed, his mouth was dry, and his face was covered with perspiration. The laziness had left him, but he was conscious still of the sick feeling in his stomach, and felt feverishly weak. He glanced at the man next to him, a sophomore starting his first big game at guard, who sat staring blankly at the floor; his face pale and drawn, and his lips tightly shut. Nervously he was rubbing one knee with his clenched fist. Watching him, he remembered how nervous he had been himself his sophomore year; he was better now, but still this waiting was hell. He wondered what it was like for soldiers before going over the top; a football game is perhaps not like fighting, but he didn't see how the waiting could be much worse. The next sixty seconds seemed hours. The coach still paced the room, smoking impatiently; he was nearly as nervous as the players. Coaches usually give their men a short 'fight-talk' before sending them onto the field, but he had not spoken a word since he had entered the room. He did not believe in 'fight-talks.' Suddenly he stopped, crushed the cigarette butt under his foot, and turned to the players. 'I'll say again what I have said every Saturday this year: tackling and blocking win football games. That's all I need to tell you.' There was a rap on the door. Two minutes! All eleven players were up on their feet, pulling on their head-guards. The coach moved toward the door, and as each man passed, he shook him by the hand. Men who shook his hand now did not need 'fight-talks.'

A roar from the stands greeted them as they trotted onto the field. He was glad they did not run through signals; they had done it last year, and he used to get out of breath running only ten yards. For some reason he was always very short of breath just before the kick-off. As the captains met in the center of the field, he tossed a ball carelessly back and forth with one of the other backs, then jogged up and down, and did a few 'rolls' on the ground to limber up. His legs were still weak. The captain returned to the side-line, and the team quickly formed a close huddle about him. The cheers became deafening; from the outside of the huddle he could hardly hear what the captain was saying. The whole stadium seemed to rock as the teams ran onto the field.

Lining up to receive the kick-off, he took his position on the ten-yard line on the far side of the field. He jogged in place and moved his arms, trying to keep well warmed up. The weakness had left his legs, but a sick, hollow feeling still remained in the pit of his stomach. The sun in his eyes half blinded him. The opposing quarterback, who seemed painfully slow, was still fixing the ball for his kick-off, and secretly he hoped the ball would not come to him. The referee on the west side-line motioned to the two captains; then the shrill sound of his whistle pierced the din of the cheering, and an expectant hush spread over the vast throng of spectators.

For an instant everything seemed to stand still. He saw the kicker hesitate, then step forward, his whole team moving with him like a battle-line. He heard the sharp thump as the kicker's foot met the ball squarely. Breathlessly he watched it come hurtling end over end down the field; the fullback was under it. He moved ahead of the runner to form interference as the opposing line charged down upon them. Overanxious, he left his feet too soon in trying to block the first lineman down the field; it was a weak attempt, and he was knocked to one side. There was a thud behind him as two tacklers crashed into the fullback.

Then came the change. Every feeling of weakness and sickness left him—he was in a football game. He no longer saw the bank of wild spectators towering above him on all sides; his ears were deaf to the roar of the cheering. He was only the field, the ball, the other players; his ears heard only the voice of the quarterback and the 'First down, ten yards to go!' It was always like that after the first play. The kick-off was sickening suspense; but the rest was football—tackling, blocking, speed, and skill—a game, yet played under a pressure of which he was always conscious. There was something more than the mechanics of each play; he would move faster and hit harder than in practice, for he was keyed-up almost to the breaking point.

Automatically he ran through his assignments; long signal drills had made the routine plays second nature to him. On more than half of them, he worked on the defensive left tackle from his right wing-back position. He found the tackle hard to move, charging low and fast, but he seemed to be playing a bit too wide, and was easy to handle on an inside tackle play. On one occasion he gave him a really good ride, the fullback was 'cleaned out,' and the play went for ten yards.

As the game progressed, the routine blocking, tackling, and covering forward passes made almost no impression upon his memory. But late in the first period his team reached the opponents' twenty-yard line, and on fourth down the quarterback called on him to kick a field goal. The angle was a difficult one; it would be a hit-or-miss try. The pass from center was good, the quarterback handled it perfectly, and he got the kick away fast. His eyes followed the ball as it rose toward the goal posts, just clearing the upstretched arms of a lineman. It seemed to hang in the air, waver, and then pass inches outside the very top of the nearer upright. He had missed by a fraction. An indelible picture of the ball's flight imprinted itself upon his mind.

During the minute's rest between the periods, he noticed a sore place on his right leg; he must have bruised the muscle.

It would get stiff if he didn't keep it limbered up.

Halfway through the second period, the quarterback threw him a short 'flat' pass, just out of reach of the defensive fullback. As he caught it and turned toward the goal, he saw two backs tearing down to cut him off. They were coming at different angles, forcing him toward the side of the field. Outrunning the center, who had cut across from behind the line of scrimmage, he dashed up the side-line. Both backs were going to get an open shot at him; he set himself. Crash! Together they hit him as he reached the ten-yard line, and all three slammed headlong into the low board fence enclosing the field. He was dazed when someone pulled him to his feet; for an instant everything looked blurred. He felt badly shaken up as he took his position in the huddle. On the next play a hole was opened on the other side of the line, and the fullback ploughed his way to the two-yard line. One more play, and the ball was over.

The teams lined up for the point-after-touchdown. His head was clear now, as he drew a line in the turf with his spikes, straight back from the spot where the quarterback would place the ball. No thought of what it might mean if he should miss entered his mind. He was concentrating on the line and the center of the cross-bar, utterly unconscious of the solid mass of spectators beyond the goal posts and the deafening roar rising from the east side of the field. The ball was passed, and snapped to the ground; stepping forward, he met it squarely. As he raised his head to follow its flight, the broad shoulders of a lineman charging straight 'up the alley' loomed before him. With a dull thud, the ball struck the lineman's chest and bounded harmlessly away; the figures on the score-board remained unchanged—six to nothing. Every detail of the picture was clear in his mind as he jogged back up the field for the next kick-off.

A minute before the end of the half, he had a narrow escape. Thinking that the end he was covering was only a decoy, he carelessly let him slip by. The passer had fooled him cleverly, looking to the right as if to throw there, then at the last instant wheeling and throwing to the left. The ball sailed over his head, and, as he turned, he saw it strike the end's outstretched hands, carom off, and fall 'incomplete' to the ground. Luck alone had saved him. Two plays later, the half ended.

Inside the warm room he threw himself down on the soft blankets stretched on the floor. Now for the first time, he realized how emotionally wrought-up he had been during the thirty minutes of play, how tired his whole body really was, and what a battering he had already been through. The excitement of the game had deadened all feeling, but now, as he tried to relax, he became acutely conscious of aching muscles in his legs and a dull pain in his bad wrist. His head buried in a loose blanket, he lay motionless on his stomach. He wanted to be left alone; he only wanted to rest. One of the trainers laid a wet towel on his neck; the water felt cold as it dribbled down his back. The doctor, moving about the room to check up on the condition of every player, leaned over him. 'How about you?' 'O.K., Doc.' He tried to forget everything, but the picture of the blocked kick kept flashing across his mind. The six-point lead looked like a mere nothing; he imagined a touchdown for the opponents, and their kick sailing squarely through the goal posts. He was well aware now of the importance of the point-after-touchdown that had been blocked. The whole game might hang on that one play. Six to nothing—two plays, and the score-board might read 'seven to six. Seven to six—seven to six—then his attempted field goal in the first period loomed before him. He saw the ball rise toward the very top of the upright, waver for an instant, and then pass just outside. Nine to nothing would have been a comfortable lead. . . . Someone tapped his shoulder; it was a manager with black coffee. He rolled over, sat up, and took the hot cup. The coffee tasted good as he sipped it slowly.

The players lay stretched on blankets, some drinking coffee, others flat on their backs with wet towels around their heads. The doctor was busy strapping the center's side with broad strips of adhesive tape. Trainers and one or two coaches moved from player to player, speaking always in low tones. No one was being bawled out, no one was being criticized; even words of encouragement were few, for above all else the men needed rest and quiet. After conferring with the doctor, the coach read off the line-up for the start of the second half; the players whose names were not read left the room with assistant coaches, trainers, and the doctor. The room became quiet.

As he watched the coach again pacing the floor, the weak

feeling came back to his stomach, but not so noticeably this time. He began to forget his tired, aching muscles. The players were getting onto their feet now and pulling on their head-guards. The coach moved toward the door, and, before opening it, turned and spoke quietly. 'They're coming back with all they've got, this next period. You've done a good job. Keep it up.'

The members of the opponents' band were just filing off to take their places in the stands as the team came out. He rubbed his stiff leg, and jogged a little to warm up before the teams took the field.

The play in the third period was a little slow, with frequent exchanges of kicks, and no sustained offensive drive by either team. The quarterback in the lead was cautious, while his opponent evidently thought it best to play conservatively, waiting for a break, rather than shoot his bolt too soon. Although the play was more conservative, there was no let-up in the fierce tackling and blocking. The tackle opposite him had changed his tactics, playing closer, and was harder to handle.

The fourth period opened with the score still six to nothing. But there the opponents began to open up, and halfway through the period came a play that changed everything. Following perfect interference, the opposing fullback broke away on a tackle play and raced into the open with only the 'safety-man' to beat. At the twenty-yard line the quarterback made a last desperate lunge, but missed, as the runner side-stepped cleverly, and dashed across the goal line standing up.

It had all come so suddenly that he hardly knew what had happened. He had seen the runner break away, and had instinctively started across the field to cut him off, but an interferer, who seemed to come from nowhere, had taken him neatly out of the play. The whole team appeared to be stunned as they lined up for the point-after-touchdown. Standing behind the goal line, a feeling of helplessness came over him as he watched the opposing quarterback and the kicker prepare for the place-kick. He could only hope now; there was nothing he could do from his halfback position except watch for a pass. But perhaps one of the linemen would break through and block the kick; perhaps the pass from center would be bad. He watched the quarterback set himself, and saw the kicker take a final look at the cross-bar. The ball was passed, and his heart seemed to stop beating as he watched it, cleanly handled by the quarterback, leave the kicker's foot, and sail directly between the uprights. For an instant he was conscious of the pandemonium in the stands. Then a feeling of bitter disappointment swept over him, and was gone, giving way to one of determination. He glanced at the clock on the score-board—nine minutes to play! There was still time to score.

In those last nine minutes he gave everything he had. Tired and battered from fifty minutes of play, he drove himself mercilessly. He hammered the tackle with every ounce of strength in his body. The minutes seemed to fly. When he glanced again at the clock, there were two minutes to go. Almost every play now was a forward pass, and he ran his heart out trying to break away from the defense. But they had shifted into a six-man line and were dropping their ends back to cover the passes, making it almost impossible to get free. An intercepted pass on third down finally gave them the ball, and a minute later the game ended.

As the crowd began to pour down onto the field, his only thought was to get out of the stadium, back to the locker room. He pushed his way with the other players through the wild crowd, finally reaching the tunnel leading out under the stands. Once inside the locker room, he slumped onto the bench by his locker and began mechanically to unlace his shoes. A feeling of bitter disappointment was gnawing at his mind. Still emotionally wrought-up, he was only half conscious of his aching muscles and a throbbing pain in his head. He noticed that his hand trembled as he pulled half-heartedly at his shoe-laces. Looking up, he noticed a player slouched on the wooden bench across the room. There were tears on his mud-stained face, and he was crying quietly to himself, like a child. He had often seen players cry, and knew that it was usually more from physical exhaustion than from disappointment. It gave relief sometimes, after the terrific tension of the game.

Players straggled in and began slowly to undress. A lineman lay on one of the rubbing-tables, wrapped in a blanket, his knee in an ice-pack; he had twisted it in the third period and had had to leave the game. Coaches went about, speaking encouraging words and helping occasionally with stubborn jerseys or shoulder-pads. One of the trainers pulled the adhesive tape from his ankles, and it made him wince. He noticed that his throat was sore as it had been once before after a hard game; he wondered why. After a hot shower, he dressed slowly; every move was an effort. Outside, the busses were waiting to take the team to the train, and he climbed into the nearest one. It felt good to sit back in a comfortable seat. Now for the first time he began to realize how exhausted he really was. He had taken a terrible physical beating, and every muscle seemed to ache; his bruised leg was becoming stiff, and his head still throbbed. He had driven his tired body without mercy, and now he began to be conscious of it. Someone sat down beside him, but said very little; he was glad, for he did not feel like talking.

Climbing out of the bus at the railroad station with his stiff leg, he felt like a lame old man. The train had just pulled in and the managers hustled the squad aboard. He went directly to the dining-car with one of the other players, and although he felt starved, not having eaten since eleven-thirty, he ate but little, for he had learned that it was a poor policy to overload a tired stomach. Soup, crackers, milk, and a little ice cream were all he took.

In the Pullman car most of the players had settled down to read or play cards. He found that the porter had already made up his berth, and though it was only seven-thirty, he was more than ready for bed, and wanted to be alone. Stealing a magazine from one of the managers, he undressed and climbed into his lower berth. He tried to read a light story, but he could not keep his mind on it, and turning the pages, he looked at the advertisements; then finally, too tired even to read, he snapped off the light at his head and stretched out his aching limbs.

He did not try to go to sleep at once; it was too much to ask his tired nerves and muscles to relax completely after all they had been through. Lying flat on his back, he closed his eyes and tried to think of anything but football. The feeling of disappointment had not left him, and he did not want to think of the game. But it was useless to try to fight against it, for every thought led back to one of those plays imprinted so clearly on his memory. Again he saw the opposing fullback break loose, felt himself taken out of the play, and saw the runner cleverly side-step the last tackler and cross the goal line. Every detail of the play came back to him.

Then the picture of the winning goal—the suspense, and finally the ball sailing squarely between the uprights. He felt a new pang of bitter disappointment as he remembered his own blocked kick. A clear image of the lineman charging toward him and crashing into the rising ball flashed across his mind. Seven to six —one thought. He thought of the field goal he had missed by inches, and he could see the ball hang in the air, then pass just wide of the mark. That would have changed everything. If he had only . . . his imagination began to run away with him; he was back on the field now. There were two minutes left to play, and in the huddle the quarterback was calling for a long forward pass on the end of a reverse play. He broke away from the defensive halfback as the ball left the passer's hand. It was a perfect throw, just within his reach, and jumping with all his might he grabbed the ball out of the air and fell across the goal line. A touchdown! Twelve to seven! That was right, wasn't it? No; seven to six, seven to six . . . if he had only . . .

He was dozing off. The porter had turned out the lights, and the sound of voices had died away; all was quiet except for the monotonous clicking of the heavy trucks on the rails as the train sped eastward.

The Colonel's Cup

By SIEGFRIED SASSOON

B Y THE END of February I had made further progress in what I believed to be an important phase of my terrestrial experience. In other words (and aided by an exceptionally mild winter) I had averaged five days a fortnight with the hounds. I had, of course, confided in Dixon my intention of entering Cockbird for the Ringwell Heavy-Weight Race. My main object now seemed to be to jump as many fences as possible before that eventful day arrived. Meets of the Dumborough had been disregarded, and a series of short visits to the Rectory had continued the 'qualifying' of Cockbird. ('Qualifying' consisted in drawing the Master's attention to the horse during each day's hunting; and I did this more than conscientiously, since Stephen and I were frequently shouted at by him for 'larking' over fences when the hounds weren't running.)

The problem of Harkaway's lack of stamina had been solved by Dixon when he suggested that I should box him into the Staghound meets. He told me that they generally had the best of their fun in the first hour, so I could have a good gallop and bring the old horse home early. This took me (by a very early train from Baldock Wood) to a new and remote part of the county, and some of the fun I enjoyed there is worth a few pages of description.

The Coshford Vale Stag Hunt, which had been in existence as a subscription pack for about half a century, had been kept on its legs by the devoted efforts of a group of prosperous hop-farmers and a family of brewers whose name was a household word in the district. Gimling's Fine Ales were a passport to popularity, and the genial activities of Mr. 'Gus' Gimling, who had been

From "Memoirs of a Fox Hunting Man," Faber and Faber, London.

Master for more years than he cared to count, had kept the Hunt flourishing and assured it of a friendly reception almost everywhere in the country over which it hunted (described in the scarlet-covered Hunting Directory as "principally pasture with very little plough"). This description encouraged me to visualize an Elysium of green fields and jumpable hedges; but the country, although it failed to come up to my preconceived idea of its charms, included a nice bit of vale; and in those days there was very little wire in the fences.

I need hardly say that, since stags were no longer indigenous to that part of England, the Coshford stag-hunters kept theirs at home (in a deer paddock a few miles from the kennels). The animal which had been selected to provide the day's sport was carried to the meet in a mysterious-looking van, driven by the deerkeeper, a ruddy faced Irishman in a brown velveteen jacket who had earned a reputation for humorous repartee, owing to the numerous inquiries of inquisitive persons on the roads who asked him what he'd got in that old hearse of his.

Provincial stag-hunts are commonly reputed to be comic and convivial gatherings which begin with an uproarious hunt-breakfast for the local farmers. Purple faced and bold with cherry brandy, they heave themselves on to their horses and set off across the country, frequently falling off in a ludicrous manner. But the Coshford sportsmen, as I knew them, were businesslike and well behaved; they were out for a good old-fashioned gallop. In fact, I think of them as a somewhat serious body of men. And since the field was mainly composed of farmers, there was nothing smart or snobbish about the proceedings.

I need hardly say that there was no levity in my own attitude of mind when I set out for my first sample of this new experiment in sportsmanship. In spite of talking big to Dixon the night before, I felt more frightened than light-hearted. For I went alone and knew no one when I got there. Dixon had talked to me about Harry Buckman, who acted as amateur huntsman and was well known as a rider at hunt races all over the country. That was about all I'd got to go on, and I gazed at Buckman with interest and admiration when he tit-tupped stylishly past me at the meet with his velvet cap cocked slightly over one ear. Buckman was a mixture of horse dealer and yeoman farmer. In the summer he

rode jumpers in the show ring. His father had hunted a pack of
harriers, and it was said that when times were bad he would go
without his dinner himself rather than stint his hounds of their
oatmeal.

Roughly speaking, young Buckman's task as huntsman was
twofold. Firstly, he was there to encourage and assist the hounds
(a scratch pack—mostly dog-hounds drafted from foxhound kennels because they were over-sized) in following the trail of their
unnaturally contrived quarry; secondly, he had to do everything
he could to prevent his hounds from 'pulling down' the deer.
With this paradoxical but humane object in view he had once
jumped a railway gate; by this feat of horsemanship he arrived
in the nick of time and saved the deer's life. Fast hunts were fairly
frequent, but there were slow hunting days when scent was bad
and the Coshford subscribers were able to canter along at their
ease enjoying a pretty bit of hound-work. Sometimes the uncarted
animal got clean away from them, and there was a special interest
attached to a meet when they drew for an outlying deer.

My first day with the Staghounds was on Christmas Eve and
I find the following entry in my diary: "Coshford; Packman's
Green. Perfect hunting day; came on wet about 2.30. Turned out
at Hazelpits Farm and ran well to Wissenden, then on by Chartley
Church and Henhurst down the hill and on towards Applestead.
Took deer ('Miss Masterful') about 2. Nine-mile point. Harkaway in good form. Took a toss over a stile toward the end. Very
nice country, especially the first bit." From this concise account
it may seem as if I had already mastered the Coshford topography,
but I suspect that my source of information was a paragraph in
a local paper.

I cannot remember how I made myself acquainted with the
name of the deer which provided the nine-mile point. But in any
case, how much is taken for granted and left unrecorded in that
shorthand description? And how helpful it would have been now
if I had written an accurately observed and detailed narrative of
the day. But since the object of these pages is to supply that de-
ficiency I must make my reminiscent deductions as best I can.
And those words from my diary do seem worth commenting on—
symbolic as they are of the equestrian equilibrium on which my
unseasoned character was trying to pattern itself. I wrote myself

down that evening as I wanted myself to be—a hard-bitten hunting man, self-possessed in his localized knowingness and stag-hunting jargon. The words might well have been penned by Mr. 'Gus' Gimling himself. "Took a toss over a stile" is the only human touch. But taking tosses was incidental to the glory of being a hard rider. What I ought to have written was—that I couldn't make up my mind whether to go at it or not, and the man behind me shouted "go on if you're going," so I felt flustered and let Harkaway rush at it anyhow and then jerked his mouth just as he was taking off, and he didn't really fall, but only pecked badly and chucked me over his head and then stood quite still waiting for me to scramble up again, and altogether it was rather an inglorious exhibition, and thank goodness Stephen wasn't there to see it. For though Stephen and I always made a joke out of every toss we took, it wouldn't have suited my dignity if he'd told me in cold blood that I was still a jolly rotten rider—the tacit assumption being that my falls were entirely due to my thrusting intrepidity.

It will be noticed that no mention is made of the method by which 'Miss Masterful' was 'taken,' although I had witnessed that performance for the first time in my life. As far as I can recollect, Miss M. having decided that the show had lasted long enough, plunged into a small pond and stood there with only her small head appearing above the muddy water. Raucous ratings and loud whip-crackings restrained the baying hounds from splashing in after her, and then genial Mr. Gimling, assisted by one of the whiskered wiseacres of the hunt (in a weather-stained black coat which came nearly down to his knees, white cord breeches, black butcher-boots, and very long spurs), began to get busy with a long rope. After Miss M. had eluded their attempts several times they succeeded in lassoing her head and she was persuaded to emerge from the pond. She was then frog-marched away to a farm building, where she awaited the arrival of her conveyance, which was cruising about the country and usually put in an appearance much earlier than might have been expected.

It can also be inferred from my diary that the weather 'came on wet' as soon as I'd started my ten-mile ride back to the railway-station and Harkaway's horse-box, and that the supporters of the Coshford Hunt departed in different directions wishing one an-

other a merry Christmas and a happy New Year. It may also be
inferred that poor Miss Masterful sweated and shivered in the
barn with heaving sides and frightened eyes. It did not occur to
me to sympathize with her as I stood at the entrance to watch
them tie her up. I only wondered how far I was from the station
and my poached eggs for tea. Any sympathy I had was reserved
for Harkaway, who looked as if he'd had more galloping than
was good for him. But when I was jogging back by Chartley
Church, with my coat collar turned up and the rain soaking my
knees, I chuckled to myself as I thought of an amusing incident
which had happened earlier in the day.

We were galloping full-tilt along a road just outside a cosy
village. An angry faced old parson was leaning over his garden
gate, and as we clattered past he shook his fist at us and shouted
"Brutes! brutes!" in a loud unclerical voice. Excited and elated
as I was, I turned in the saddle and waved my whip derisively at
him. Silly old buffer! And what a contrast to that jolly sporting
parson in a low-crowned top-hat who went so well and came up
and talked to me so nicely while Miss Masterful was being hauled
out of the pond!

I have analysed the orthodox entry in my diary more fully
than I had intended. But how lifelessly I recover the breathing
reality of which those words are the only relics. The night before
hunting; the anxious wonderings about the weather; lying awake
for a while with busy thoughts about tomorrow that grow blurred
with the beginning of an untroubled sleep. And then Miriam
battering on the door with "It's twenty to seven, sir," and the
first look at the quiet morning greyness, and the undefinable feeling produced by the yellow candlelight and the wintry smelling
air from the misty garden. Such was the impermanent fabric as it
unfolded: memory enchants even the dilatory little train journey
which carried my expectant simplicity into the freshness of a
country seen for the first time. All the sanguine guesswork of
youth is there, and the silliness; all the novelty of being alive and
impressed by the urgency of tremendous trivialities.

The end of February became the beginning of March, and
this unavoidable progression intensified my anticipations of the
date in April which meant so much to me. Cockbird had done
his eight qualifying days without the slightest mishap or the least

sign of unsoundness. He was so delightfully easy to handle that my assurance as a rider had increased rapidly. But in the period of preparation Dixon and I, between us, carried a large invisible load of solicitude and suspense. Our conversational demeanour was jauntily portentous. But when I was alone with myself and indoors, I often felt so nervous that the month-long remoteness of the point-to-points became almost unbearable. My confidence in Cockbird's ability to carry off the Colonel's Cup served only to magnify my imaginations of what might go wrong in the race through my own lack of experience.

I consoled myself with day-dreams in which I won in every way that my limited racing repertory could contrive. There was cantering home an easy winner; and there was winning cleverly by half a length; and there was coming up with a rush to score sensationally in the last stride. Each winner lacked intensity; I would have preferred something more spectacular and heroic. But this was difficult to manage; I couldn't win with my arm in a sling unless I started in that condition, which would be an anti-climax. On the whole I was in favour of a fine finish with Stephen, although even this seemed inappropriate because Jerry was believed to be much slower than Cockbird, and could only hope to win if I fell—a thought which reduced my suppositions to reality.

Meanwhile Cockbird existed unperturbed, munching large feeds of crushed oats (with which Dixon mixed some water, for he had an idea that this was good for his wind) and doing three hours' steady work on the road every day. Once a week we took him to a ten-acre field on a hillside, which a well-disposed farmer allowed us to use for gallops. Round and round we went with set and serious faces (Dixon riding Harkaway), until we had done three presumptive miles up and down hill. When we pulled up Dixon would jump off, and I would jump off to stand meekly by the horses' snorting heads while he fussed around Cockbird with as much solemnity and solicitude as if he were a Grand National favourite. And, so far as we were concerned, the 'National' (which was to be run ten days before the Ringwell Heavy-Weight Race) was quite a secondary affair, though we sometimes talked about it in an offhand way which might have led a stranger to suppose that either of us might slip up to Liverpool to see it, provided that we could spare the time. Neither of us doubted that

Cockbird himself could 'get round Aintree' if asked to do so. He was, we agreed, a regular National stamp of horse, and though I had never seen an Aintree fence, I was quite sure that no fence was too big for him.

On some such afternoon (for we always went out in the afternoon, though before breakfast would have been more correct, but it would have made the day so long and empty), on some such afternoon, when Cockbird had done his gallop to our mutual satisfaction and we were jogging quietly home, with the sun making haloes on the fleeces of the sheep who watched us pass—on some such afternoon, I repeat, I was reminded of the old days when I was learning to ride the cob Sheila, and of how I used to ask Dixon to pretend to be Mr. MacDoggart winning the Hunt Cup. Such a suggestion now would have struck both of us as unseemly; this was no time for such childish nonsense as that (though, when one came to think of it, twelve years ago wasn't such a very long time and 'the twenty hop-kilns' were still down there in the valley to remind me of my childish excitement about them). But the thought passed through my mind, and at the same moment the warning whistle of a train going along the Weald would remind me of that interrogative railway journey which the three of us would be making in not much more than two weeks' time—was it really as near as that now?

The thought of Mr. MacDoggart's remote victories at Dumborough Races made me wish that I could ask Dixon for some first-hand information about race-riding. But although he had once worked in a racing-stable, he'd never had an opportunity of riding in a race. And I was shy of asking him questions which would expose my ignorance of things which, for some reason, I supposed that I ought to have known; so I had to make the best of such hints as he dropped me.

And then there was the difficulty of dress, a subject on which he never offered advice. Desperately in need of information, I asked myself what I was to wear on my head. Stephen had worn some sort of cap last year, but the idea of buying a jockey-cap seemed somehow ludicrous. (I remembered the old brown corduroy one I wore on my first day with the Dumborough.)

On this particular afternoon I had shortened my stirrups by several holes. I had observed, in some steeplechasing photographs in an illustrated paper, that the jockeys rode with their knees ever so much higher than mine. This experiment caused me to feel important and professional but less secure in the saddle. And when Cockbird made a sudden swerve (quite needlessly alarmed by a blackbird that flew out of the hedge which we hugged so as to make the field as large as possible) I almost lost my balance; in fact I nearly fell off. Dixon said nothing until we were on our way home, and then he merely remarked that he'd never believed in riding very short. "They always say that for a point-to-point there's nothing like sticking to the old-fashioned hunting seat." I took the hint, which was a wise one.

Much depended on Cockbird; but much more depended on me. There were moments when I felt acutely conscious of the absolute nullity of my past as a race-rider. It wasn't so easy to discuss the event when one was limited by a tacit avowal that one had no idea what it would feel like. The void in my experience caused circumlocutions. My only authority was Stephen, whose well-known narrative of last year's race I was continually para-phrasing. The fact that the Ringwell country was so far away from our own familiar haunts added to the anxious significance of my attempt. How could we—humble denizens of an inglorious un-hunted region—hope to invade successfully the four-day-a-week immensity which contained the Colonel and his coveted Cup?

Such was the burden of my meditations while I lugged the garden roller up and down the tennis lawn after tea, while the birds warbled and scolded among the laurels and arbutuses in the latening March twilight and Aunt Evelyn tinkled Handel's 'Har-monious Blacksmith' on the piano in the drawing-room.

It will have been observed that, in the course of my career as a sportsman, I was never able to believe that I could do a thing until I had done it. Whatever quality it was which caused this tentative progress toward proficiency, it gave intensity to every-thing that I did. I do not claim that it was unusual—this nervous-ness of mine about my first point-to-point race. On the contrary, I am sure that it was a normal and exemplary state of mind. Any-one who cares to do so is at liberty to make fun of the trepidations which a young man carries about with him and conceals. But there is a risk in such ridicule. As I remember and write, I grin, but not unkindly, at my distant and callow self and the absurdities which constitute his chronicle. To my mind the only thing that matters is the resolve to do something. Middle-aged retrospection may decide that it wasn't worth doing; but the perceptions of maturity are often sapless and restrictive; and "the thoughts of youth are long, long thoughts," even though they are only about buying a racing-cap.

A week before the Races I went to London and bought a cap with a jutting peak; it was made of black silk, with strings that hung down on each side until they had been tied in front. I had remarked, quite casually, to Stephen, that I supposed a top-hat was rather uncomfortable for racing, and he had advised me about the cap, telling me to be sure to get one which came well down over my ears, "for there's nothing that looks so unworkmanlike as to have a pair of red ears sticking out under your cap." Whereupon he pulled one of mine, which, as he said, were big enough to catch any wind there was.

I also bought a weight-cloth. The Heavy-Weight Racers had to carry fourteen stone, and after Dixon had weighed me and my hunting saddle on the old weighing machine in the harness-room, we came to the conclusion that, assuming our antiquated machine to be accurate, I should be required to carry twelve pounds of lead.

"Thank heaven it wasn't thirteen," I thought, as I went into the stable to give Cockbird a few well-washed carrots.

He certainly was looking an absolute picture, though Dixon said he'd like to get a shade more of the meat off him. As he nipped playfully at my sleeve I marvelled at my good fortune in being the possessor of such unparalleled perfection.

With an access of elation, I ran back to the house in a hail-storm. The sun was out again by the time I was upstairs brushing my hair for luncheon. I got out my new cap and tried it on before the glass. Then Miriam bumped into the room with a can of hot water, and as I hadn't time to snatch it off I stood there with the strings hanging down, looking, no doubt, a bit of a fool.

"Oh, sir, you did give me a turn!" she ejaculated, "I'd hardly have known you in that there jockey-cap!" She added that I'd be the death of them all before I'd done.

During luncheon Aunt Evelyn remarked that she did so hope it wouldn't be wet for the point-to-points. She had never seen one in her life, but she had once been to Dumborough Races, which she considered dangerous. Fortunately for her peace of mind, she still visualized a point-to-point as a sort of paper-chase, and I had said nothing to counteract this notion, although I did not want to minimize the grandeur of next week's events. Aunt Evelyn's intense love of horses made Cockbird the object of an admiration which almost equalled my own. This, combined with her unshakeable faith in Dixon, gave her a comfortable feeling that I was quite safe on Cockbird. But when Miriam, rather tactlessly, blurted out, "Mr. George hasn't half got a lovely jockey-cap!" she showed symptoms of alarm.

"Oh, I do hope the jumps won't be very big!" she exclaimed. To which I replied, somewhat boastfully, that I meant to get over them whatever they might be like.

"I'm going over to walk round the course with Stephen on Sunday. He says it's a course that wants knowing," I said, helping myself to some more tapioca pudding.

Stephen had warned me that I shouldn't be able to stay at the Rectory for the Race, because his mother was already "in such a muck-sweat about it" that the topic was never touched on in her presence. So I bicycled to Dumbridge, took the slow train which explored Sussex on Sunday mornings, got out at a wayside station, and then bicycled another seven miles to the course. (The seven-mile ride saved me from going on to Downfield and changing on to the branch line which went to the station close by the course.) These exertions were no hardship at all on that dusty spring day; had it been necessary, I would gladly have bicycled all the whole thirty miles from Butley and back again. Nothing in my life had ever appeared more imperative than that I should walk round that "three and a half miles of fair hunting country" and memorize each obstacle in the sequence. I wanted to carry home in my cranium every inch of the land over which Cockbird would, I strenuously hoped, stride with his four legs.

In the meantime I had plenty to occupy my mind pleasantly as I pedalled seriously along the leafless lanes. I already knew that part of the Ringwell country moderately well; I could identify most of the coverts by their names, and I ruminated affectionately on the rainy February days when I had gone round and through them in a flustered gallop with the mud from the man

in front of me flying past my head. Eagerly I recognized the
hedges and heave-gates which I had jumped, and the ruddy faces
of the Ringwell sportsmen occupied my meditations in amicable
clusters.

Memories within memories; those red and black and brown
coated riders return to me without any beckoning, bringing
along with them the wintry smelling freshness of the woods and
fields. And how could I forget them, those evergreen country
characters whom once I learnt to know by heart, and to whom
I have long since waved my last farewell (as though at the end of
a rattling good day). Sober-faced squires, with their civil greet-
ings and knowing eyes for the run of a fox; the landscape belonged to them and they to the homely landscape. Weather-beaten
farmers, for whom the activities of the Hunt were genial inter-
ludes in the stubborn succession of good or bad seasons out of
which they made a living on their low-lying clay or wind-swept
downland acres. These people were the pillars of the Hunt—the
land-owners and the farmers. The remainder were merely subscribers; and a rich-flavoured collection of characters they were,
although I only half-recognized them as such while I was with
them.

There was loquacious old Mr. Dearborn; formerly a none too
successful stockbroker, and now a gentleman of leisure, who enjoyed himself on a couple of spavined screws which (he continually asserted) were worth at least a couple of hundred apiece and
as clever as cats, though he'd never given more than thirty pounds
for a horse, and rarely went as high as that; both of them, as
Stephen said, looked lonely without a gig behind them. Old
Dearborn jabbered his way through the days, attaching himself to
one group of riders after another until a fox was found; at the
end of a good hunt he would always turn up again, puffing and
blowing and purple in the face, but voluble with enthusiasm for
the way his horse had got over "one of the ugliest places you ever
saw in your life." However tedious he may have been, the Ringwell field wouldn't have been the same without him.

Many an exuberant voice and lively countenance I could
revive from that vanished cavalcade. But I can't help thinking
that the best man of them all was 'Gentleman George,' as we
called him. George was a grey-haired groom; Mr. Clampton, his

middle-aged master, was 'something in the City'—a natty untalkative little man, who came out in queerly cut clothes and a low-crowned hat. Mr. Clampton kept three stout-hearted weight-carriers, but he seldom hunted more than one day a week. George put in as many days as possible; he called it "keeping the guv'nor's 'osses." At the most remote meets he would trot up—his fine-featured open face subdued to the decorum of servitude and a jolly twinkle for ever lurking in his keen eyes. (He was a man who could condense more meaning into a single wink than most political speakers can put into a peroration.) Always he had his free and easy hail for the hunt-servants (to whom he could generally give some useful information during the day); for the gentry he reserved a respectful rap of his hat-brim and a sonorous "Mornin', sir." However curt his utterances were, the tones of his voice seemed to imply the underlying richness and vigor of his vitality. He knew every inch of the country backwards, and the short-tailed grey who was his favorite had done fourteen seasons with those hounds since Mr. Clampton first bought him as a five-year-old from a farm in County Waterford.

The great joke about George was his method of acting as second horseman when his worthy master was out hunting. This, of course, should have meant that he kept as much as possible to the roads and handed the horse over to his employer as soon as the first horse had done as much galloping and jumping as was considered good for him. Not so George, who was seldom more than two fields away from hounds however hard they ran. Times without number I have seen him come crashing through some black-looking fence and then turn to shout back at the irresolute Mr. Clampton, "Shove 'im at it, sir; there's a big old ditch on the landing side!" And at the end of a gallop, when both horses were smoking hot, he would dismount with the utmost gravity and exchange horses with his master, who had even been known to go home first, leaving his privileged retainer to knock holes in the fences in a late afternoon hunt.

In him I seem to be remembering all that was warm-hearted and exhilarating in my days with the Ringwell, for he showed a special interest in Stephen Colwood and myself, and was never so well contented as when he was showing us the way over an awkward place or giving us the benefit of his ripe experience and intimate knowledge. There was something noble about him. And so (I choose to think) it was for 'Gentleman George' that I kept the kindliest of my meditations as I was bicycling to the point-to-point course.

It was peaceful and pleasant to be squatting on a gate and opening the package of sandwiches that Miriam had made me. The gate opened on to a boggy lane which ran through Crutchett's Wood—a well-known covert. But Crutchett's Wood was beginning to look more idyllic than sporting now; it was dotted with primrose bunches, and the wild anemones were numerous. Although I saw them with placid appreciation my uppermost thought was that the country was drying up nicely; deep going was believed to be a disadvantage to Cockbird, who was supposed to possess a turn of speed which he would have more chance of showing if the ground were dry.

The early afternoon was quiet and Sunday-like as I sat with half a ham-sandwich in my hand; a saffron butterfly fluttered aimlessly along the hedge; miles away the grey-green barrier of the downs overlooked the inactive Weald, and I thought I'd rather like to be up there, by the old windmill on Ditchbury Beacon.

Discarding this unsportsmanlike notion I went on my way; half an hour later my uncompanioned identity had been merged in my meeting with Stephen and we were very deliberately inspecting the first few fences. There was a stake-and-bound hedge on a bank which we didn't much like the look of. While we were still planted in front of it the cheery voice of Arthur Brandwick hailed us with "That's a place where you'll have to take a pull at your old horse, Steve." With him was Nigel Croplady, wearing white gaiters and puffing a cigar; his somewhat supercilious recognition of my existence made me feel that I had no business to be there at all. Croplady was on the Point-to-Point Committee; he had helped to plan out the course and had supervised the making up and trimming of the fences.

"I'm not at all sure we oughtn't to have made the course a bit stiffer," he remarked.

Brandwick replied that he wouldn't be saying that if he were having a bump round it himself.

Croplady expressed regret that he wasn't able to ride the horse he'd entered for the Heavy Weights. "That infernal knee of mine went groggy again while I was playing golf on Thursday. But I've got 'Boots' Brownrigg to ride him for me, so he ought to be in the picture all right."

I gathered that 'Boots' Brownrigg was in the 'Blues' and had "ridden a clinking good finish at the Guards' Meeting at Hawthorn Hill the other day."

Brandwick told us that he'd asked Roger Pomfret to ride his young horse. "He's a mutton-fisted beggar; but the horse is a bit nappy, and young Roger'll be the man to keep him going at his fences."

Every syllable they uttered made my own private aspirations more preposterous and perishable: my optimism was at a very low ebb as we plodded across a wet pasture to the next obstacle, which had a wide ditch on the take-off side.

"There's another place where there'll be trouble for somebody!" Brandwick's jolly voice seemed to be glorying in the prospect of horses refusing and riders shooting up their necks, or even over their ears. He turned to me. "Let's see, you're running that nice-looking bay of yours, aren't you?"

I replied, "Yes, I'm having a ride."

Croplady became knowledgeable about the entries, which had long been a subject for speculation between Stephen and myself. "Quite a hot lot for the Heavy Weights this year. Two of those Cavalry thrusters who keep their nags in Downfield. They're always rather an unknown quantity."

Stephen remarked that the Colonel's Cup was well worth winning, and Croplady agreed that it was a much better pot than the Light-Weight one, and must have cost the old boy five-and-twenty quid at least.

Silent and disheartened, I longed to be alone again; the presence of the other two made it impossible for me to talk naturally to Stephen, and I couldn't help feeling that they regarded me as an entry which could be ruled out of all serious consideration. The whole affair had become bleakly detached from my previous conception of it. I was just a greenhorn. What chance had I got against Brownrigg of the 'Blues,' or those ferociously efficient Cavalry officers? Bicycling back to the station with only just time to catch the train, I visualized myself refusing the first fence and colliding with Roger Pomfret, who was associated in my memory with all my most inglorious experiments with the Dumborough.

Aunt Evelyn found me an uncommunicative companion that evening; and it wasn't easy to talk to Dixon about the course when I went to the stable next morning. "I hear there's a very hot lot entered for the Heavy Weights," I said, as I watched him polishing away at Cockbird's glossy coat. My tone was, perhaps, a shade extenuatory. I couldn't bring myself to speak of Brownrigg of the 'Blues.'

Dixon straightened himself and passed his hand along Cockbird's back. "Don't you worry about that. I'll bet our horse gives some of 'em a shaking up!" he replied.

Cockbird gave a playful hoist of his hind quarters and then snatched a mouthful of hay from his rack. I wished that the confidence of my confederates was a little more infectious.

The races were to be on Wednesday. After exercising our minds on the problem how best to convey Cockbird to the course by two o'clock on that afternoon, we decided against his spending the previous night in Downfield. I suggested that he would probably sleep better in his own stable, which struck me at the time as being improperly expressed, though it was necessary that he should lie down and shut his eyes like everybody else who has something important to do next day. In this connection I should like to mention an odd fact, which is that when I dream about horses, as I often do, they usually talk like human beings, although the things they say, as in most dreams, are only confused fantasias on ordinary speech.

Anyhow, it was arranged that Dixon should ride Cockbird to Dumbridge on Wednesday morning, box him to Downfield, put him up at Whatman's 'Hunting and Livery Stables' for two or three hours, and then jog him quietly out to the course, which was about four miles from Downfield. In the meantime I was to ride Harkaway to Dumbridge (I felt that this ride would be better for me than if I drove in the dog-cart), catch a later train, and find my way out to the course as best I could. The bag holding my coat, boots, cap, spurs, and weight-cloth would go by the carrier. (I mention these details because they did seem so vastly important at the time.)

Cockbird's night's rest was, I imagine, normal, and it didn't occur to me to speculate about Dixon's. My own slumbers were what I should then have considered inadequate; that is to say, I lay awake for a couple of hours and then slept like a top until Miriam called me at eight.

I came down to breakfast reticent and self-conscious. Patient Miriam's anxiety that I should eat a good breakfast wasn't well received, and Aunt Evelyn's forced cheerfulness made me feel as if I were going to be hanged in the afternoon. She had never made any reference to the possibility of her going to see the Races. I have no doubt that she was as sensitive to the precarious outcome of the adventure as I was. For me the whole day, until my race started, was pervaded by the sinking sensation which is commonly called being in a blue funk. But when the stable-boy (his face clearly showing his awareness that he was at close quarters with momentous happenings) had led Harkaway out of the stable, and I had mounted and was trotting through the village, I was conscious of being as fit as I'd ever been in my life, and of being in some way harmonious with the mild, half-clouded April morning which contained me.

The morning tasted good; but it had only one meaning; it was the morning of the point-to-points. To have understood the gusto of that physical experience would have been to destroy the illusion which we call youth and immaturity—that unforeseeing actuality which retrospection can transmute into a lucid and orderly emotion. The April morning, as I see it now, symbolized a stage which I had then reached in my earthly pilgrimage.

But whatever "bright shoots of everlastingness" my body may have felt, my ordinary mind manifested itself only by instructing me to feel in my coat pocket for the half-sheet of notepaper on which I had written "This is to certify that Mr. G. Sherston's bay gelding Cockbird has been fairly and regularly hunted with the Ringwell Hounds"; to which the M.F.H. had appended his signature, adding the figures of the current hunting season, which I had carelessly omitted. This document had to be shown at the scales, although when I actually got there the Clerk of the Scales forgot to ask me for it. When I was making sure that it was still in my pocket I was still under the misapprehension that unless I could produce it in the weighing tent I should be disqualified from riding in my race.

In the middle of the village I met John Homeward and his

van. He was setting out on his monotonous expedition to the county town, and I stopped for a few words with him. His benevolent bearded face made me feel more confident, and so did his gruff voice when he took a stumpy clay pipe out of his mouth to wish me luck.

"I've asked Tom to put half a crown on for me," he said; "it'll be a great day for Butley if you win!" His blunt nod, as I left him sitting under the shadow of his hooded van, was a send-off which stiffened my faltering ambition to prove myself worthy of being the owner of Cockbird.

Remembering how I'd bicycled off to the Ringwell Meeting twelve months before, I thought how flabbergasted I should have been if I'd been told that I should be riding in a race there next year. And in spite of that persistent sinking sensation, I was thankful that, at any rate, I had got as far as 'having a bump round.' For whatever might happen, I was much superior to any of the spectators. Taking my cap off to two elderly ladies, the Miss Pattons, who passed me on their tricycles with bobs and smiles, I wondered whether it was going to rain. Perhaps the sun came out to show that it was going to be a fine afternoon. When I was on the main road I passed Joey, the lizard-faced stone-breaker, who looked up from his flint-hammering to salute me with a grin.

The sun was still shining when I got to the course; but it was now less easy to believe that I had engaged myself to contribute to the entertainment which was attracting such a crowd of cheerful country folk. I felt extraneous and forlorn. Everyone else seemed intent on having as good a time as possible on such a lovely afternoon. I had come briskly out from Downfield on a two-horse charabanc which was waiting outside the station. The journey cost half a crown. Several of my fellow passengers were 'bookies' and their clerks, with their name-boards and giant umbrellas; their jocosities accentuated the crudity of the impact on my mind made by the realistic atmosphere of racing. I did my best to feel as much like a 'gentleman-rider' as I could, and to forget that I was making my first appearance in a race.

The air smelt of trodden turf as I lugged my bag (loaded with fourteen one-pound lead weights) into the dressing-room, which was in a farm building under some elms on the crest of the rising ground which overlooked the sparsely flagged course. After dumping the bag in a corner of the dry-mud floored barn, I went out to look for Cockbird and Dixon. They were nowhere to be seen, so I returned to the dressing-room, reminding myself that Dixon had said he wouldn't bring 'our horse' out there any earlier than he was obliged to, since it would only excite him; I also realized that I should get 'rattled' myself unless I kept quiet and reserved my energies for three o'clock.

The first race was run at two, and mine was the third event on the card, so I bought that absorbing document and perched myself on an old corn-bin to peruse it. "Riders are requested to return their number-cloths to the Clerk of the Scales immediately after each race." I had forgotten that number-cloths existed, so that was news to me. "These Steeplechases are held subject to National Hunt Rules as to corrupt and fraudulent practices." A moment's reflection convinced me that I need not worry about that admonition; it was sufficiently obvious that I had a clean sheet under National Hunt Rules, though it flattered me to feel that I was at last within their jurisdiction.

After these preliminaries I looked inside the card, at the entries. Good heavens, there were fourteen in my race! Several of the names I didn't know. Captain Silcock's 'Crumpet.' M. F. Duckwith's 'Grasshopper.' Those must be the soldiers who hunted from Downfield. Mr. G. Bagwell's 'Kilgrubbin III.' That might be—yes, of course it was—the fat little man on the weedy chestnut, who was always refusing small timber out hunting. Not much danger from him as long as I kept well out of his way at the first fence; and probably he, and several of the others, wouldn't go to the post after all. My own name looked nice.

A blue-jowled man in a yellow waistcoat hurried in, exclaiming, "Can anybody lend me a weight-cloth?" I glanced at my bag and resolved that nothing would induce me to lend him mine (which had yet to receive its baptismal instalment of sweat). Several riders were now preparing for the first race, but no one took any notice of me until ginger-haired Roger Pomfret came in. He had been inspecting the fences, and he wiped his fleshy red face with his sleeve as he sat down and started rummaging in his bag. Tentatively I asked him what he thought of the course. I was quite glad to see someone I knew, though I'd have preferred

to see someone else. He chucked me a surly nod, which he supple-
mented with—"Course? I don't mind telling you, this course would
break the heart of a buffalo. It's nothing but twists and turns,
and there isn't a fence you could go fast at without risking your
neck, and a nice hope I've got on that sketchy jumper of Brandwick's!"

Before I could think of an answer his boon companion in
blasphemy, Bill Jaggett, came in (embellished with a brown billy-
cock hat and black and white check breeches). Jagget began
chaffing him about the unhealthy ride he was going to have in
the Heavy Weights. "I'll lay you a tenner to a fiver you don't
get round without falling," he guffawed. Pomfret took the bet and
called him a pimply faced bastard into the bargain.

I thought I might as well get dressed up: when I had pulled
my boots on and was very deliberately tucking the straps in with
a boot-hook, Stephen strolled in; he was already wearing his faded
pink cap, and the same elongated and anxious countenance which
I'd seen a year ago. No doubt my own face matched his. When
we'd reassured one another about the superlative fitness of our
horses he asked if I'd had any lunch, and as I hadn't he produced
a bar of chocolate and an orange, which I was glad to get. Stephen
was always thoughtful of other people.

The shouts of the bookies were now loudening outside in the
sunlight, and when I'd slipped on my raincoat we went out to
see what we could of the Light-Weight Race.

The first two races were little more than the clamour and
commotion of a passing procession. The 'Open Race' was the
main excitement of the afternoon; it was run 'in colours,' and
there were about a dozen dashing competitors, several of them
well-known winners in such events.

But everything connected with this contest reached me as
though from a long way off, since I was half-stupefied by yawning
nervousness. They appeared to be accomplishing something incredible by galloping round the course. I had got to do it myself
in half an hour; and what was worse, Dixon was relying on me
to put in a creditable performance. He even expected me to give
the others 'a shaking-up.' Stephen had ceased to be any moral
support at all. In spite of his success last year he was nearly as
nervous as I was, and when the field for the Open Race had filed

out of the hurdle-guarded enclosure, which did duty as the paddock, he disappeared in the direction of Jerry and I was left to
face the future alone.

Also, as far as I knew, my horse hadn't yet arrived, and it was
with a new species of alarm that I searched for him after I had
seen the race start; the Paddock and its environs now looked unfriendly and forsaken.

I discovered my confederates in a quiet corner under a hay-
rick. They seemed a discreet and unassuming pair, but Dixon
greeted me with an invigorative grin. "I kept him away from the
course as long as I could," he said confidentially; "he's quiet as a
sheep, but he knows what he's here for; he's staled twice since we
got here." He told me that Mr. Gaffikin was about and had been
looking for me. "He says our horse stands a jolly good chance with
the going as good as it is."

I said there was one place, in and out of a lane, where I'd have
to be careful.

We then escorted Cockbird to the Paddock; by the time we
were there and I'd fetched my weight-cloth, the Open Race was
over and the spectators were trooping back again. Among them
was Mr. Gaffikin, who hailed me companionably with "Hullo,
old chap; jolly sporting of you to be having a ride!" and thereafter
took complete charge of me in a most considerate manner, going
with me to the weighing tent with the weight-cloth over his arm,
while I, of course, carried my saddle.

The winner of the Open Race was weighing in when we arrived, and I stepped diffidently on to the machine immediately
after his glorified and perspiring vacation of the seat. Mr. Gaffikin
doled out a few leads for me to slip into the leather pouches on
the dark blue cloth until I tipped the scale at fourteen stone. The
Clerk of the Scales, an unsmiling person with a large sallow face
—he was a corn-merchant—verified my name on the card and
handed me my number-cloth and armlet; my number was seven:
under less exacting conditions I might have wondered whether it
was a lucky number, but I was pushed out of the way by Pomfret.
Arthur Brandwick (in a grey bowler) was at his elbow, talking
nineteen to the dozen; I caught a glimpse of Stephen's serious
face; Colonel Hesmon was with him, behaving exactly the same
as last year, except that, having already 'given the boy the horse,'

he could no longer say that he was going to do so if he won the race.

While Dixon was putting the last testing touches to Cockbird's straps and buckles, the little Colonel came across to assure me that if Jerry didn't win there was no one he'd rather see first past the judge's wagon than me. He added that he'd taken a lot of trouble in choosing the Cup—"very nice goblet shape—got it from Stegman & Wilks—excellent old firm in the City." But his eye wandered away from Cockbird; his sympathies were evidently strongly implicated in Jerry, who was as unperturbed as if he were being put into a brougham to fetch someone from the station.

Near him, Nigel Croplady was fussing round his horse, with quite a crowd round him.

The terrific 'Boots' Brownrigg was puffing a cigarette with apparent unconcern; his black cap was well over his eyes and both hands were plunged in the pockets of a short blue overcoat; from one of the pockets protruded a short cutting whip. His boots were perfection. Spare built and middle sized, he looked absolutely undefeatable; and if he had any doubts about his own abilities he concealed them well.

Stifling another yawn, I did my best to imitate his demeanour. The bookies were bawling "Two to one bar one." Cockbird, stimulated by publicity, now began to give himself the airs of a real restive racehorse, chucking his head about, flattening his ears, and capering sideways in a manner which caused the onlookers to skip hastily out of range of his heels.

"I say, that's a classy looking quad!" exclaimed a youth who appeared to have purchased the Paddock. He consulted his card, and I overheard his companion, as they turned away, saying something about "his jockey looking a bit green." "We'd better back Nigel's horse. They say he'll win for a cert."

For want of anything else to do at this critical moment I asked Dixon whether he'd put Homeward's half-crown on. He said, "Yes, sir; Mr. Gaffikin's man has just done it for me, and I've got a bit on for myself. It's a good thing; they're laying five to one about him. Mr. Stephen's horse is at two's."

Mr. Gaffikin chimed in with "Mikado's a hot favorite. Two to one on, all along the line!" Mikado was Croplady's horse.

Mr. Gaffikin then tied the strings of my cap in a very tight bow; a bell jangled and a stentorian voice shouted, "Now then, gentlemen, I'm going down to the post." The blue sky suddenly went white; my heart bumped; I felt dazed and breathless. Then Mr. Gaffikin's remote voice said, "Let me give you a leg up, old chap"; I grabbed hold of the reins, lifted an awkward foot, and was lifted airily on the slippery saddle: Cockbird gave one prance and then stood still; Dixon was holding him firmly by the head. Pressing my knees into the saddle I heard Mr. Gaffikin's ultimate advice. "Don't go in front unless you can help it; but keep well with 'em." They both wished me luck and released me to my destiny.

I felt as if I'd never been on Cockbird's back before; everything around me appeared unreal and disconnected from all my previous experience. As I followed Stephen out of the Paddock in a sort of equestrian trance, I caught sight of his father's face, pale and fixed in its most strenuous expression; his eyes followed his son, on whose departure he was too intent to be able to take in anyone else. We filed through a gate under some trees: 'Gentleman George' was standing by the gate; he stared up at me as I passed. "That's the 'oss for my money," was all that he said, but his measured tone somehow brought me to my senses, and I was able to look about me when we got down to the starting place.

But even then I was much more a passenger than a resolute rider with his wits about him to 'pinch' a good start. There were seven others. I kept close to Stephen. We lined up uneasily; while the starter (on his dumpy grey cob) was instructing us to keep the red flags on the right and the white flags on the left (which we already knew) I noticed Pomfret (on a well-bred, excitable brown) , and Brownrigg (Croplady's bright chestnut looking very compact) already stealing forward on the side furthest from him.

When he said "Go" I went with the others, albeit with no sense of initiative. The galloping hoofs sounded strange. But Cockbird felt strong under me and he flicked over the first fence with level and unbroken stride; he was such a big jumper and so quick over his fences that I had to pull him back after each one in order to keep level with Jerry, who was going his best pace all the way. One of the soldiers (in a top-hat) was making the running with Brownrigg and Pomfret close behind him. At the awkward fifth fence (the one on a bank) Pomfret's horse jumped

sideways and blundered as he landed; this caused Pomfret to
address him in uncomplimentary language, and at the next obstacle (another awkward one) he ran out to the left, taking one
of the soldiers with him. This, to my intense relief, was the last
I saw of him. I took it at a place where a hole had been knocked
in it in the previous races. The next thing I remember was the
brook, which had seemed wide and intimidating when I was on
foot and had now attracted a small gathering of spectators. But
water-jumps are deceptive things and Cockbird shot over this one
beautifully: (Stephen told me afterwards that he'd "never seen a
horse throw such an enormous leap"). We went on up a long
slope of firm pasture-land, and I now became aware of my responsibility; my arms were aching and my fingers were numb and
I found it increasingly difficult to avoid taking the lead, for after
jumping a couple more fences and crossing a field of light plough-
land we soared over a hedge with a big drop and began to go
down the other side of the hill. Jerry was outpaced and I was
level with Mikado and the Cavalry soldier who had been cutting
out the work. As Stephen dropped behind he said, "Go on,
George; you've got 'em stone-cold."

We were now more than three parts of the way round, and
there was a sharp turn left-handed where we entered on the last
half-mile of the course. I lost several lengths here by taking a
wide sweep round the white flag, which Brownrigg almost touched
with his left boot. At the next fence the soldier went head over
heels, so it was just as well for me that I was a few lengths behind
him. He and his horse were still rolling about on the ground when
I landed well clear of them. Brownrigg looked round and then
went steadily on across a level and rather wet field which compelled me to take my last pull at Cockbird. Getting on to better
ground, I remembered Mr. Gaffikin's advice, and let my horse go
after him. When I had drawn up to him it was obvious that
Cockbird and Mikado were the only ones left in it. I was alone
with the formidable Brownrigg. The difference between us was
that he was quite self-contained and I was palpitating with excitement.

We were side by side: approaching the fourth fence from the
finish he hit his horse and went ahead; this caused Cockbird to
quicken his pace and make his first mistake in the race by going

too fast at the fence. He hit it hard and pecked badly; Brownrigg, of course, had steadied Mikado for the jump after the quite legitimate little piece of strategy which so nearly caused me to 'come unstuck.' Nearly, but not quite. For after my arrival at Cockbird's ears his recovery tipped me half-way back again and he cantered on across the next field with me clinging round his neck. At one moment I was almost in front of his chest. I said to myself, "I won't fall off," as I gradually worked my way back into the saddle. My horse was honestly following Mikado, and my fate depended on whether I could get into the saddle before we arrived at the next fence. This I just succeeded in doing, and we got over somehow. I then regained my stirrups and set off in urgent pursuit.

After that really remarkable recovery of mine, life became lyrical, beatified, ecstatic, or anything else you care to call it. To put it tersely, I just galloped past Brownrigg, sailed over the last two fences, and won by ten lengths. Stephen came in a bad third. I also remember seeing Roger Pomfret ride up to Jaggett in the Paddock and inform him in a most aggressive voice that he'd got to "well pay up and look pleasant."

Needless to say that Dixon's was the first face I was aware of; his eager look and the way he said, "Well done," were beyond all doubt the quintessence of what my victory meant for me. All else was irrelevant at that moment, even Stephen's unselfish exultation and Mr. Gaffikin's loquacious enthusiasm. As for Cockbird, no words could ever express what we felt about him. He had become the equine equivalent of Divinity.

Excited as I was, an inward voice cautioned me to control my volubility. So when I had weighed in and returned with my saddle to find a cluster of knowing ones casting an eye over the winner, I just waited soberly until Dixon had rubbed him down, mounted, and ridden serenely out of sight. The colonel was on the spot to congratulate me on my 'nailing good performance' and, better still, to give Dixon his due for having got Cockbird so fit. Those few lofty minutes when he was making much of his horse were Dixon's reward for all the trouble he had taken since Cockbird has been in his charge. He had needed no such incentive, but he asked for nothing more. While he was on his way back to Downfield he may also have thought to himself how he had made me

into a good enough rider to have got round the course without
a catastrophe. (He had yet to hear the full details of the race—
including my peculiar acrobatics toward the end, which had been
witnessed by no one except the rider of Mikado, who had been
kind enough to tell Croplady that he never saw such a thing in
his life, which was, I hoped, intended as a compliment.)

When I had watched Dixon's departure I found that public
interest was being focused on the Yeomanry Team-Race. I was
glad to slip away by myself: a few fields out in the country I relaxed my legs on a five-barred gate and contemplated my achievement with as much mental detachment as I could muster. Even
in those days I had an instinct for getting the full flavour of an
experience. Perhaps I was fortunate in not yet having become
aware that the winner of the last race is forgotten as soon as the
next one starts.

Forty minutes later I had claimed my cup. (There was no
ceremony of presentation.) Having crammed the ebony pedestal
into my kit-bag I came out into the Paddock with the cup in my
other hand. It was convenient to carry, for it had handles to it.

Good-natured Arthur Brandwick came up and offered me a
lift back to Downfield. While he was patting me on the back I
caught sight of a figure which seemed somehow familiar. A loose-
built ruddy faced young sportsman was talking to a couple of
jovial whiskered farmers; he sat on a shooting-stick with his thin
neatly gaitered legs straightened; a brown felt hat was tipped well
over his blunt nose, for the five o'clock sun was glaring full in
his eyes. I wondered who it was he reminded me of. Brandwick
answered my unspoken question.

"D'you twig who that is?" I shook my head. "Well, take another good look at him. It's our new Master, and a hell of a good
lad he is, from all I've heard. Up till a month ago everyone
thought the country'd have to be hunted by a Committee next
season. There was something fishy about every one of the coves
who'd applied for the Mastership. And then this chap wrote and
offered to hunt the hounds himself and put up fifteen hundred
a year if we guaranteed him another two thousand. Hardly a soul
knew about it till to-day. We're lucky to get him. He's been hunting a good rough country in Ireland the last two seasons and
showing rare sport. He's run across for a couple of days to have

a look at us." As we walked away the new Master turned his head and favoured us with a slow and rather blank stare.

"What did you say his name was?" I asked, when we were out of earshot. Brandwick informed me that his name was Milden— Denis Milden—and I knew that I'd known it all the time, though I hadn't set eyes on him since I was eleven years old.

Aquamarine and celestial were the shoals of sunset as I hacked pensively home from Dumbridge. The Colonel's Cup clinked and joggled against my saddle. Time was irrelevant. But I was back at Butley by eight o'clock, and Cockbird, who had returned by an earlier train, was safe and sound; a little uneasily he wandered around his loose-box, rustling the deep straw, but always going back to the manger for another mouthful of clover-hay. Dixon serenely digested triumph with his tea; presently he would go out to the 'Rose and Crown' to hand Homeward his multiplied half-crown and overawe the gossips with his glory.

Absolved and acquiescent was the twilight as I went quietly across the lawn and in at the garden door to the drawing-room. Aunt Evelyn's arm-chair scrooped on the beeswaxed floor as she pushed it back and stood up with her bottle of smelling-salts in her hand. For the first time since my success I really felt like a hero. And Miriam served the dinner with the tired face of a saint that seemed lit with foreknowledge of her ultimate reward. But at that time I didn't know what her goodness meant.

At the end of our evening, when they had gone upstairs with my highly coloured history of the day in their heads, I strolled out into the garden; for quite a long time I stared at the friendly lights that twinkled from the railway station and along the dark Weald. I had brought something home with me as well as the Cup. There was this new idea of Denis Milden as Master. For I hadn't forgotten him, and my persistent studying of Horse and Hound and The Hunting Directory had kept me acquainted with his career as an amateur huntsman since he had left Oxford. A dog barked and a train went along the Weald . . . the last train to London, I thought. . . .

Going back to the drawing-room, I lit a pair of candles which made their miniature gold reflections on the shining surface of the massive Cup. I couldn't keep my eyes away from it. I looked round the shadowed room on which all my childhood and adolescence had converged, but everything led back to the talisman; while I gazed and gazed on its lustre I said to myself, aloud, "It can't be true that it's really there on the table!" The photograph of Watts's 'Love and Death' was there on the wall; but it meant no more to me than the strangeness of the stars which I had seen without question, out in the quiet spring night. I was secure in a cosy little universe of my own, and it had rewarded me with the Colonel's Cup. My last thought before I fell asleep was, "Next season I'll come out in a pink coat."

Trinket's Colt

By E. O. SOMERVILLE and MARTIN ROSS

IT WAS petty sessions day in Skebawn, a cold, grey day of February. A case of trespass had dragged its burden of cross summonses and cross swearing far into the afternoon, and when I left the bench my head was singing from the bellowings of the attorneys, and the smell of their clients was heavy upon my palate.

The streets still testified to the fact that it was market day, and I evaded with difficulty the sinuous course of carts full of soddenly screwed people, and steered an equally devious one for myself among the groups anchored around the doors of the public-houses. Skebawn possesses, among its legion of public-houses, one establishment which timorously, and almost imperceptibly, proffers tea to the thirsty. I turned in there, as was my custom on court days, and found the little dingy den, known as the Ladies' Coffee-Room, in the occupancy of my friend Mr. Florence McCarthy Knox, who was drinking strong tea and eating buns with serious simplicity. It was a first and quite unexpected glimpse of that domesticity that has now become a marked feature in his character.

"You're the very man I wanted to see," I said as I sat down beside him at the oilcloth-covered table; "a man I know in England who is not much of a judge of character has asked me to buy him a four-year-old down here, and as I should rather be stuck by a friend than a dealer, I wish you'd take over the job."

Flurry poured himself out another cup of tea, and dropped three lumps of sugar into it in silence.

From "Some Experiences of an Irish R. M.," Longmans, Green, London.

Finally he said, "There isn't a four-year-old in this country that I'd be seen dead with at a pig fair."

This was discouraging, from the premier authority on horse-flesh in the district.

"But it isn't six weeks since you told me you had the finest filly in your stables that was ever foaled in the County Cork," I protested; "what's wrong with her?"

"Oh, is it that filly?" said Mr. Knox with a lenient smile; "she's gone these three weeks from me. I swapped her and £6 for a three-year-old Ironmonger colt, and after that I swapped the colt and £19 for that Bandon horse I rode last week at your place, and after that again I sold the Bandon horse for £75 to old Welply, and I had to give him back a couple of sovereigns luck-money. You see I did pretty well with the filly after all."

"Yes, yes—oh, rather," I assented, as one dizzily accepts the propositions of a bimetallist; "and you don't know of anything else—?"

The room in which we were seated was closely screened from the shop by a door with a muslin-curtained window in it; several of the panes were broken, and at this juncture two voices that had for some time carried on a discussion forced themselves upon our attention.

"Begging your pardon for contradicting you, ma'am," said the voice of Mrs. McDonald, proprietress of the tea-shop, and a leading light in Skebawn Dissenting circles, shrilly tremulous with indignation, "if the servants I recommend you won't stop with you, it's no fault of mine. If respectable young girls are set picking grass out of your gravel, in place of their proper work, certainly they will give warning!"

The voice that replied struck me as being a notable one, well-bred and imperious.

"When I take a barefooted slut out of a cabin, I don't expect her to dictate to me what her duties are!"

Flurry jerked up his chin in a noiseless laugh. "It's my grandmother!" he whispered. "I bet you Mrs. McDonald don't get much change out of her!"

"If I set her to clean the pig-sty I expect her to obey me," continued the voice in accents that would have made me clean forty pig-sties had she desired me to do so.

"Very well, ma'am," retorted Mrs. McDonald, "if that's the way you treat your servants, you needn't come here again looking for them. I consider your conduct is neither that of a lady nor a Christian!"

"Don't you, indeed?" replied Flurry's grandmother. "Well, your opinion doesn't greatly distress me, for, to tell you the truth, I don't think you're much of a judge."

"Didn't I tell you she'd score?" murmured Flurry, who was by this time applying his eye to a hole in the muslin curtain. "She's off," he went on, returning to his tea. "She's a great character! She's eighty-three if she's a day, and she's as sound on her legs as a three-year-old! Did you see that old shandrydan of hers in the street a while ago, and a fellow on the box with a red beard on him like Robinson Crusoe? That old mare that was on the near side—Trinket her name is—is mighty near clean bred. I can tell you her foals are worth a bit of money."

I had heard of old Mrs. Knox of Aussolas; indeed, I had seldom dined out in the neighbourhood without hearing some new story of her and her remarkable menage, but it had not yet been my privilege to meet her.

"Well, now," went on Flurry in his slow voice, "I'll tell you a thing that's just come into my head. My grandmother promised me a foal of Trinket's the day I was one-and-twenty, and that's five years ago, and deuce a one I've got from her yet. You never were at Aussolas? No, you were not. Well, I tell you the place there is like a circus with horses. She has a couple of score of them running wild in the woods, like deer."

"Oh, come," I said, "I'm a bit of a liar myself—"

"Well, she has dozens of them anyhow, rattling good colts too, some of them, but they might as well be donkeys for all the good they are to me or any one. It's not once in three years she sells one, and there she has them walking after her for bits of sugar, like a lot of dirty lapdogs," ended Flurry with disgust.

"Well, what's your plan? Do you want me to make her a bid for one of the lapdogs?"

"I was thinking," replied Flurry, with great deliberation, "that my birthday's this week, and maybe I could work a four-year-old colt of Trinket's she has out of her in honour of the occasion."

"And sell your grandmother's birthday present to me?"

'Just that, I suppose," answered Flurry with a slow wink.

A few days afterwards a letter from Mr. Knox informed me that he had "squared the old lady, and it would be all right about the colt." He further told me that Mrs. Knox had been good enough to offer me, with him, a day's snipe shooting on the celebrated Aussolas bogs, and he proposed to drive me there the following Monday, if convenient. Most people found it convenient to shoot the Aussolas snipe bog when they got the chance. Eight o'clock on the following Monday morning saw Flurry, myself, and a groom packed into a dogcart, with portmanteaus, gun-cases, and two rampant red setters.

It was a long drive, twelve miles at least, and a very cold one. We passed through long tracts of pasture country, fraught, for Flurry, with memories of runs, which were recorded for me, fence by fence, in every one of which the biggest dog-fox in the country had gone to ground, with not two feet—measured accurately on the handle of the whip—between him and the leading hound; through bogs that imperceptibly melted into lakes, and finally down and down into a valley, where the fir-trees of Aussolas clustered darkly round a glittering lake, and all but hid the grey roofs and pointed gables of Aussolas Castle.

"There's a nice stretch of a demesne for you," remarked Flurry, pointing downward with the whip, "and one little old woman holding it all in the heel of her fist. Well able to hold it she is, too, and always was, and she'll live twenty years yet, if it's only to spite the whole lot of us, and when all's said and done goodness knows how she'll leave it!"

"It strikes me you were lucky to keep her up to her promise about the colt," I said.

Flurry administered a composing kick to the ceaseless strivings of the red setters under the seat.

"I used to be rather a pet with her," he said, after a pause; "but mind you, I haven't got him yet, and if she gets any notion I want to sell him I'll never get him, so say nothing about the business to her."

The tall gates of Aussolas shrieked on their hinges as they admitted us, and shut with a clang behind us, in the faces of an old mare and a couple of young horses, who, foiled in their break for the excitements of the outer world, turned and galloped defiantly on either side of us. Flurry's admirable cob hammered on, regardless of all things save his duty.

"He's the only one I have that I'd trust myself here with," said his master, flicking him approvingly with the whip; "there are plenty of people afraid to come here at all, and when my grandmother goes out driving she has a boy on the box with a basket full of stones to peg at them. Talk of the dickens, here she is herself!"

A short, upright old woman was approaching, preceded by a white woolly dog with sore eyes and a bark like a tin trumpet; we both got out of the trap and advanced to meet the lady of the manor.

I may summarise her attire by saying that she looked as if she had robbed a scarecrow; her face was small and incongruously refined, the skinny hand that she extended to me had the grubby tan that bespoke the professional gardener, and was decorated with a magnificent diamond ring. On her head was a massive purple velvet bonnet.

"I am very glad to meet you, Major Yeates," she said with an old-fashioned precision of utterance; "your grandfather was a dancing partner of mine in old days at the Castle, when he was a handsome young aide-de-camp there, and I was—you may judge for yourself what I was."

She ended with a startling little hoot of laughter, and I was aware that she quite realised the world's opinion of her, and was indifferent to it.

Our way to the bogs took us across Mrs. Knox's home farm, and through a large field in which several young horses were grazing.

"There now, that's my fellow," said Flurry, pointing to a fine-looking colt, "the chestnut with the white diamond on his forehead. He'll run into three figures before he's done, but we'll not tell that to the old lady!"

The famous Aussolas bogs were as full of snipe as usual, and a good deal fuller of water than any bogs I had ever shot before. I was on my day, and Flurry was not, and as he is ordinarily an infinitely better snipe shot than I, I felt at peace with the world and all men as we walked back, wet through, at five o'clock.

The sunset had waned, and a big white moon was making the eastern tower of Aussolas look like a thing in a fairy tale or a play when we arrived at the hall door. An individual, whom I recognised as the Robinson Crusoe coachman, admitted us to a hall, the like of which one does not often see. The walls were panelled with dark oak up to the gallery that ran round three sides of it, the balusters of the wide staircase were heavily carved, and blackened portraits of Flurry's ancestors on the spindle side stared sourly down on their descendant as he tramped upstairs with the bog mould on his hobnailed boots.

We had just changed into dry clothes when Robinson Crusoe shoved his red beard round the corner of the door, with the information that the mistress said we were to stay for dinner. My heart sank. It was then barely half-past five. I said something about having no evening clothes and having to get home early.

"Sure the dinner'll be in another half-hour," said Robinson Crusoe, joining hospitably in the conversation; "and as for evening clothes—God bless ye!"

The door closed behind him.

"Never mind," said Flurry, "I dare say you'll be glad enough to eat another dinner by the time you get home." He laughed. "Poor Slipper!" he added inconsequentially, and only laughed again when I asked for an explanation.

Old Mrs. Knox received us in the library, where she was seated by a roaring turf fire, which lit the room a good deal more effectively than the pair of candles that stood beside her in tall silver candlesticks. Ceaseless and implacable growls from under her chair indicated the presence of the woolly dog. She talked with confounding culture of the books that rose all round her to the ceiling; her evening dress was accomplished by means of an additional white shawl, rather dirtier than its congeners; as I took her into dinner she quoted Virgil to me, and in the same breath screeched an objurgation at a being whose matted head rose suddenly into view from behind an ancient Chinese screen, as I have seen the head of a Zulu woman peer over a bush.

Dinner was as incongruous as everything else. Detestable soup in a splendid old silver tureen that was nearly as dark in hue as Robinson Crusoe's thumb; a perfect salmon, perfectly cooked, on a chipped kitchen dish; such cut glass as is not easy to find nowadays; sherry that, as Flurry subsequently remarked, would burn the shell off an egg; and a bottle of port, draped in immemorial cobwebs, wan with age, and probably priceless. Throughout the vicissitudes of the meal Mrs. Knox's conversation flowed on undismayed, directed sometimes at me—she had installed me in the position of friend of her youth, and talked to me as if I were my own grandfather—sometimes at Crusoe, with whom she had several heated arguments, and sometimes she would make a statement of remarkable frankness on the subject of her horse-farming affairs to Flurry, who, very much on his best behaviour, agreed with all she said, and risked no original remark. As I listened to them both, I remembered with infinite amusement how he had told me once that "a pet name she had for him was 'Tony Lumpkin,' and no one but herself knew what she meant by it." It seemed strange that she made no allusion to Trinket's colt or to Flurry's birthday, but, mindful of my instructions, I held my peace.

As, at about half-past eight, we drove away in the moonlight, Flurry congratulated me solemnly on my success with his grandmother. He was good enough to tell me that she would marry me to-morrow if I asked her, and he wished I would, even if it was only to see what a nice grandson he'd be for me. A sympathetic giggle behind me told me that Michael, on the back seat, had heard and relished the jest.

We had left the gates of Aussolas about half a mile behind when, at the corner of a by-road, Flurry pulled up. A short squat figure arose from the black shadow of a furze bush and came out into the moonlight, swinging its arms like a cabman and cursing audibly.

"Oh murdher, oh murdher, Misther Flurry! What kept ye at all? 'Twould perish the crows to be waiting here the way I am these two hours—"

"Ah, shut your mouth, Slipper!" said Flurry, who, to my surprise, had turned back the rug and was taking off his driving coat, "I couldn't help it. Come on, Yeates, we've got to get out here."

"What for?" I asked, in not unnatural bewilderment.

"It's all right. I'll tell you as we go along," replied my companion, who was already turning to follow Slipper up the by-

road. "Take the trap on, Michael, and wait at the River's Cross."
He waited for me to come up with him, and then put his hand
on my arm. "You see, Major, this is the way it is. My grandmother's given me that colt right enough, but if I waited for her
to send him over to me I'd never see a hair of his tail. So I just
thought that as we were over here we might as well take him
back with us, and maybe you'll give us a help with him; he'll not
be altogether too handy for a first go off."

I was staggered. An infant in arms could scarcely have failed
to discern the fishiness of the transaction, and I begged Mr. Knox
not to put himself to this trouble on my account, as I had no
doubt I could find a horse for my friend elsewhere. Mr. Knox
assured me that it was no trouble at all, quite the contrary, and
that, since his grandmother had given him the colt, he saw no
reason why he should not take him when he wanted him; also,
that if I didn't want him he'd be glad enough to keep him himself; and finally, that I wasn't the chap to go back on a friend,
but I was welcome to drive back to Shreelane with Michael this
minute if I liked.

Of course I yielded in the end. I told Flurry I should lose
my job over the business, and he said I could then marry his
grandmother, and the discussion was abruptly closed by the
necessity of following Slipper over a locked five-barred gate.

Our pioneer took us over about half a mile of country, knocking down stone gaps where practicable and scrambling over tall
banks in the deceptive moonlight. We found ourselves at length
in a field with a shed in one corner of it; in a dim group of farm
buildings a little way off a light was shining.

"Wait here," said Flurry to me in a whisper; "the less noise
the better. It's an open shed, and we'll just slip in and coax him
out."

Slipper unwound from his waist a halter, and my colleagues
glided like spectres into the shadow of the shed, leaving me to
meditate on my duties as Resident Magistrate, and on the questions that would be asked in the House by our local member
when Slipper had given away the adventure in his cups.

In less than a minute three shadows emerged from the shed,
where two had gone in. They had got the colt.

"He came out as quiet as a calf when he winded the sugar,"

said Flurry; "it was well for me I filled my pockets from grand-mamma's sugar basin."

He and Slipper had a rope from each side of the colt's head; they took him quietly across a field towards a gate. The colt stepped daintily between them over the moonlit grass; he snorted occasionally, but appeared on the whole amenable.

The trouble began later, and was due, as trouble often is, to the beguilements of a short cut. Against the maturer judgment of Slipper, Flurry insisted on following a route that he assured us he knew as well as his own pocket, and the consequence was that in about five minutes I found myself standing on top of a bank hanging on to a rope on the other end of which the colt dangled and danced, while Flurry, with the other rope, lay prone in the ditch, and Slipper administered to the bewildered colt's hindquarters such chastisement as could be ventured on.

I have no space to narrate in detail the atrocious difficulties and disasters of the short cut. How the colt set to work to buck, and went away across the field, dragging the faithful Slipper, literally ventre-a-terre, after him, while I picked myself in ig-nominy out of a briar patch, and Flurry cursed himself black in the face. How we were attacked by ferocious cur dogs, and I lost my eyeglass; and how, as we neared the River's Cross, Flurry espied the police patrol on the road, and we all hid behind a rick of turf, while I realised in fulness what an exceptional ass I was, to have been beguiled into an enterprise that involved hiding with Slipper from the Royal Irish Constabulary.

Let it suffice to say that Trinket's infernal offspring was finally handed over on the highroad to Michael and Slipper, and Flurry drove me home in a state of mental and physical overthrow.

I saw nothing of my friend Mr. Knox for the next couple of days, by the end of which time I had worked up a high polish on my misgivings, and had determined to tell him that under no circumstances would I have anything to say to his grandmother's birthday present. It was like my usual luck that, instead of writing a note to this effect, I thought it would be good for my liver to walk across the hills to Tory Cottage and tell Flurry so in person.

It was a bright, blustery morning, after a muggy day. The feeling of spring was in the air, the daffodils were already in bud, and crocuses showed purple in the grass on either side of the avenue. It was only a couple of miles to Tory Cottage by the way across the hills; I walked fast, and it was barely twelve o'clock when I saw its pink walls and clumps of evergreens below me. As I looked down at it the chiming of Flurry's hounds in the kennels came to me on the wind; I stood still to listen, and could almost have sworn that I was hearing again the clash of Magdalen bells, hard at work on May morning.

The path that I was following led downwards through a larch plantation to Flurry's back gate. Hot wafts from some hideous caldron at the other side of a wall apprised me of the vicinity of the kennels and their cuisine, and the fir-trees round were hung with gruesome and unknown joints. I thanked Heaven that I was not a master of hounds, and passed on as quickly as might be to the hall door.

I rang two or three times without response; then the door opened a couple of inches and was instantly slammed in my face. I heard the hurried paddling of bare feet on oilcloth, and a voice, "Hurry, Bridgie, hurry! There's quality at the door!"

Bridgie, holding a dirty cap on with one hand, presently arrived and informed me that she believed Mr. Knox was out about the place. She seemed perturbed, and she cast scared glances down the drive while speaking to me.

I knew enough of Flurry's habits to shape a tolerably direct course for his whereabouts. He was, as I had expected, in the training paddock, a field behind the stable-yard, in which he had put up practice jumps for his horses. It was a good-sized field with clumps of furze in it, and Flurry was standing near one of these with his hands in his pockets, singularly unoccupied. I supposed that he was prospecting for a place to put up another jump. He did not see me coming and turned with a start as I spoke to him. There was a queer expression of mingled guilt and what I can only describe as divilment in his grey eyes as he greeted me. In my dealings with Flurry Knox, I have since formed the habit of sitting tight, in a general way, when I see that expression.

"Well, who's coming next, I wonder!" he said, as he shook hands with me; "it's not ten minutes since I had two of your d——d peelers here searching the whole place for my grandmother's colt!"

"What!" I exclaimed, feeling cold all down my back; "do you mean the police have got hold of it?"

"They haven't got hold of the colt anyway," said Flurry, looking sideways at me from under the peak of his cap, with the glint of the sun in his eye. "I got word in time before they came."

"What do you mean?" I demanded; "where is he? For Heaven's sake don't tell me you've sent the brute over to my place!"

"It's a good job for you I didn't," replied Flurry, "as the police are on their way to Shreelane this minute to consult you about it. You!" He gave utterance to one of his short diabolical fits of laughter. "He's where they'll not find him, anyhow. Ho! ho! It's the funniest hand I ever played!"

"Oh yes, it's devilish funny, I've no doubt," I retorted, beginning to lose my temper, as is the manner of many people when they are frightened; "but I give you fair warning that if Mrs. Knox asks me any questions about it, I shall tell her the whole story."

"All right," responded Flurry; "and when you do, don't forget to tell her how you flogged the colt out on to the road over her own bounds ditch."

"Very well," I said hotly, "I may as well go home and send in my papers. They'll break me over this—"

"Ah, hold on, Major," said Flurry soothingly, "it'll be all right. No one knows anything. It's only on the spec the old lady sent the bobbies here. If you'll keep quiet it'll all blow over."

"I don't care," I said, struggling hopelessly in the toils; "if I meet your grandmother, and she asks me about it, I shall tell her all I know."

"Please God you'll not meet her! After all, it's not once in a blue moon that she—" began Flurry. Even as he said the words his face changed. "Holy fly!" he ejaculated, "isn't that her dog coming into the field? Look at her bonnet over the wall! Hide, hide for your life!" He caught me by the shoulder and shoved me down among the furze bushes before I realised what had happened.

"Get in there! I'll talk to her."

I may as well confess that at the mere sight of Mrs. Knox's purple bonnet my heart had turned to water. In that moment I knew what it would be like to tell her how I, having eaten her salmon, and capped her quotations, and drunk her best port, had gone forth and helped to steal her horse. I abandoned my dignity, my sense of honour; I took the furze prickles to my breast and wallowed in them.

Mrs. Knox had advanced with vengeful speed; already she was in high altercation with Flurry at no great distance from where I lay; varying sounds of battle reached me, and I gathered that Flurry was not—to put it mildly—shrinking from that economy of truth that the situation required.

"Is it that curby, long-backed brute? You promised him to me long ago, but I wouldn't be bothered with him!"

The old lady uttered a laugh of shrill derision. "Is it likely I'd promise you my best colt? And still more, is it likely that you'd refuse him if I did?"

"Very well, ma'am." Flurry's voice was admirably indignant. "Then I suppose I'm a liar and a thief."

"I'd be more obliged to you for the information if I hadn't known it before," responded his grandmother with lightning speed; "if you swore to me on a stack of Bibles you knew nothing about my colt I wouldn't believe you! I shall go straight to Major Yeates and ask his advice. I believe him to be a gentleman, in spite of the company he keeps!"

I writhed deeper into the furze bushes, and thereby discovered a sandy rabbit run, along which I crawled, with my cap well over my eyes, and the furze needles stabbing me through my stockings. The ground shelved a little, promising profounder concealment, but the bushes were very thick, and I laid hold of the bare stem of one to help my progress. It lifted out of the ground in my hand, revealing a freshly-cut stump. Something snorted, not a yard away; I glared through the opening, and was confronted by the long, horrified face of Mrs. Knox's colt, mysteriously on a level with my own.

Even without the white diamond on his forehead I should have divined the truth; but how in the name of wonder had Flurry persuaded him to couch like a woodcock in the heart of a furze brake? For a full minute I lay as sill as death for fear of frightening him, while the voices of Flurry and his grandmother raged on alarmingly close to me. The colt snorted, and blew long breaths through his wide nostrils, but he did not move. I crawled an inch or two nearer, and after a few seconds of cautious peering I grasped the position. They had buried him.

A small sandpit among the furze had been utilized as a grave; they had filled him in up to his withers with sand, and a few furze bushes, artistically disposed round the pit, had done the rest. As the depth of Flurry's guile was revealed, laughter came upon me like a flood; I gurgled and shook apoplectically, and the colt gazed at me with serious surprise, until a sudden outburst of barking close to my elbow administered a fresh shock to my tottering nerves.

Mrs. Knox's woolly dog had tracked me into the furze, and was now baying the colt and me with mingled terror and indignation. I addressed him in a whisper, with perfidious endearments, advancing a crafty hand towards him the while, made a snatch for the back of his neck, missed it badly, and got him by the ragged fleece of his hind-quarters as he tried to flee. If I had flayed him alive he could hardly have uttered a more deafening series of yells, but, like a fool, instead of letting him go, I dragged him towards me, and tried to stifle the noise by holding his muzzle. The tussle lasted engrossingly for a few seconds, and then the climax of the nightmare arrived.

Mrs. Knox's voice, close behind me, said, "Let go my dog this instant, sir! Who are you—"

Her voice faded away, and I knew that she also had seen the colt's head.

I positively felt sorry for her. At her age there was no knowing what effect the shock might have on her. I scrambled to my feet and confronted her.

"Major Yeates!" she said. There was a deathly pause. "Will you kindly tell me," said Mrs. Knox slowly, "am I in Bedlam, or are you? And what is that?"

She pointed to the colt, and that unfortunate animal, recognising the voice of his mistress, uttered a hoarse and lamentable whinny. Mrs. Knox felt around her for support, found only furze prickles, gazed speechlessly at me, and then, to her eternal honour, fell into wild cackles of laughter.

So, I may say, did Flurry and I. I embarked on my explanation and broke down; Flurry followed suit and broke down too. Overwhelming laughter held us all three, disintegrating our very souls. Mrs. Knox pulled herself together first.

"I acquit you, Major Yeates, I acquit you, though appearances are against you. It's clear enough to me you've fallen among thieves." She stopped and glowered at Flurry. Her purple bonnet was over one eye. "I'll thank you, sir," she said, "to dig out that horse before I leave this place. And when you've dug him out you may keep him. I'll be no receiver of stolen goods!"

She broke off and shook her fist at him. "Upon my conscience, Tony, I'd give a guinea to have thought of it myself!"

Lisheen Races, Second-Hand

By E. O. SOMERVILLE and MARTIN ROSS

I T MAY or may not be agreeable to have attained the age of thirty-eight, but, judging from old photographs, the privilege of being nineteen has also its drawbacks. I turned over page after page of an ancient book in which were enshrined portraits of the friends of my youth, singly, in David and Jonathan couples, and in groups in which I, as it seemed to my mature and possibly jaundiced perception, always contrived to look the most immeasurable young bounder of the lot. Our faces were fat, and yet I cannot remember ever having been considered fat in my life; we indulged in low-necked shirts, in "Jemima" ties with diagonal stripes; we wore coats that seemed three sizes too small, and trousers that were three sizes too big; we also wore small whiskers.

I stopped at last at one of the David and Jonathan memorial portraits. Yes, here was the object of my researches; this dour and earnestly romantic youth was Leigh Kelway, and that fatuous and chubby young person seated on the arm of his chair was myself. Leigh Kelway was a young man ardently believed in by a large circle of admirers, headed by himself and seconded by me, and for some time after I had left Magdalen for Sandhurst, I maintained a correspondence with him on large and abstract subjects. This phase of our friendship did not survive; I went soldiering to India, and Leigh Kelway took honours and moved suitably on into politics, as is the duty of an earnest young Radical with useful family connections and an independent income. Since then I had at intervals seen in the papers the name of the Honourable Basil Leigh Kelway mentioned as a speaker at elections, as a

From "Some Experiences of an Irish R. M.," Longmans, Green, London.

writer of thoughtful articles in the reviews, but we had never met, and nothing could have been less expected by me than the letter, written from Mrs. Raverty's Hotel, Skebawn, in which he told me he was making a tour in Ireland with Lord Waterbury, to whom he was private secretary. Lord Waterbury was at present having a few days' fishing near Killarney, and he himself, not being a fisherman, was collecting statistics for his chief on various points connected with the Liquor Question in Ireland. He had heard that I was in the neighbourhood, and was kind enough to add that it would give him much pleasure to meet me again.

With a stir of the old enthusiasm I wrote begging him to be my guest for as long as it suited him, and the following afternoon he arrived at Shreelane. The stout young friend of my youth had changed considerably. His important nose and slightly prominent teeth remained, but his wavy hair had withdrawn intellectually from his temples; his eyes had acquired a statesmanlike absence of expression, and his neck had grown long and bird-like. It was his first visit to Ireland, as he lost no time in telling me, and he and his chief had already collected much valuable information on the subject to which they had dedicated the Easter recess. He further informed me that he thought of popularising the subject in a novel, and therefore intended to, as he put it, "master the brogue" before his return.

During the next few days I did my best for Leigh Kelway. I turned him loose on Father Scanlan; I showed him Mohona, our champion village, that boasts fifteen public-houses out of twenty buildings of sorts and a railway station; I took him to hear the prosecution of a publican for selling drink on a Sunday, which gave him an opportunity of studying perjury as a fine art, and of hearing a lady, on whom police suspicion justly rested, profoundly summed up by the sergeant as "a woman who had th' appairance of having knocked at a back door."

The net result of these experiences has not yet been given to the world by Leigh Kelway. For my own part, I had at the end of three days arrived at the conclusion that his society, when combined with a note-book and a thirst for statistics, was not what I used to find it at Oxford. I therefore welcomed a suggestion from Mr. Flurry Knox that we should accompany him to some typical country races, got up by the farmers at a place called Lisheen, some twelve miles away. It was the worst road in the district, the races of the most grossly unorthodox character; in fact, it was the very place for Leigh Kelway to collect impressions of Irish life, and in any case it was a blessed opportunity of disposing of him for the day.

In my guest's attire next morning I discerned an unbending from the role of cabinet minister towards that of sportsman; the outlines of the note-book might be traced in his breast pocket, but traversing it was the strap of a pair of field-glasses, and his light grey suit was smart enough for Goodwood.

Flurry was to drive us to the races at one o'clock, and we walked to Tory Cottage by the short cut over the hill, in the sunny beauty of an April morning. Up to the present the weather had kept me in a more or less apologetic condition; any one who has entertained a guest in the country knows the unjust weight of responsibility that rests on the shoulders of the host in the matter of climate, and Leigh Kelway, after two drenchings, had become sarcastically resigned to what I felt he regarded as my mismanagement.

Flurry took us into the house for a drink and a biscuit, to keep us going, as he said, till "we lifted some luncheon out of the Castle Knox people at the races," and it was while we were thus engaged that the first disaster of the day occurred. The dining-room door was open, as also was the window of the little staircase just outside it, and through the window travelled sounds that told of the close proximity of the stable-yard; the clattering of hoofs on the cobble stones, and voices uplifted in loud conversation. Suddenly from this region there arose a screech of the laughter peculiar to kitchen flirtation, followed by the clank of a bucket, the plunging of a horse, and then an uproar of wheels and galloping hoofs. An instant afterwards Flurry's chestnut cob, in a dogcart, dashed at full gallop into view, with the reins streaming behind him, and two men in hot pursuit. Almost before I had time to realise what had happened, Flurry jumped through the half-opened window of the dining-room like a clown at a pantomime, and joined in the chase; but the cob was resolved to make the most of his chance, and went away down the drive and out of sight at a pace that distanced every one save the kennel terrier, who sped in shrieking ecstasy after him.

"Oh merciful hour!" exclaimed a female voice behind me. Leigh Kelway and I were by this time watching the progress of events from the gravel, in company with the remainder of Flurry's household. "The horse is desthroyed! Wasn't that the quare start he took! And all in the world I done was to slap a bucket of wather at Michael out the windy, and 'twas himself got it in place of Michael!"

"Ye'll never ate another bit, Bridge Dunnigan," replied the cook, with the exulting pessimism of her kind. "The master'll have your life!"

Both speakers shouted at the top of their voices, probably because in spirit they still followed afar the flight of the cob.

Leigh Kelway looked serious as we walked on down the drive. I almost dared to hope that a note on the degrading oppression of Irish retainers was shaping itself. Before we reached the bend of the drive all the rescue party was returning with the fugitive all, with the exception of the kennel terrier, looking extremely gloomy. The cob had been confronted by a wooden gate, which he had unhesitatingly taken in his stride, landing on his head on the farther side with the gate and the cart on top of him, and had arisen with a lame foreleg, a cut on his nose, and several other minor wounds.

"You'd think the brute had been fighting the cats, with all the scratches and scrapes he has on him!" said Flurry, casting a vengeful eye at Michael, "and one shaft's broken and so is the dashboard. I haven't another horse in the place; they're all out at grass, and so there's an end of the races!"

We all three stood blankly on the hall-door steps and watched the wreck of the trap being trundled up the avenue.

"I'm very sorry you're done out of your sport," said Flurry to Leigh Kelway, in tones of deplorable sincerity; "perhaps, as there's nothing else to do, you'd like to see the hounds—?"

I felt for Flurry, but of the two I felt more for Leigh Kelway as he accepted this alleviation. He disliked dogs, and held the newest views on sanitation, and I knew what Flurry's kennels could smell like. I was lighting a precautionary cigarette, when we caught sight of an old man riding up the drive. Flurry stopped short.

"Hold on a minute," he said; "here's an old chap that often

brings me horses for the kennels; I must see what he wants."

The man dismounted and approached Mr. Knox, hat in hand, towing after him a gaunt and ancient black mare with a big knee.

"Well, Barrett," began Flurry, surveying the mare with his hands in his pockets, "I'm not giving the hounds meat this month, or only very little."

"Ah, Master Flurry," answered Barrett, "it's you that's pleasant! Is it give the like o' this one for the dogs to ate! She's a vallyble strong young mare, no more than shixteen years of age, and ye'd sooner be lookin' at her goin' under a side-car than eatin' your dinner."

"There isn't as much meat on her as 'd fatten a jackdaw," said Flurry, clinking the silver in his pockets as he searched for a matchbox. "What are you asking for her?"

The old man drew cautiously up to him.

"Master Flurry," he said solemnly, "I'll sell her to your honour for five pounds, and she'll be worth ten after you give her a month's grass."

Flurry lit his cigarette; then he said imperturbably, "I'll give you seven shillings for her."

Old Barrett put on his hat in silence, and in silence buttoned his coat and took hold of the stirrup leather. Flurry remained immovable.

"Master Flurry," said old Barrett suddenly, with tears in his voice, "you must make it eight, sir!"

"Michael!" called out Flurry with apparent irrelevance, "run up to your father's and ask him would he lend me a loan of his side-car."

Half-an-hour later we were, improbable as it may seem, on our way to Lisheen races. We were seated upon an outside-car of immemorial age, whose joints seemed to open and close again as it swung in and out of ruts, whose tattered cushions stank of rats and mildew, whose wheels staggered and rocked like the legs of a drunken man. Between the shafts jogged the latest addition to the kennel larder, the eight-shilling mare. Flurry sat on one side, and kept her going at a rate of not less than four miles an hour; Leigh Kelway and I held on to the other.

"She'll get us as far as Lynch's anyway," said Flurry, abandoning his first contention that she could do the whole distance, as he pulled her on to her legs after her fifteenth stumble, "and he'll lend us some sort of ა horse, if it was only a mule."

"Do you notice that these cushions are very damp?" said Leigh Kelway to me, in a hollow undertone.

"Small blame to them if they are!" replied Flurry. "I've no doubt but they were out under the rain all day yesterday at Mrs. Hurley's funeral."

Leigh Kelway made no reply, but he took his note-book out of his pocket and sat on it.

We arrived at Lynch's at a little past three, and were there confronted by the next disappointment of this disastrous day. The door of Lynch's farmhouse was locked, and nothing replied to our knocking except a puppy, who barked hysterically from within.

"All gone to the races," said Flurry philosophically, picking his way round the manure heap. "No matter, here's the filly in the shed here. I know he's had her under a car."

An agitating ten minutes ensued, during which Leigh Kelway and I got the eight-shilling mare out of the shafts and the harness, and Flurry, with our inefficient help, crammed the young mare into them. As Flurry had stated that she had been driven before, I was bound to believe him, but the difficulty of getting the bit into her mouth was remarkable, and so also was the crab-like manner in which she sidled out of the yard, with Flurry and myself at her head, and Leigh Kelway hanging on to the back of the car to keep it from jamming in the gateway.

"Sit up on the car now," said Flurry when we got out on to the road; "I'll lead her on a bit. She's been ploughed away; one side of her mouth's as tough as a gad!"

Leigh Kelway threw away the wisp of grass with which he had been cleaning his hands, and mopped his intellectual forehead; he was very silent. We both mounted the car, and Flurry, with the reins in his hands, walked beside the filly, who, with her tail clasped in, moved onward in a succession of short jerks.

"Oh, she's all right!" said Flurry, beginning to run, and dragging the filly into a trot; "once she gets started—" Here the filly spied a pig in a neighbouring field, and despite the fact that she had probably eaten out of the same trough with it, she gave a violent side spring, and broke into a gallop.

"Now we're off!" shouted Flurry, making a jump at the car and clambering on; "if the traces hold we'll do!"

The English language is powerless to suggest the view-halloo with which Mr. Knox ended his speech, or to do more than indicate the rigid anxiety of Leigh Kelway's face as he regained his balance after the preliminary jerk, and clutched the back rail. It must be said for Lynch's filly that she did not kick; she merely fled, like a dog with a kettle tied to its tail, from the pursuing rattle and jingle behind her, with the shafts buffeting her dusty sides as the car swung to and fro. Whenever she showed any signs of slackening, Flurry loosed another yell at her that renewed her panic, and thus we precariously covered another two or three miles of our journey.

Had it not been for a large stone lying on the road, and had the filly not chosen to swerve so as to bring the wheel on top of it, I dare say we might have got to the races; but by an unfortunate coincidence both these things occurred, and when we recovered from the consequent shock, the tire of one of the wheels had come off, and was trundling with cumbrous gaiety into the ditch. Flurry stopped the filly and began to laugh; Leigh Kelway said something startlingly unparliamentary under his breath.

"Well, it might be worse," Flurry said consolingly as he lifted the tire on to the car; "we're not half a mile from a forge."

We walked that half-mile in funeral procession behind the car; the glory had departed from the weather, and an ugly wall of cloud was rising up out of the west to meet the sun; the hills had darkened and lost colour, and the white bog cotton shivered in a cold wind that smelt of rain.

By a miracle the smith was not at the races, owing, as he explained, to his having "the toothaches," the two facts combined producing in him a morosity only equalled by that of Leigh Kelway. The smith's sole comment on the situation was to unharness the filly, and drag her into the forge, where he tied her up. He then proceeded to whistle viciously on his fingers in the direction of a cottage, and to command, in tones of thunder, some unseen creature to bring over a couple of baskets of turf. The turf arrived in process of time, on a woman's back, and was arranged in a circle in a yard at the back of the forge. The tire was bedded in it, and the turf was with difficulty kindled at different points.

"Ye'll not get to the races this day," said the smith, yielding a sardonic satisfaction; "the turf's wet, and I haven't one to do a hand's turn for me." He laid the wheel on the ground and lit his pipe.

Leigh Kelway looked pallidly about him over the spacious empty landscape of brown mountain slopes patched with golden furze and seamed with grey walls; I wondered if he were as hungry as I. We sat on stones opposite the smouldering ring of turf and smoked, and Flurry beguiled the smith into grim and calumnious confidences about every horse in the country. After about an hour, during which the turf went out three times, and the weather became more and more threatening, a girl with a red petticoat over her head appeared at the gate of the yard, and said to the smith:

"The horse is gone away from ye."

"Where?" exclaimed Flurry, springing to his feet.

"I met him walking wesht the road there below, and when I thought to turn him he commenced to gallop."

"Pulled her head out of the headstall," said Flurry, after a rapid survey of the forge. "She's near home by now."

It was at this moment that the rain began; the situation could scarcely have been better stage-managed. After reviewing the position, Flurry and I decided that the only thing to do was to walk to a public-house a couple of miles farther on, feed there if possible, hire a car, and go home.

It was an uphill walk, with mild generous raindrops striking thicker and thicker on our faces; no one talked, and the grey clouds crowded up from behind the hills like billows of steam. Leigh Kelway bore it all with egregious resignation. I cannot pretend that I was at heart sympathetic, but by virtue of being his host I felt responsible for the breakdown, for his light suit, for everything, and divined his sentiment of horror at the first sight of the public-house.

It was a long, low cottage, with a line of dripping elm-trees overshadowing it; empty cars and carts round its door, and a babel

from within made it evident that the racegoers were pursuing a
gradual homeward route. The shop was crammed with steaming
countrymen, whose loud brawling voices, all talking together,
roused my English friend to his first remark since we had left
the forge.

"Surely Yeates, we are not going into that place?" he said
severely; "those men are all drunk."

"Ah, nothing to signify!" said Flurry, plunging in and driving
his way through the throng like a plough. "Here, Mary Kate!"
he called to the girl behind the counter, "tell your mother we
want some tea and bread and butter in the room inside."

The smell of bad tobacco and spilt porter was choking; we
worked our way through it after him towards the end of the shop,
intersecting at every hand discussions about the races.

"Tom was very nice. He spared his horse all along, and then
he put into him—" "Well, at Goggin's corner the third horse was
before the second, but he was goin' wake in himself." "I tell ye
the mare had the hind leg fasht in the fore." "Clancy was dipping
in the saddle." " 'Twas a dam nice race whatever—"

We gained the inner room at last, a cheerless apartment,
adorned with sacred pictures, a sewing-machine, and an array of
supplementary tumblers and wineglasses; but, at all events, we
had it so far to ourselves. At intervals during the next half-hour
Mary Kate burst in with cups and plates, cast them on the table
and disappeared, but of food there was no sign. After a further
period of starvation and of listening to the noise in the shop,
Flurry made a sortie, and, after lengthy and unknown adventures,
reappeared carrying a huge brown teapot, and driving before him
Mary Kate with the remainder of the repast. The bread tasted
of mice, the butter of turf-smoke, the tea of brown paper, but we
had got past the critical stage. I had entered upon my third round
of bread and butter when the door was flung open, and my valued
acquaintance, Slipper, slightly advanced in liquor, presented himself to our gaze. His bandy legs sprawled consequentially, his
nose was redder than a coal of fire, his prominent eyes rolled
crookedly upon us, and his left hand swept behind him the attempt of Mary Kate to frustrate his entrance.

"Good-evening to my vinerable friend, Mr. Flurry Knox!" he

began, in the voice of a town crier, "and to the Honourable Major Yeates, and the English gintleman!"

This impressive opening immediately attracted an audience from the shop, and the doorway filled with grinning faces as Slipper advanced farther into the room.

"Why weren't ye at the races, Mr. Flurry?" he went on, his roving eye taking a grip of us all at the same time; "sure the Miss Bennetts and all the ladies was asking where were ye."

"It'd take some time to tell them that," said Flurry, with his mouth full; "but what about the races, Slipper? Had you good sport?"

"Sport is it? Divil so pleasant an afternoon ever you seen," replied Slipper. He leaned against a side table, and all the glasses on it jingled. "Does your honour know O'Driscoll?" he went on irrelevantly. "Sure you do. He was in your honour's stable. It's what we were all sayin'; it was a great pity your honour was not there, for the likin' you had to Driscoll."

"That's thrue," said a voice at the door.

"There wasn't one in the Barony but was gethered in it, through and fro," continued Slipper, with a quelling glance at the interrupter; "and there was tints for sellin' porther, and whisky as pliable as new milk, and boys goin' round the tints outside, feeling for heads with the big ends of their blackthorns, and all kinds of recreations, and the Sons of Liberty's piffler and dhrum band from Skebawn; though faith! there was more of thim runnin' to look at the races than what was playin' in it; not to mintion different occasions that the band-masther was atin' his lunch within in the whisky tint."

"But what about Driscoll?" said Flurry.

"Sure it's about him I'm tellin' ye," replied Slipper, with the practised orator's watchful eye on his growing audience. " 'Twas within in the same whisky tint meself was, with the bandmasther and a few of the lads, an' we buyin' a ha'porth o' crackers, when I seen me brave Driscoll landin' into the tint, and a pair o' thim long boots on him; him that hadn't a shoe nor a stocking to his foot when your honour had him picking grass out o' the stones behind in your yard. 'Well,' says I to meself, 'we'll knock some spoort out of Driscoll!'

" 'Come here to me, acushla!' says I to him; 'I suppose it's some way wake in the legs y'are,' says I, 'and the docthor put them on ye the way the people wouldn't thrample ye!'

" 'May the divil choke ye!' says he, pleasant enough, but I knew by the blush he had he was vexed.

" 'Then I suppose 'tis a left-tenant colonel y'are,' says I; 'yer mother must be proud out o' ye!' says I, 'an' maybe ye'll lend her a loan o' thim waders when she's rinsin' yer bauneen in the river!' says I.

" 'Therell be work out o' this!' says he, lookin' at me both sour and bitther.

" 'Well indeed, I was thinkin' you were blue moulded for want of a batin',' says I. He was for fighting us then, but afther we had him pacificated with about a quarther of a naggin o' sperrits, he told us he was goin' ridin' in a race.

" 'An' what'll ye ride?' says I.

" 'Owld Bocock's mare,' says he.

" 'Knipes!' says I, sayin' a great curse; 'is it that little staggeen from the mountains; sure she's somethin' about the one age with meself,' says I. 'Many's the time Jamesy Geoghegan and meself used to be dhrivin' her to Macroom with pigs an' all soorts,' says I; 'an' is it leppin' stone walls ye want her to go now?'

" 'Faith, there's walls and every vari'ty of obstackle in it,' says he.

" 'It'll be the best o' your play, so,' says I, 'to leg it away home out o' this.'

" 'An' who'll ride her, so?' says he.

" 'Let the divil ride her,' says I."

Leigh Kelway, who had been leaning back seemingly half asleep, obeyed the hypnotism of Slipper's gaze, and opened his eyes.

"That was now all the conversation that passed between himself and meself," resumed Slipper, "and there was no great delay afther that till they said there was a race startin' and the dickens a one at all was goin' to ride only two, Driscoll, and one Clancy. With that then I seen Mr. Kinahane, the Petty Sessions clerk, goin' round clearin' the coorse, an' we walked the fields hither and over till we seen the most of th' obstackles.

" 'Stand easy now by the plantation,' says I; 'if they get to

come as far as this, believe me ye'll see spoort,' says I, 'an' 'twill
be a convenient spot to encourage the mare if she's anyway wake
in herself,' says I, cuttin' somethin' about five foot of an ash
sapling out o' the plantation.

" 'That's yer sort!' says owld Bocock, that was thravellin' the
racecoorse, peggin' a bit o' paper down with a thorn in front of
every lep, the way Driscoll 'd know the handiest place to face
her at it.

"Well, I hadn't barely thrimmed the ash plant—"

"Have you any jam, Mary Kate?" interrupted Flurry, whose
meal had been in no way interfered with by either the story or
the highly-scented crowd who had come to listen to it.

"We have no jam, only thraycle, sir," replied the invisible
Mary Kate.

"I hadn't the switch barely thrimmed," repeated Slipper
firmly, "when I heard the people screechin', an' I seen Driscoll
an' Clancy comin' on, leppin' all before them, an' owld Bocock's
mare bellusin' an' powdherin' along, an' bedad! whatever obstackle wouldn't throw her down, faith, she'd throw it down, an'
there's the thraffic they had in it.

" 'I declare to me sowl,' says I, 'if they continue on this way
there's a great chance some one o' thim'll win,' says I.

" 'Ye lie!' says the bandmasther, bein' a thrifle fulsome after
his luncheon.

" 'I do not,' says I, 'in regard of seein' how soople them two
boys is. Ye might observe,' says I, 'that if they have no convanient
way to sit on the saddle, they'll ride the neck o' the horse till such
time as they gets an occasion to lave it,' says I.

" 'Arragh, shut yer mouth!' says the bandmasther; 'they're
puckin' out this way now, an' may the divil admire me!' says he,
'but Clancy has the other bet out, and the divil such leatherin'
and beltin' of owld Bocock's mare ever you seen as what's in it!'
says he.

"Well, when I seen them comin' to me, and Driscoll about the
length of the plantation behind Clancy, I let out a couple of bawls.

" 'Skelp her, ye big brute!' says I. 'What good's in ye that ye
aren't able to skelp her?' "

The yell and the histrionic flourish of his stick with which
Slipper delivered this incident brought down the house. Leigh

Kelway was sufficiently moved to ask me in an undertone if "skelp" was a local term.

"Well, Mr. Flurry, and gintlemen," recommenced Slipper, "I declare to ye when owld Bocock's mare heard thim roars she sthretched out her neck like a gandher, and when she passed me out she give a couple of grunts, and looked at me as ugly as a Christian.

" 'Hah!' says I, givin' her a couple o' dhraws o' th' ash plant across the butt o' the tail, the way I wouldn't blind her; 'I'll make ye grunt!' says I, 'I'll nourish ye!'

"I knew well she was very frightful of th' ash plant since the winter Tommeen Sullivan had her under a sidecar. But now, in place of havin' any obligations to me, ye'd be surprised if ye heard the blaspheemious expressions of that young boy that was ridin' her; and whether it was over-anxious he was, turnin' around the way I'd hear him cursin', or whether it was some slither or slide came to owld Bocock's mare, I dunno, but she was bet up agin the last obstackle but two, and before ye could say 'Schnipes,' she was standin' on her two ears beyond in th' other field! I declare to ye, on the vartue of me oath, she stood that way till she reconnoithered what side would Driscoll fall an' she turned about then and rolled on him as cosy as if he was meadow grass!"

Slipper stopped short; the people in the doorway groaned appreciatively; Mary Kate murmured "The Lord save us!"

"The blood was dhruv out through his nose and ears," continued Slipper, with a voice that indicated the cream of the narration, "and you'd hear his bones crackin' on the ground! You'd have pitied the poor boy."

"Good heavens!" said Leigh Kelway, sitting up very straight in his chair.

"Was he hurt, Slipper?" asked Flurry casually.

"Hurt is it?" echoed Slipper in high scorn; "killed on the spot!" He paused to relish the effect of the denouement on Leigh Kelway. "Oh, divil so pleasant an afthernoon ever you seen; and indeed, Mr. Flurry, it's what we were all sayin', it was a great pity your honour was not there for the likin' you had for Driscoll."

As he spoke the last word there was an outburst of singing and cheering from a car-load of people who had just pulled up at the door. Flurry listened, leaned back in his chair, and began to laugh.

"It scarcely strikes one as a comic incident," said Leigh Kelway, very coldly to me; "in fact, it seems to me that the police ought—"

"Show me Slipper!" bawled a voice in the shop; "show me that dirty little undherlooper till I have his blood! Hadn't I the race won only for he souring the mare on me! What's that you say? I tell you he did! He left seven slaps on her with the handle of a hay-rake—"

There was in the room in which we were sitting a second door, leading to the back yard, a door consecrated to the unobtrusive visits of so-called "Sunday travellers." Through it Slipper faded away like a dream, and, simultaneously, a tall young man, with a face like a red-hot potato tied up in a bandage, squeezed his way from the shop into the room.

"Well, Driscoll," said Flurry, "since it wasn't the teeth of the rake he left on the mare, you needn't be talking!"

Leigh Kelway looked from one to the other with a wilder expression in his eye than I had thought it capable of. I read in it a resolve to abandon Ireland to her fate.

At eight o'clock we were still waiting for the car that we had been assured should be ours directly it returned from the races. At half-past eight we had adopted the only possible course that remained, and had accepted the offers of lifts on the laden cars that were returning to Skebawn, and I presently was gratified by the spectacle of my friend Leigh Kelway wedged between a roulette table and its proprietor on one side of a car, with Driscoll and Slipper, mysteriously reconciled and excessively drunk, seated, locked in each other's arms, on the other. Flurry and I, somewhat similarly placed, followed on two other cars. I was scarcely surprised when I was informed that the melancholy white animal in the shafts of the leading car was Owld Bocock's much-enduring steeplechaser.

The night was very dark and stormy, and it is almost superfluous to say that no one carried lamps; the rain poured upon us, and through wind and wet Owld Bocock's mare set the pace at a rate that showed she knew from bitter experience what was expected from her by gentlemen who had spent the evening in a public-house; behind her the other two tired horses followed closely, incited to emulation by shouting, singing, and a liberal allowance of whip. We were a good ten miles from Skebawn, and never had the road seemed so long. For mile after mile the half-seen low walls slid past us, with occasional plunges into caverns of darkness under trees. Sometimes from a wayside cabin a dog would dash out to bark at us as we rattled by; sometimes our cavalcade swung aside to pass, with yells and counter-yells, crawling carts filled with other belated race-goers.

I was nearly wet through, even though I received considerable shelter from a Skebawn publican, who slept heavily and irrepressibly on my shoulder. Driscoll, on the leading car, had struck up an approximation to the "Wearing of the Green," when a wavering star appeared on the road ahead of us. It grew momently larger; it came towards us apace. Flurry, on the car behind me, shouted suddenly—

"That's the mail car, with one of the lamps out! Tell those fellows ahead to look out!"

But the warning fell on deaf ears.

> *"When laws can change the blades of grass*
> *From growing as they grow—"*

howled five discordant voices, oblivious of the towering proximity of the star.

A Biancoli mail car is nearly three times the size of an ordinary outside car, and when on a dark night it advances, Cyclops-like, with but one eye, it is difficult for even a sober driver to calculate its bulk. Above the sounds of melody there arose the thunder of heavy wheels, the splashing trample of three big horses, then a crash and a turmoil of shouts. Our cars pulled up just in time, and I tore myself from the embrace of my publican to go to Leigh Kelway's assistance.

The wing of the Biancoli had caught the wing of the smaller car, flinging Owld Bocock's mare on her side and throwing her freight headlong on top of her, the heap being surmounted by the roulette table. The driver of the mail car unshipped his solitary lamp and turned it on the disaster. I saw that Flurry had already got hold of Leigh Kelway by the heels, and was dragging him from under the others. He struggled up hatless, muddy, and gasping, with Driscoll hanging on by his neck, still singing the "Wearing of the Green."

A voice from the mail car said incredulously, "Leigh Kelway!" A spectacled face glared down upon him from under the dripping spikes of an umbrella.

It was the Right Honourable the Earl of Waterbury, Leigh Kelway's chief, returning from his fishing expedition.

Meanwhile Slipper, in the ditch, did not cease to announce that "Divil so pleasant an afthernoon ever ye seen as what was in it!"

Don
The Story of a Lion Dog

By ZANE GREY

I T HAS TAKEN me years to realize the greatness of a dog; and often as I have told the story of Don—his love of freedom and hatred of men—how I saved his life and he saved mine— it never was told as I feel it now.

I saw Don first at Flagstaff, Arizona, where arrangements had been made for me to cross the desert with Buffalo Jones and a Mormon caravan en route to Lee's Ferry on the Colorado River. Jones had brought a pack of nondescript dogs. Our purpose was to cross the river and skirt the Vermilion Cliffs, and finally work up through Buckskin Forest to the north rim of the Grand Canyon, where Jones expected to lasso mountain lions and capture them alive. The most important part of our outfit, of course, was the pack of hounds. Never had I seen such a motley assembly of canines. They did not even have names. Jones gave me the privilege of finding names for them.

Among them was a hound that seemed out of place because of his superb proportions, his sleek, dark, smooth skin, his noble head, and great, solemn black eyes. He had extraordinarily long ears, thick-veined and faintly tinged with brown. Here was a dog that looked to me like a thoroughbred. My friendly overtures to him were unnoticed. Jones said he was part bloodhound and had belonged to an old Mexican don in southern California. So I named him Don.

We were ten days crossing the Painted Desert, and protracted horseback-riding was then so new and hard for me that I had no

Harper & Brothers.

enthusiasm left to scrape acquaintance with the dogs. Still, I did
not forget and often felt sorry for them as they limped along,
clinking their chains under the wagons. Even then I divined that
horses and dogs were going to play a great part in my Western
experience.

At Lee's Ferry we crossed the Colorado and I was introduced
to the weird and wild canyon country, with its golden-red walls
and purple depths. Here we parted with the caravan and went
on with Jones's rangers, Jim and Emmet, who led our outfit into
such a wonderful region as I had never dreamed of. We camped
several days on the vast range where Jones let his buffalo herd
run wild. One day the Arizonians put me astride a white mustang
that apparently delighted in carrying a tenderfoot. I did not
then know what I was soon to learn—that the buffalo always
chased this mustang off the range. When I rode up on the herd,
to my utter amaze and terror they took after me and— But I am
digressing, and this is a dog story.

Once across the river, Jones had unchained the dogs and let
them run on ahead or lag behind. Most of them lagged. Don for
one, however, did not get sore feet. Beyond the buffalo range we
entered the sage, and here Jones began to train the dogs in earnest.
He carried on his saddle an old blunderbuss of a shotgun, about
which I had wondered curiously. I had supposed he meant to
use it to shoot small game.

Moze, our black-and-white dog, and the ugliest of the lot,
gave chase to a jack rabbit.

"Hyar, you Moze, come back!" bawled Jones in stentorian
tones. But Moze paid no attention. Jones whipped out the old
shotgun and before I could utter a protest he had fired. The
distance was pretty far—seventy yards or more—but Moze howled
piercingly and came sneaking and limping back. It was remarkable to see him almost crawl to Jones's feet.

"Thar! That'll teach you not to chase rabbits. You're a lion
dog!" shouted the old plainsman as if he were talking to a human.

At first I was so astounded and furious that I could not speak.
But presently I voiced my feeling.

"Wal, it looks worse than it is," he said, with his keen gray-
blue eyes on me. "I'm usin' fine birdshot an' it can't do any more
than sting. You see, I've no time to train these dogs. It's necessary

to make them see quick that they're not to trail or chase any varmints but lions."

There was nothing for me to do but hold my tongue, though my resentment appeared to be shared by Jim and Emmet. They made excuses for the old plainsman. Jim said: "He shore can make animals do what he wants. But I never seen the dog or hoss that cared two bits for him."

We rode on through the beautiful purple sageland, gradually uphill, toward a black-fringed horizon that was Buckskin Forest. Jack rabbits, cottontails, coyotes and foxes, prairie dogs and pack rats infested the sage and engaged the attention of our assorted pack of hounds. All the dogs except Don fell victim to Jones's old blunderbuss; and surely stubborn Moze received a second peppering, this time at closer range. I espied drops of blood upon his dirty white skin. After this it relieved me greatly to see that not even Moze transgressed again. Jones's method was cruel, but effective. He had captured and subdued wild animals since his boyhood. In fact, that had been the driving passion of his life, but no sentiment entered into it.

"Reckon Don is too smart to let you ketch him," Jim once remarked to our leader.

"Wal, I don't know," responded Jones, dubiously. "Mebbe he just wouldn't chase this sage trash. But wait till we jump some deer. Then we'll see. He's got bloodhound in him, and I'll bet he'll run deer. All hounds will, even the best ones trained on bear an' lion."

Not long after we entered the wonderful pine forest the reckoning of Don came as Jones had predicted. Several deer bounded out of a thicket and crossed ahead of us, soon disappearing in the green blur.

"Ahuh! Now we'll see," ejaculated Jones, deliberately pulling out the old shotgun.

The hounds trotted along beside our horses, unaware of the danger ahead. Soon we reached the deer tracks. All the hounds showed excitement. Don let out a sharp yelp and shot away like a streak on the trail.

"Don, come hyar!" yelled Jones, at the same time extending his gun. Don gave no sign he had heard. Then Jones pulled trigger and shot him. I saw the scattering of dust and pine needles all

around Don. He doubled up and rolled. I feared that he might
be badly injured. But he got up and turned back. It seemed
strange that he did not howl. Jones drew his plunging horse to
a halt and bade us all stop.

"Don, come back hyar," he called in a loud, harsh, commanding voice.

The hound obeyed, not sneakingly or cringingly. He did not
put his tail between his legs. But he was frightened and no doubt
pretty badly hurt. When he reached us I saw that he was trembling
all over and that drops of blood dripped from his long ears. What
a somber, sullen gaze in his eyes!

"See hyar," bellowed Jones. "I knowed you was deer-chaser.
Wal, now you're a lion dog."

Later that day, when I had recovered sufficiently from my
disapproval, I took Jones to task about this matter of shooting
the dogs. I wanted to know how he expected the hounds to learn
what he required of them.

"Wal, that's easy," he replied curtly. "When we strike a lion
trail I'll put them on it—let them go. They'll soon learn."

It seemed plausible, but I was so incensed that I doubted the
hounds would chase anything; and I resolved that if Jones shot
Don again I would force the issue and end the hunt unless assured
there would be no more of such drastic training methods.

Soon after this incident we made camp on the edge of a
beautiful glade where a snow-bank still lingered and a stream of
water trickled down into a green swale. Before we got camp
pitched a band of wild horses thudded by, thrilling me deeply.
My first sight of wild horses! I knew I should never forget that
splendid stallion, the leader, racing on under the trees, looking
back at us over his shoulder.

At this camp I renewed my attempts to make friends with
Don. He had been chained apart from the other dogs. He ate
what I fetched him, but remained aloof. His dignity and distrust
were such that I did not risk laying a hand on him then. But I
resolved to win him if it were possible. His tragic eyes haunted
me. There was a story in them I could not read. He always seemed
to be looking afar. On this occasion I came to the conclusion that
he hated Jones.

Buckskin Forest was well named. It appeared to be full of

deer, the large black-tailed species known as mule deer. This species must be related to the elk. The size and beauty of them, the way they watched with long ears erect and then bounded off as if on springs, never failed to thrill me with delight.

As we traveled on, the forest grew wilder and more beautiful. In the park-like glades a bleached white grass waved in the wind and bluebells smiled wanly. Wild horses outnumbered the deer, and that meant there were some always in sight. A large gray grouse flew up now and then, and most striking of the forest creatures to fascinate me was a magnificent black squirrel, with a long bushy white tail, and tufted ears, and a red stripe down its glossy sides.

We rode for several days through this enchanting wilderness, gradually ascending, and one afternoon we came abruptly to a break in the forest. It was the north rim of the Grand Canyon. My astounded gaze tried to grasp an apalling abyss of purple and gold and red, a chasm too terrible and beautiful to understand all at once. The effect of that moment must have been tremendous, for I have never recovered from it. To this day the thing that fascinates me most is to stand upon a great height—canyon wall, or promontory, or peak—and gaze down into the mysterious colorful depths.

Our destination was Powell's Plateau, an isolated cape jutting out into the canyon void. Jones showed it to me—a distant gold-rimmed, black-fringed promontory, seemingly inaccessible and unscalable. The only trail leading to it was a wild-horse hunter's trail, seldom used, exceedingly dangerous. It took us two days over this canyon trail to the Saddle—a narrow strip of land dipping down from the Plateau and reaching up to the main rim. We camped under a vast looming golden wall, so wonderful that it kept me from sleeping. That night lions visited our camp. The hounds barked for hours. This was the first chance I had to hear Don. What a voice he had! Deep, ringing, wild, like the bay of a wolf!

Next morning we ascended the Saddle, from the notch of which I looked down into the chasm still asleep in purple shadows; then we climbed a narrow deer trail to the summit of the Plateau. Here indeed was the grand, wild, isolated spot of my dreams. Indeed, I was in an all-satisfying trance of adventure.

I wanted to make camp on the rim, but Jones laughed at me. We rode through the level, stately forest of pines until we came to a ravine on the north side of which lay a heavy bank of snow. This was very necessary, for there was no water on the Plateau. Jones rode off to scout while the rest of us pitched camp. Before we had completed our task a troop of deer appeared across the ravine, and motionless they stood watching us. There were big and little deer, blue-gray in color, sleek and graceful, so tame that to me it seemed brutal to shoot at them.

Don was the only one of the dogs that espied the deer. He stood up to gaze hard at them, but he did not bark or show any desire to chase them. Yet there seemed to me to be a strange yearning light in his dark eyes. I had never failed to approach Don whenever opportunity afforded, to continue my overtures of friendship. But now, as always, Don turned away from me. He was cold and somber. I had never seen him wag his tail or whine eagerly, as was common with most hounds.

Jones returned to camp jubilant and excited, as far as it was possible for the old plainsman to be. He had found lion trails and lion tracks, and he predicted a great hunt for us.

The Plateau resembled in shape the ace of clubs. It was perhaps six miles long and three or four wide. The body of it was covered with a heavy growth of pine, and the capes that sloped somewhat toward the canyon were thick with sage and cedar. This lower part, with its numerous swales and ravines and gorges, all leading down into the jungle of splintered crags and thicketed slopes of the Grand Canyon, turned out to be a paradise for deer and lion.

We found many lion trails leading down from the cedared broken rim to the slopes of yellow and red. These slopes really constituted a big country, and finally led to the sheer perpendicular precipices, three thousand feet lower.

Deer were numerous and as tame as cattle on a range. They grazed with our horses. Herds of a dozen or more were common. Once we saw a very large band. Down in the sage and under the cedars and in ravines we found many remains of deer. Jones called these lion-kills. And he frankly stated that the number of deer killed yearly upon the Plateau would be incredible to any one who had not seen the actual signs.

In two days we had three captive lions tied up to pine saplings near camp. They were two-year-olds. Don and I had treed the first lion; I had taken pictures of Jones lassoing him; I had jumped off a ledge into a cedar to escape another; I had helped Jones hold a third; I had scratches from lion claws on my chaps, and— But I keep forgetting that this is not a story about lions. Always before when I had told it I have slighted Don.

One night, a week or more after we had settled in camp, we sat round a blazing red fire and talked over the hunt of the day. We all had our parts to tell. Jones and I had found where a lioness had jumped a deer. He showed me where the lioness had crouched upon a little brushy knoll, and how she had leaped thirty feet to the back of the deer. He showed me the tracks the deer had made—bounding, running, staggering with the lioness upon its back—and where, fully a hundred paces beyond, the big cat had downed its prey and killed it. There had been a fierce struggle. Then the lioness had dragged the carcass down the slope, through the sage, to the cedar tree where her four two-year-old cubs waited. All that we found of the deer were the ragged hide, some patches of hair, cracked bones, and two long ears. These were still warm.

Eventually we got the hounds on this trail and soon put up the lions. I found a craggy cliff under the rim and sat there watching and listening for hours. Jones rode to and fro above me, and at last dismounted to go down to join the other men. The hounds treed one of the lions. How that wild canyon slope rang with barks and bays and yells! Jones tied up this lion. Then the hounds worked up the ragged slope toward me, much to my gratification and excitement. Somewhere near me the lions had taken to cedars or crags, and I strained my eyes searching for them.

At last I located a lion on top of an isolated crag right beneath me. The hounds, with Don and Ranger leading, had been on the right track. My lusty yells brought the men. Then the lion stood up—a long, slender, yellowish cat—and spat at me. Next it leaped off that crag, fully fifty feet to the slope below, and bounded down, taking the direction from which the men had come. The hounds gave chase, yelping and baying. Jones bawled at them, trying to call them off, for what reason I could not guess. But I was soon to learn. They found the lion Jones had captured and left lying tied under a cedar, and they killed it, then took the trail of the other. They treed it far down in the rough jumble of rocks and cedars.

One by one we had ridden back to camp that night, tired out. Jim was the last in and he told his story last. And what was my amazement and fright to learn that all the three hours I had sat upon the edge of the caverned wall, the lioness had crouched on a bench above me. Jim on his way up had seen her, and then located her tracks in the dust back of my position. When this fact burst upon me I remembered how I had at first imagined I heard faint panting breaths near me somewhere. I had been too excited to trust my ears.

"Wal," said Jones, standing with the palms of his huge hands to the fire, "we had a poor day. If we had stuck to Don there'd have been a different story. I haven't trusted him. But now I reckon I'll have to. He'll make the greatest lion dog I ever had. Strikes me queer, too, for I never guessed it was in him. He has faults, though. He's too fast. He outruns the other hounds, an' he's goin' to be killed because of that. Some day he'll beat the pack to a mean old Tom lion or a lioness with cubs, an' he'll get his everlastin'. Another fault is, he doesn't bark often. That's bad, too. You can't stick to him. He's got a grand bay, shore, but he saves his breath. Don wants to run an' trail an' fight alone. He's got more nerve than any hound I ever trained. He's too good for his own sake—an' it'll be his death."

Naturally I absorbed all that Buffalo Jones said about dogs, horses, lions, everything pertaining to the West, and I believed it as if it had been gospel. But I observed that the others, especially Jim, did not always agree with our chief in regard to the hounds. A little later, when Jones had left the fire, Jim spoke up with his slow Texas drawl:

"Wal, what does he know about dawgs, I'll tell you right heah, if he hadn't shot Don we'd had the best hound that ever put his nose to a track. Don is a wild, strange hound, shore enough. Mebbe he's like a lone wolf. But it's plain he's been mistreated by men. An' Jones has just made him wuss."

Emmet inclined to Jim's point of view. And I respected this giant Mormon who was famous on the desert for his kindness to men and animals. His ranch at Lee's Ferry was overrun with dogs, cats, mustangs, burros, sheep and tamed wild animals that he had succored.

"Yes, Don hates Jones and, I reckon, all of us," said Emmet. "Don's not old, but he's too old to change. Still, you can never tell what kindness will do to animals. I'd like to take Don home with me and see. But Jones is right. That hound will be killed."

"Now I wonder why Don doesn't run off from us?" inquired Jim.

"Perhaps he thinks he'd get shot again," I ventured.

"If he ever runs away it'll not be here in the wilds," replied Emmet. "I take Don to be about as smart as any dog ever gets. And that's pretty close to human intelligence. People have to live lonely lives with dogs before they understand them. I reckon I understand Don. He's either loved one master once and lost him, or else he has always hated all men."

"Humph! That's shore an idee," ejaculated Jim, dubiously. "Do you think a dog can feel like that?"

"Jim, I once saw a little Indian shepherd dog lie down on its master's grave and die," returned the Mormon, sonorously.

"Wal, dog-gone me!" exclaimed Jim, in mild surprise.

One morning Jim galloped in, driving the horses pell-mell into camp. Any deviation from the Texan's usual leisurely manner of doing things always brought us up short with keen expectation.

"Saddle up," called Jim. "Shore that's a chase on. I seen a big red lioness up heah. She must have come down out of the tree what I hang my meat. Last night I had a haunch of venison. It's gone. . . . Say, she was a beauty. Red as a red fox."

In a very few moments we were mounted and riding up the ravine, with the eager hounds sniffing the air. Always over-anxious in my excitement, I rode ahead of my comrades. The hounds trotted with me. The distance to Jim's meat tree was a short quarter of a mile. I knew well where it was and, as of course the lion trail would be fresh, I anticipated a fine opportunity to watch Don. The other hounds had come to regard him as their leader. When we neared the meat tree, which was a low-branched oak shaded by thick silver spruce, Don elevated his nose high in the air. He had caught a scent even at a distance. Jones had said more than once that Don had a wonderful nose. The other hounds, excited by Don, began to whine and yelp and run around with noses to the ground.

I had eyes only for Don. How instinct he was with life and fire! The hair on his neck stood up like bristles. Suddenly he let out a wild bark and bolted. He sped away from the pack and like a flash passed that oak tree, running with his head high. The hounds strung out after him and soon the woods seemed full of a baying chorus.

My horse, Black Bolly, well knew the meaning of the medley and did not need to be urged. He broke into a run and swiftly carried me up out of the hollow and through a brown-aisled pine-scented strip of forest to the canyon.

I rode along the edge of one of the deep indentations on the main rim. The hounds were bawling right under me at the base of a low cliff. They had jumped the lioness. I could not see them, but that was not necessary. They were running fast towards the head of this cove, and I had hard work to hold Black Bolly to a safe gait along that rocky rim. Suddenly she shied, and then reared, so that I fell out of the saddle as much as I dismounted. But I held the bridle, and then jerked my rifle from the saddle sheath. As I ran toward the rim I heard the yells of the men coming up behind. At the same instant I was startled and halted by sight of something red and furry flashing up into a tree right in front of me. It was the red lioness. The dogs had chased her into a pine the middle branches of which were on a level with the rim.

My skin went tight and cold and my heart fluttered. The lioness looked enormous, but that was because she was so close. I could have touched her with a long fishing-pole. I stood motionless for an instant, thrilling in every nerve, reveling in the beauty and wildness of that great cat. She did not see me. The hounds below engaged all her attention. But when I let out a yell, which I could not stifle, she jerked spasmodically to face me. Then I froze again. What a tigerish yellow flash of eyes and fangs! She hissed. She could have sprung from the tree to the rim and upon me in two bounds. But she leaped to a ledge below the rim, glided along that, and disappeared.

I ran ahead and with haste and violence clambered out upon

a jutting point of the rim, from which I could command the situation. Jones and the others were riding and yelling back where I had left my horse. I called for them to come.

The hounds were baying along the base of the low cliff. No doubt they had seen the lioness leap out of the tree. My eyes roved everywhere. This cove was a shallow V-shaped gorge, a few hundred yards deep and as many across. Its slopes were steep, with patches of brush and rock.

All at once my quick eye caught a glimpse of something moving up the opposite slope. It was a long red pantherish shape. The lioness! I yelled with all my might. She ran up the slope and at the base of the low wall she turned to the right. At that moment Jones strode heavily over the rough loose rocks of the promontory toward me.

"Where's the cat?" he boomed, his gray eyes flashing. In a moment more I had pointed her out. "Ha! I see. . . . Don't like that place. The canyon boxes. She can't get out. She'll turn back."

The old hunter had been quick to grasp what had escaped me. The lioness could not find any break in the wall, and manifestly she would not go down into the gorge. She wheeled back along the base of this yellow cliff. There appeared to be a strip of bare clay or shale rock against which background her red shape stood out clearly. She glided along, slowing her pace, and she turned her gaze across the gorge.

Then Don's deep bay rang out from the slope to our left. He had struck the trail of the lioness. I saw him running down. He leaped in long bounds. The other hounds heard him and broke for the brushy slope. In a moment they had struck the scent of their quarry and given tongue.

As they started down Don burst out of the willow thicket at the bottom of the gorge and bounded up the opposite slope. He was five hundred yards ahead of the pack. He was swiftly climbing. He would run into the lioness.

Jones gripped my arm in his powerful hand.

"Look!" he shouted. "Look at that fool hound! . . . Runnin' uphill to get to that lioness. She won't run. She's cornered. She'll meet him. She'll kill him. . . . Shoot her! Shoot her!"

I scarcely needed Jones's command to stir me to save Don, but it was certain that the old plainsman's piercing voice made me tremble. I knelt and leveled my rifle. The lioness showed red against the gray—a fine target. She was gliding more and more slowly. She saw or heard Don. The gunsight wavered. I could not hold steady. But I had to hurry. My first bullet struck two yards below the beast, puffing the dust. She kept on. My second bullet hit behind her. Jones was yelling in my ear. I could see Don out of the tail of my eye. . . . Again I shot. Too high! But the lioness jumped and halted. She lashed with her tail. What a wild picture! I strained—clamped every muscle, and pulled trigger. My bullet struck right under the lioness, scattering a great puff of dust and gravel in her face. She bounded ahead a few yards and up into a cedar tree. An instant later Don flashed over the bare spot where she had waited to kill him, and in another his deep bay rang out under the cedar.

"Treed, by gosh!" yelled Jones, joyfully pounding me on the back with his huge fist. "You saved that fool dog's life. She'd have killed him shore. . . . Wal, the pack will be there pronto, an' all we've got to do is go over an' tie her up. But it was a close shave for Don."

That night in camp Don was not in the least different from his usual somber self. He took no note of my proud proprietorship or my hovering near him while he ate the supper I provided, part of which came from my own plate. My interest and sympathy had augmented to love.

Don's attitude toward the captured and chained lions never ceased to be a source of delight and wonder to me. All the other hounds were upset by the presence of the big cats. Moze, Sounder, Tiger, Ranger would have fought these collared lions. Not so Don! For him they had ceased to exist. He would walk within ten feet of a hissing lioness without the slightest sign of having seen or heard her. He never joined in the howling chorus of the dogs. He would go to sleep close to where the lions clanked their chains, clawed the trees, whined and spat and squalled.

Several days after that incident of the red lioness we had a long and severe chase through the brushy cedar forest on the left wing of the Plateau. I did well to keep the hounds within earshot. When I arrived at the end of that run I was torn and blackened by the brush, wet with sweat, and hot as fire. Jones, lasso in hand, was walking round a large cedar tree under which the pack of hounds was clamoring. Jim and Emmet were seated on a stone, wiping their red faces.

"Wal, I'll rope him before he rests up," declared Jones.

"Wait till—I get—my breath," panted Emmet.

"We shore oozed along this mawnin'," drawled Jim.

Dismounting, I untied my camera from the saddle and then began to peer up into the bushy cedar.

"It's a Tom lion," declared Jones. "Not very big, but he looks mean. I reckon he'll mess us up some."

"Haw! Haw!" shouted Jim, sarcastically. The old plainsman's imperturbability sometimes wore on our nerves.

I climbed a cedar next to the one in which the lion had taken refuge. From a topmost fork, swaying to and fro, I stood up to photograph our quarry. He was a good-sized animal, tawny in hue, rather gray of face, and a fierce-looking brute. As the distance between us was not far, my situation was as uncomfortable as thrilling. He snarled at me and spat viciously. I was about to abandon my swinging limb when the lion turned away from me to peer down through the branches.

Jones was climbing into the cedar. Low and deep the lion growled. Jones held in one hand a long pole with a small fork at the end, upon which hung the noose of his lasso. Presently he got far enough up to reach the lion. Usually he climbed close enough to throw the rope, but evidently he regarded this beast as dangerous. He tried to slip the noose over the head of the lion. One sweep of a big paw sent pole and noose flying. Patiently Jones made ready and tried again, with similar result. Many times he tried. His patience and perseverance seemed incredible. One attribute of his great power to capture and train wild animals here asserted itself. Finally the lion grew careless or tired, on which instant Jones slipped the noose over its head.

Drawing the lasso tight, he threw his end over a thick branch and let it trail down to the men below. "Wait now!" he yelled and quickly backed down out of the cedar. The hounds were leaping eagerly.

"Pull him off that fork an' let him down easy so I can rope one of his paws."

It turned out, however, that the lion was hard to dislodge. I could see his muscles ridge and bulge. Dead branches cracked, the tree top waved. Jones began to roar in anger. The men replied with strained hoarse voices. I saw the lion drop from his perch and, clawing the branches, springing convulsively, he disappeared from my sight.

Then followed a crash. The branch over which Jones was lowering the beast had broken. Wild yells greeted my startled ears and a perfect din of yelps and howls. Pandemonium had broken loose down there. I fell more than I descended from that tree.

As I bounded erect I espied the men scrambling out of the way of a huge furry wheel. Ten hounds and one lion comprised that brown whirling ball. Suddenly out of it a dog came hurtling. He rolled to my feet, staggered up.

It was Don. Blood was streaming from him. Swiftly I dragged him aside, out of harm's way. And I forgot the fight. My hands came away from Don wet and dripping with hot blood. It shocked me. Then I saw that his throat had been terribly torn. I thought his jugular vein had been severed. Don lay down and stretched out. He looked at me with those great somber eyes. Never would I forget! He was going to die right there before my eyes.

"Oh, Don! Don! What can I do?" I cried in horror.

As I sank beside Don one of my hands came in contact with snow. It had snowed that morning and there were still white patches in shady places. Like a flash I ripped off my scarf and bound it round Don's neck. Then I scraped up a double handful of snow and placed that in my bandana handkerchief. This also I bound tightly round his neck. I could do no more. My hope left me then, and I had not the courage to sit there beside him until he died.

All the while I had been aware of a bedlam near at hand. When I looked I saw a spectacle for a hunter. Jones, yelling at the top of his stentorian voice, seized one hound after the other by the hind legs and, jerking him from the lion, threw him down the steep slope. Jim and Emmet were trying to help while at the same time they avoided close quarters with that threshing beast. At last they got the dogs off and the lion stretched out. Jones got up, shaking his shaggy head. Then he espied me and his hard face took on a look of alarm.

"Hyar—you're all—bloody," he panted plaintively, as if I had been exceedingly remiss.

Whereupon I told him briefly about Don. Then Jim and Emmet approached and we all stood looking down on the quiet dog and the patch of bloody snow.

"Wal, I reckon he's a goner," said Jones, breathing hard. "Shore I knew he'd get his everlastin'."

"Looks powerful like the lion has aboot got his, too," added Jim.

Emmet knelt by Don and examined the bandage round his neck. "Bleeding yet," he muttered, thoughtfully. "You did all that was possible. Too bad! . . . The kindest thing we can do is to leave him here."

I did not question this, but I hated to consent. Still, to move him would only bring on more hemorrhage and to put him out of his agony would have been impossible for me. Moreover, while there was life there was hope! Scraping up a goodly ball of snow, I rolled it close to Don so that he could lick it if he chose. Then I turned aside and could not look again. But I knew that tomorrow or the following day I would find my way back to this wild spot.

The accident to Don and what seemed the inevitable issue weighed heavily upon my mind. Don's eyes haunted me. I very much feared that the hunt had reached an unhappy ending for me. Next day the weather was threatening and, as the hounds were pretty tired, we rested in camp, devoting ourselves to needful tasks. A hundred times I thought of Don, alone out there in the wild brakes. Perhaps merciful death had relieved him of suffering. I would surely find out on the morrow.

But the indefatigable Jones desired to hunt in another direction next day and, as I was by no means sure I could find the place where Don had been left, I had to defer that trip. We had a thrilling, hazardous, luckless chase, and I for one gave up before it ended.

Weary and dejected, I rode back. I could not get Don off my conscience. The pleasant woodland camp did not seem the same place. For the first time the hissing, spitting, chain-clinking, tail-lashion lions caused me irritation and resentment. I would have none of them. What was the capture of a lot of spiteful, vicious cats to the life of a noble dog? Slipping my saddle off, I turned Black Bolly loose.

Then I imagined I saw a beautiful black long-eared hound enter the glade. I rubbed my eyes. Indeed there was a dog coming. Don! I shouted my joy and awe. Running like a boy, I knelt by him, saying I knew not what. Don wagged his tail! He licked my hand! These actions seemed as marvelous as his return. He looked sick and weak, but he was all right. The handkerchief was gone from his neck but the scarf remained, and it was stuck tight where his throat had been lacerated.

Later Emmet examined Don and said we had made a mistake about the jugular vein being severed. Don's injury had been serious, however, and without the prompt aid I had so fortunately given he would soon have bled to death. Jones shook his gray old locks and said: "Reckon Don's time hadn't come. Hope that will teach him sense." In a couple of days Don had recovered and on the next he was back leading the pack.

A subtle change had come over Don in his relation to me. I did not grasp it so clearly then. Thought and memory afterward brought the realization to me. But there was a light in his eyes for me which had never been there before.

One day Jones and I treed three lions. The larger leaped and ran down into the canyon. The hounds followed. Jones strode after them, leaving me alone with nothing but a camera to keep those two lions up that tree. I had left horse and gun far up the slope. I protested; I yelled after him, "What'll I do if they start down?"

He turned to gaze up at me. His grim face flashed in the sunlight.

"Grab a club an' chase them back," he replied.

Then I was left alone with two ferocious-looking lions in a pinon tree scarcely thirty feet high. While they heard the baying of the hounds they paid no attention to me, but after that ceased they got ugly. Then I hid behind a bush and barked like a dog. It worked beautifully. The lions grew quiet. I barked and yelped and bayed until I lost my voice. Then they got ugly again! They started down. With stones and clubs I kept them up there, while all the time I was wearing to collapse. When at last I was about to give up in terror and despair I heard Don's bay, faint and far away. The lions had heard it before I had. How they strained! I could see the beating of their hearts through their lean sides. My own heart leaped. Don's bay floated up, wild and mournful. He was coming. Jones had put him on the back trail of the lion that had leaped from the tree.

Deeper and clearer came the bays. How strange that Don should vary from his habit of seldom baying! There was something uncanny in this change. Soon I saw him far down the rocky slope. He was climbing fast. It seemed I had long to wait, yet my fear left me. On and up he came, ringing out that wild bay. It must have curdled the blood of those palpitating lions. It seemed the herald of that bawling pack of hounds.

Don espied me before he reached the pinon in which were the lions. He bounded right past it and up to me with the wildest demeanor. He leaped up and placed his forepaws on my breast. And as I leaned down, excited and amazed, he licked my face. Then he whirled back to the tree, where he stood up and fiercely bayed the lions. While I sank down to rest, overcome, the familiar baying chorus of the hounds floated up from below. As usual they were far behind the fleet Don, but they were coming.

Another day I found myself alone on the edge of a huge cove that opened down into the main canyon. We were always getting lost from one another. And so were the hounds. There were so many lion trails that the pack would split, some going one way, some another, until it appeared each dog finally had a lion to himself.

It was a glorious day. From far below, faint and soft, came the strange roar of the Rio Colorado. I could see it winding, somber and red, through the sinister chasm. Adventure ceased to exist for me. I was gripped by the grandeur and loveliness, the desolation and loneliness, of the supreme spectacle of nature.

Then as I sat there, absorbed and chained, the spell of enchantment was broken by Don. He had come to me. His mouth was covered with froth. I knew what that meant. Rising, I got my canteen from the saddle and poured water into the crown of my sombrero. Don lapped it. As he drank so thirstily I espied a bloody scratch on his nose.

"Aha! A lion has bated you one, this very morning," I cried. "Don—I fear for you."

He rested while I once more was lost in contemplation of the glory of the canyon. What significant hours these on the lonely heights! But then I only saw and felt.

Presently I mounted my horse and headed for camp, with Don trotting behind. When we reached the notch of the cove the hound let out his deep bay and bounded down a break in the low wall. I dismounted and called. Only another deep bay answered me. Don had scented a lion or crossed one's trail. Suddenly several sharp deep yelps came from below, a crashing of brush, a rattling of stones. Don had jumped another lion.

Quickly I threw off sombrero and coat and chaps. I retained my left glove. Then, with camera over my shoulder and revolver in my belt, I plunged down the break in the crag. My boots were heavy soled and studded with hobnails. The weeks on these rocky slopes had trained me to fleetness and surefootedness. I plunged down the sliding slant of weathered stone, crashed through the brush, dodged under the cedars, leaped from boulder to ledge and down from ledge to bench. Reaching a dry stream bed, I espied in the sand the tracks of a big lion, and beside them smaller tracks that were Don's. And as I ran I yelled at the top of my lungs, hoping to help Don tree the lion. What I was afraid of was that the beast might wait for Don and kill him.

Such strenuous exertion required a moment's rest now and then, during which I listened for Don. Twice I heard his bay, and the last one sounded as if he had treed the lion. Again I took to my plunging, jumping, sliding descent; and I was not long in reaching the bottom of that gorge. Ear and eye had guided me unerringly, for I came to an open place near the main jump-off into the canyon, and here I saw a tawny shape in a cedar tree. It belonged to a big Tom lion. He swayed the branch and leaped to a ledge, and from that down to another, and then vanished round a corner of wall.

Don could not follow those high steps. Neither could I. We worked along the ledge, under cedars, and over huge slabs of rock toward the corner where our quarry had disappeared. We were close to the great abyss. I could almost feel it. Then the glaring light of a void struck my eyes like some tangible thing.

At last I worked out from the shade of rocks and trees and, turning the abrupt jut of wall, I found a few feet of stone ledge between me and the appalling chasm. How blue, how fathomless! Despite my pursuit of a lion I was suddenly shocked into awe and fear.

Then Don returned to me. The hair on his neck was bristling. He had come from the right, from round the corner of wall where the ledge ran, and where surely the lion had gone. My blood was up and I meant to track that beast to his lair, photograph him if possible, and kill him. So I strode on to the ledge and round the point of wall. Soon I espied huge cat tracks in the dust, close to the base. A well-defined lion trail showed there. And ahead I saw the ledge—widening somewhat and far from level—stretch before me to another corner.

Don acted queerly. He followed me, close at my heels. He whined. He growled. I did not stop to think then what he wanted to do. But it must have been that he wanted to go back. The heat of youth and the wildness of adventure had gripped me and fear and caution were not in me.

Nevertheless, my sensibilities were remarkably acute. When Don got in front of me there was something that compelled me to go slowly. Soon, in any event, I should have been forced to that. The ledge narrowed. Then it widened again to a large bench with cavernous walls overhanging it. I passed this safe zone to turn on to a narrowing edge of rock that disappeared round another corner. When I came to this point I must have been possessed, for I flattened myself against the wall and worked round it.

Again the way appeared easier. But what made Don go so cautiously? I heard his growls; still, no longer did I look at him. I felt this pursuit was nearing an end. At the next turn I halted short, suddenly quivering. The ledge ended—and there lay the lion, licking a bloody paw.

Tumultuous indeed were my emotions, yet on that instant I did not seem conscious of fear. Jones had told me never, in close quarters, to take my eyes off a lion. I forgot. In the wild excitement of a chance for an incomparable picture I forgot. A few precious seconds were wasted over the attempt to focus my camera.

Then I heard quick thuds. Don growled. With a start I jerked up to see the lion had leaped or run half the distance. He was coming. His eyes blazed purple fire. They seemed to paralyze me, yet I began to back along the ledge. Whipping out my re-

volver I tried to aim. But my nerves had undergone such a shock
that I could not aim. The gun wobbled. I dared not risk shooting.
If I wounded the lion it was certain he would knock me off that
narrow ledge.

So I kept on backing, step by step. Don did likewise. He
stayed between me and the lion. Therein lay the greatness of that
hound. How easily he could have dodged by me to escape the
ledge! But he did not do it.

A precious opportunity presented when I reached the widest
part of the bench. Here I had a chance and I recognized it. Then,
when the overhanging wall bumped my shoulder, I realized too
late. I had come to the narrowing part of the ledge. Not reason
but fright kept me from turning to run. Perhaps that might have
been the best way out of the predicament. I backed along the
strip of stone that was only a foot wide. A few more blind steps
meant death. My nerve was gone. Collapse seemed inevitable. I
had a camera in one hand and a revolver in the other.

That purple-eyed beast did not halt. My distorted imagination
gave him a thousand shapes and actions. Bitter despairing thoughts
flashed through my mind. Jones had said mountain lions were
cowards, but not when cornered—never when there was no avenue
of escape!

Then Don's haunches backed into my knees. I dared not look
down, but I felt the hound against me. He was shaking, yet he
snarled fiercely. The feel of Don there, the sense of his courage,
caused my cold thick blood to burst into hot gushes. In another
second he would be pawed off the ledge or he would grapple with
this hissing lion. That meant destruction for both, for they would
roll off the ledge.

I had to save Don. That mounting thought was my salvation.
Physically, he could not have saved me or himself, but this grand
spirit somehow pierced to my manhood.

Leaning against the wall, I lifted the revolver and steadied
my arm with my left hand, which still held the camera. I aimed
between the purple eyes. That second was an eternity. The gun
crashed. The blaze of one of those terrible eyes went out.

Up leaped the lion, beating the wall with heavy thudding
paws. Then he seemed to propel himself outward, off the ledge
into space—a tawny spread figure that careened majestically over

and over, down—down—down to vanish in the blue depths.

Don whined. I stared at the abyss, slowly becoming unlocked from the grip of terror. I staggered a few steps forward to a wider part of the ledge and there I sank down, unable to stand longer. Don crept to me, put his head in my lap.

I listened. I strained my ears. How endlessly long seemed that lion in falling! But all was magnified. At last puffed up a sliding roar, swelling and dying until again the terrific silence of the canyon enfolded me.

Presently Don sat up and gazed into the depths. How strange to see him peer down! Then he turned his sleek dark head to look at me. What did I see through the somber sadness of his eyes? He whined and licked my hand. It seemed to me Don and I were more than man and dog. He moved away then round the narrow ledge, and I had to summon energy to follow. Shudderingly I turned my back on that awful chasm and held my breath while I slipped round the perilous place. Don waited there for me, then trotted on. Not until I had gotten safely off that ledge did I draw a full breath. Then I toiled up the steep rough slope to the rim. Don was waiting beside my horse. Between us we drank the rest of the water in my canteen, and when we reached camp night had fallen. A bright fire and a good supper broke the gloom of my mind. My story held those rugged Westerners spellbound. Don stayed close to me, followed me of his own accord, and slept beside me in my tent.

There came a frosty morning when the sun rose red over the ramparts of colored rock. We had a lion running before the misty shadows dispersed from the canyon depths.

The hounds chased him through the sage and cedar into the wild brakes of the north wing of the Plateau. This lion must have been a mean old Tom, for he did not soon go down the slopes.

The particular section he at last took refuge in was impassable for man. The hounds gave him a grueling chase, then one by one they crawled up, sore and thirsty. All but Don! He did not come. Jones rolled out his mighty voice, which pealed back in mocking hollow echoes. Don did not come. At noonday Jones and the men left for camp with the hounds.

I remained. I had a vigil there on the lofty rim, along where

I could peer down the yellow-green slope and beyond to the sinister depths. It was a still day. The silence was overpowering. When Don's haunting bay floated up it shocked me. At long intervals I heard it, fainter and fainter. Then no more!

Still I waited and watched and listened. Afternoon waned. My horse neighed piercingly from the cedars. The sinking sun began to fire the Pink Cliffs of Utah, and then the hundred miles of immense chasm over which my charmed gaze held dominion. How lonely, how terrifying that stupendous rent in the earth! Lion and hound had no fear. But the thinking, feeling man was afraid. What did they mean—this exquisitely hued and monstrous canyon —the setting sun—the wildness of a lion, the grand spirit of a dog —and the wondering sadness of a man?

I rode home without Don. Half the night I lay awake waiting, hoping. But he did not return by dawn, nor through the day. He never came back.

The Silver Horn

By GORDON GRAND

ON A SPARKLING summer morning in early September I was breakfasting under the fine old gnarled apple tree that stands off the corner of my house. I was in a tingling, buoyant state and well I might be for we had had a rare cubbing morning and many things had contributed to my well-being since my return, and other pleasant things were in the immediate offing. Those that had happened included a swim in the pool, the feel of a fresh pongee suit, the taste of an iced cantaloupe, and a first cup of coffee. Those in the offing were two boiled eggs whose natal day I could vouch for, three slices of crisp bacon, a second cup of coffee, a smoke, and the morning paper.

I was in the act of pouring the second cup of coffee when the morning mail was placed on the table. The mail had no interest for me until I noticed a generous envelope postmarked London and addressed in Colonel John Weatherford's handwriting.

When I had finished breakfast I lit a cigarette, took my coffee and the letter over to a comfortable lounge chair, opened the letter and read:

Dear Pendleton:
I had a delightful chance meeting with Florence in London the other morning. The enclosed tells the story. "Good hunting" to you. I will be home soon.
Faithfully,
J. W.

From "The Silver Horn," Derrydale Press.

THE SILVER HORN
A NOCTURNE OF OLD LONDON TOWN

I said to the head waiter of that venerable hotel on Albemarle Street, "Make my compliments to the lady who has just come in to breakfast and is sitting over in the corner and say I very particularly commend broiled finnan haddie."

The pompous and ponderous dignitary returned a moment later. "The lady is much obliged, Sir, but told me to say, Sir, that she has quite a different idea about her breakfast. Quite different, if I might say so, Sir—thank you, Sir—and the lady says, Sir, as how she would be obliged if you would stop and speak with her on your way out, Sir."

When I had finished my own finnan haddie, I stopped to wish Florence "the top of the morning."

"A man who will eat finnan haddie," she said mysteriously, "doesn't deserve to hear hunting horns under a summer moon."

"What do you mean?" I asked.

"Didn't you hear him?"

"Hear whom?"

"The lone huntsman of Albemarle street?"

"No, my rooms are on the Dover street side."

"Oh," said Florence, "what bad luck! You missed the most delightful thing." And then she told me this story:

Returning from the theater and supper she had drifted off into a sound sleep, from which she was gently and fancifully awakened without sensing the cause. Her watch showed three o'clock. The roar and rumble of London had faded to its lowest murmur. A midsummer moon filtered through and illuminated the street below. What was it that had so illusively awakened the sleeper? Again she listened. The faint mellow note of a hunting horn drifted up from Piccadilly.

Now a hunting horn is one thing to some people, and a very different thing to some other people. In Mrs. Grundy's family it represents only a noise; in Florence's family and to Florence herself it is a mystic spring which unlocks myriad memories and pictures; so at 3 a.m. Florence was hanging far out of a front window of her hotel, her eyes searching the moonlit London street.

A solitary figure was strolling at his leisure up the center of the street. To the tutored eye of the lady of the balcony, there was the slightest tinge of a roll to his gait. There is much of romance in Florence, and her coffee grew colder and colder as the description ran on. The gleam of his white waistcoat, the cut of his dress coat, the sheen of his silk hat worn just a bit toward the back of the head, the cane hooked over his left arm, and— touch of touches—the gleam of a silver horn tucked between the white tie and top shirt stud. "Mind you," said Florence, "just exactly where a huntsman would carry it. Oh, it was too delicious." Well, this reveler of the night halted in front of Florence's window. Why just there, I did not inquire, but Florence had said she was hanging out of the window.

With feet far apart and leaning back on his cane, the gentle reveler plucked forth his horn, and made old Albemarle street resound. Twang. Twang. Twang. Then he warmed to his task. "Hoick, Hoick! Furrier has it. Hoick! For'ard to Furrier! Hold hard, gentlemen! Hold hard, please! Ah, Rattler Boy. Hoick! For'ard to Furrier! Steady, gentlemen, please. Let hounds get out of covert. Let them get straightened away. Please don't press hounds." And then, in a glorious, resounding voice that rolled on from street to street, "Gone away—gone away—Hoick! For'ard!" After three more sharp notes of the horn indicating that hounds had found and gone away, and as a signal and final exhortation to any hounds that might be left in covert, the horn was once more inserted between the white tie and top shirt stud.

The lone Huntsman, cheering and encouraging his hounds, passed on toward Grafton street. Hounds ran a burning line with fine head up Albemarle street, but at The Royal Institute they dwelled on the line and faulted.

The Huntsman cast them up the noble steps of the Institute and then in a narrow service alley at the Piccadilly side of the building. In the alley he was met by the bewildered guardian hurrying out to see what the hue and cry might be.

"Hold hard, Sir. Dash it, Sir! Don't you see hounds are casting? You will have their heads up in a minute. Hold hard!"

Then Furrier opened, the pack honored, and away they flew toward Grafton street. Of course, Albemarle street ends at Grafton, and there was a great to-do as to whether the fox had turned right-handed to Old Bond street or left-handed to Dover street. Again hounds faulted and up went their heads. Again the twang of the horn calling hounds to him, and then patiently he cast a little way toward Old Bond—then a little toward Dover—and finally a bit back on Albemarle. On this latter cast he encountered the old guardian of the venerable Institute standing in the middle of the road, his eyes agog.

"That's right, my man, that's right. Never fuss about when hounds are at fault."

"Of course, I think he should have cast first toward Dover street," said Florence, "because the breeze was blowing toward Hyde Park corner."

Then he cast them up on to the porch of Quaritch's, that great book shop on Grafton street, into Bunting's, the bootmaker's on Dover, and even as far back as Boss's, the master gunmaker's shop on Albemarle, probably thinking that the fox might have been turned at the Institute and headed back toward Piccadilly.

At last the riddle was solved. The true line ran toward Dover street and so down Little Hay Hill where Huntsman and horn drifted out of hearing; but Florence said she heard the horn once more across Berkeley Square and about opposite Dartmouth House on Charles street. She said she then went to bed and to sleep, but I rather think she fell to romancing.

When Florence told me this tale, and I thought of those hounds of the imagination casting for the line around Quaritch's, I could but wonder what all the old English worthies depicted in word and illustration in Quaritch's first editions would have thought of that young English blade of this year of grace alone at three o'clock in the morning hunting his hounds in the heart of moonlit old London town. I do believe there must have been many a good British sportsman tucked away in his bed close to the line of the hunted fox that night, whose heart beat a bit faster as he listened to the twang of that horn and the cheery "Hoick! For'ard!" and those who had long since resigned from the pigskin must have had mellow memories of their own youth awakened.

When I stopped at the mail desk, a ruby-faced old gentleman was saying to the mail clerk, "I say, what a go that young chap was having last night—splendid voice for a huntsman—splendid! Reminded me of my days with the Earl of Fitzwilliams' hounds.

When I heard him turn down Little Hay Hill I said to myself, 'Ah, now there's a sweet stretch to watch hounds race down.' Blest if I could get back to sleep for an hour. Of course, I thought it a bit nervy to call his hound Furrier, after George Osbaldston's great hound, but it might jolly well be that he thought he was the Square or old Meynell. Oh, youth—that's the thing to know that you made good use of it."

The old gentleman pulled on his gloves, squared his shoulders, slipped his stick on his arm, and marched off, looking, I thought, very fit.

Ting-a-ling

By DAVID GRAY

THEY WERE sitting on the balcony which distinguished the bridal suite, in the sun of the June morning. Below was the main street, animated mildly with the shopping of a dormant New England community. A few ancient carriages, reliquaries of the first families, mingled with the buggies and the delivery-wagons, and at dignified intervals a horse-car jingled past and disappeared in the vista of elms.

"It's ten minutes past eleven," he observed, looking at his watch. "We have five hours to wait for the four-ten train, but I believe we dine at twelve."

"Are you hungry?" she asked. "I dare say we could get something even before dinner—perhaps a pie."

They both laughed. "This is an awful place," he said, "isn't it? No more historic New England for me."

They leaned lazily upon the balcony rail, and sat with their heads together, looking down into the street. A grocer's clerk was putting things into a wagon, and they wondered who was going to have asparagus, and how big a family it might be which needed six quarts of strawberries. Presently, with the noises of the street, came the pingling of the periodic horse-car, and they turned and watched it approach.

"That is not a bad-looking horse," he said judicially.

"Look!" she exclaimed. There was a note of pity and indignation in her voice. The car, as it drew near, appeared to bulge with passengers.

"It's rather a joke," he said. "Those are women delegates to the Society for the Prevention of Cruelty to Animals convention."

"It's shameful," she said.

From "Gallops II," Houghton Mifflin Company.

The car stopped on the corner in front of the hotel for another passenger to worm himself into the jam on the rear platform. The horse, a big, showy chestnut, stood panting, his nostrils red and dilated. His neck was white with lather. Wet streaks extended up his ears. His body dripped, and the sweat was running down his legs.

As the two strokes of the conductor's bell gave the signal to start, he plunged forward almost before the driver had loosened the brakes. There was a clatter of hoofs on the cobblestones, and a mighty straining. The heavy car began to move, and the chestnut horse went trotting down the street, tail up and neck arched like a cavalry horse on parade.

"He's game," he said.

She put her hand on his arm. "I can't bear to see it," she whispered.

He looked down at her. Her eyes were brimming.

"Don't be a little goose," he said gently; but there was a queer feeling in his throat. He rose to his feet. "I'll be back in a few minutes," he added. "I want to go down to the office." He bent down and kissed her, and left the balcony.

She waited half an hour, and then went down to the corridor. He was not at the office. She decided to go out. As she was on the hotel steps, she met him coming in, and at the same moment a coach-horn sounded, and they saw a coach and four come around the corner.

He looked back. "Oh, Lord!" he exclaimed, "we're caught. There's your brother, and the Appleton girls, and Frank Crewe, and Winthrop, and most of your bridesmaids. I suppose they are on their way to Lenox."

"What shall we do?" she asked.

A great uproar arose from the people on the coach.

"Hello!" said Curtis.

"Hello!" yelled the people on the coach. Mr. Crewe got possession of the horn and produced fragments of the "Lohengrin Wedding March." The people in the street and the hangers-on about the hotel began to gather around.

Her brother waved his hand from the coach. "Well," he said, "how are you getting on? Quarreled yet? I am sorry, but we are completely out of rice."

"I don't understand," said Curtis, looking at the crowd in dismay. "This is a beautiful country, Willie. Historic battlefields and all that sort of thing; besides, they breed some good horses all about here. We have been picking up one or two."

"For the bride!" called Winthrop, and he generously threw her an enormous bunch of wild roses which Crewe that morning had patiently pulled from the roadside bushes at the cost of no small suffering, and had presented to the elder Appleton girl.

Curtis ignored the episode. His eye at that moment caught a stable-boy leading a big chestnut horse toward the hotel. "Here's one we've just bought," he said. "I think he's likely to make a jumper." He felt his hand, which was behind him, squeezed surreptitiously, and he was aware of beaming somewhat foolishly. He was glad that the people on the coach had turned their attention to the horse.

"Where did you find that?" asked Winthrop.

Curtis hesitated a moment. "Over that way," he said vaguely, waving his hand over an arc which extended from east to west. "It's a great country for horses."

Her brother had been inspecting the horse in silence. "My son," he said to the stable-boy, "how did you gall that race-horse's shoulder?"

"That's a collar-mark," said the boy. "Pulling a street-car is hard work."

Peals of laughter came from the coach.

"You needn't laugh," said the boy. "He's a horse all right."

She had moved to the horse's head. "I believe you," she said to the boy. "He's game."

"He is, ma'am," said the boy.

"Well, Ting-a-ling," said her brother, addressing the chestnut horse, "we can't stop to admire you all day. You're not a bad-looking horse, but if you are a street-car horse, as unfortunately you are, you have the nature that will jump until you get tired, and then you'll roll over things, and make my sister an attractive widow. I wouldn't have you at any price."

"Then everybody is satisfied," said Curtis.

"I am," she said. She gave him a little look that meant that she was satisfied with him, and Curtis felt that he was beaming again. He turned away.

The horse began to rub his nose against her arm and sniffed.

"He's looking for sugar," said the boy. "I give it to him sometimes."

"You are a very nice boy," she said. "What's your name?"

"Tim," said the boy.

"Let's have him take the horse down for us," she said to her husband. "We might keep him, too."

"All right," he said. "But let's get out of this crowd." They slipped away and hurried around the block.

"You were good to get him," she said in a low tone. "The way he acted made me feel that he wasn't meant for street-car work. What shall we call him?"

"I am afraid that brother Willie has already named him," he answered.

"What?" she demanded.

"Ting-a-ling," he replied.

"But he ought to be called Sultan or Emperor, or something like that," she insisted.

"You and I," he said, "we know what a heart he has; but, after all, he is a street-car horse. We'd better accept the facts."

"Well, then it's Ting-a-ling," she said.

It was November; three years had slipped away. The race for the Hunt Club cup was coming off in the afternoon, and everybody was lunching at the club. She was patiently chaperoning the elder Appleton girl and Frank Crewe at a table on the glass-closed veranda overlooking the polo-field.

"We'll give you some lunch," she said to Winthrop, who was passing.

"I'm with Willie," he answered.

"Willie can come too," she said.

He thanked her and sat down.

"Is Ting-a-ling pretty fit?" he asked.

"I think so," she replied; "but of course he's never been steeple-chased, so we don't know what he can do."

"He is certainly a good horse to hounds," said Winthrop.

"He's never been down," she said.

"Please don't say that on the day of the race," he interrupted; "it's unlucky."

Just then Willie joined them.

"Still talking steeplechase," he observed. "I suppose your husband is going to win."

"I don't know about that," she answered; "but he'll beat you."

"I'll bet he won't," he retorted. "It's a sure thing. I am not going to ride. They tell me that I am too fat, but that isn't the reason. I am afraid. Hello! here's the steeplechase jockey," he said to Curtis, who came in. "Have you provided liberally for me in your will? Haven't I always been a good brother-in-law?"

"Always," said Curtis, "and no doubt you need the money; but I am not making wills to-day."

"You'd better," said Willie, cheerfully. "I'd hate to have that street-car horse roll you out and have no other consolation than the thought that you had loved me." His tone became less playful. "Bequeath me my nephew, and your widow can take the property."

"If that blessed boy of yours," Crewe said to Mrs. Curtis, "isn't ruined by the indulgence of his foolish old uncle, I shall be much surprised."

"Taisez-vous!" retorted Willie, "and get a nephew of your own."

Winthrop turned to Curtis. "How has the horse shown in his training?" he asked.

"He rates pretty well, and I have a good deal of confidence in his jumping," Curtis answered. "He's rather a pet, you know, so that perhaps my judgment is prejudiced."

"He'll go until he gets tired," put in Willie, "and then he'll shut up and go through his fences. Those big half-breds are all alike."

"How do you know he's a half-bred?" said Curtis.

"I don't know that he is anything," Willie retorted. "You got him out of a street-car."

"I think we would better change the subject," said his sister; "you're becoming disagreeable. Remember," she added to the party, "you are all coming in this evening to play bridge. You can't come to dinner, because the cook is sick."

From the hill back of the club-house they watched the race. A horse of Winthrop's, with Crewe up, made the running for the first mile. Then Curtis took Ting-a-ling out of the bunch, and went away apparently without effort. At the two-mile flag Curtis was a hundred yards in the lead. The other horses seemed to be racing for the place.

"He seems to have things all his own way," said Winthrop to Mrs. Curtis. "My horse is done."

"He is going well," she whispered. She was very much excited.

Toward the middle of the third mile the four horses that were running in the second flight drew up, and it became a race again. Her heart almost stopped beating. "Is he tiring?" she murmured. The five went at the board fence near the third-mile flag in a bunch. As they took off, there was crowding on the outside. Then four horses jumped cleanly; one fell, and the four went on again.

A rustle of apprehension ran through the crowd.

"Who's down?" exclaimed the elder Appleton girl in a low tone.

"Is he hurt?" asked her sister.

"It's Ting-a-ling!" murmured Mrs. Curtis.

The horse got up, and galloped riderless after the leaders. A moment later the rider got up and started across the field on foot.

"He's not hurt," said Winthrop. "I'm awful sorry. He would have won."

"That's good of you," she replied. But she suspected that he was only softening the bitterness of the disappointment. Willie was right. The horse ran himself tired and stopped. She felt that she was very white and made an effort to talk. "That's your horse ahead with Frank Crewe," she said; "he's got the race."

It was so, and the crowd was already surging down to the finish-flags to congratulate the winner. Mrs. Curtis drove her cart across the meadow to meet the dismounted rider.

Their eyes met as she pulled up.

"It's too bad," she said. "Are you hurt?"

"I think my collar-bone is gone," he answered. "I'll see Tim and send the horse home, and then I'll go to the club and get bandaged."

He gave his orders to the boy.

"You was fouled, sir," said Tim. He was much excited. "I seen Mr. Crewe pull across you about two lengths from the fence."

"Not at all," said Curtis, shortly. "Walk him home at once and do him up."

"Is it so?" she asked. "Were you fouled?"

"I don't think I'd say it," he answered. "I rode very badly. It was my fault. I shouldn't have pulled him back into the crowd."

She said nothing. She saw that he was very much disappointed. But the hardest for her to bear was that her confidence in Ting-a-ling was gone.

At the club-house Willie was on the veranda.

"I'm awfully sorry," he said. "But, seriously, you had better shoot that horse. You'll not be so lucky another time."

Curtis looked up angrily to reply, and then turned away with his lips tightly closed.

"I'll be ready in half an hour," he said to his wife.

In rather less than that time he came from his dressing-room, his arm in bandages and the hand in a sling. He sent for his trap, and found Mrs. Curtis in the tea-room.

"I think we had better go," he said. "They have just telephoned from the house, saying the baby isn't very well. I told the doctor to come along as soon as he could. Don't say anything to Willie about the little chap," he added. "He'll tag along and make a fuss and irritate me."

She rose and followed him. The trap was at the door, and they drove away.

Earlier, the November afternoon had been flooded with a damp sunshine, and there had been a still and unnatural mildness in the air. Toward four, as they left the club, the sky became overcast, and out of the west a mass of blue-black cloud began to rise and stretch across the horizon. Soon it threw the western part of the plain and the hills beyond into darkness. Overhead it was still light, but the shadow drew on and began to chill the day.

Curtis looked apprehensively toward the west and touched the horse with the whip. His wife had the reins.

"It's growing colder," she said.

He bent forward and tucked the robe about her feet.

Uncertain drafts of wind rattled the brown leaves on the oaks and made the dead goldenrods along the roadside bow excitedly.

"I am afraid that we are going to get wet," he said.

The gusts became stronger. The blackness from the west had spread until it was overhead, and light clouds were moving eastwardly across the face of the sky.

"I felt a drop of rain," she observed.

He urged the horse to a gallop.

"So did I," said he a moment later.

"It will be a good night to stay home and read," he went on. "Don't you think I am getting to be quite a reader? Two books already this month; one of them had three hundred and twelve pages. But there were a good many pictures," he added conscientiously.

She smiled, but said nothing.

He watched her as they drove along. Presently he broke the silence.

"I wouldn't worry about the baby," he said. "Probably he has a little cold or a stomach-ache. The nurse is terrified if he sneezes."

"That's probably all," she said; "you know what a goose I am."

As they turned into the driveway the rain began to pour down. Under the porte-cochere she got out of the trap and went in while he held the horse.

Presently a man came from the stable, and he too went in. He was taking off his coat when his wife came down from the nursery.

"Well?" he asked.

"He's about the same," she answered. "He seems to have a little fever. What time did the doctor say he would be here?"

"About six," said Curtis. He looked at his watch. "It will be an hour yet. It's begun to snow," he added.

They went to the library, which looked toward the west, and watched the breaking storm.

"It was too bad about Ting-a-ling," she said after a pause.

"Well," he answered, "we have to take things as they come. I should like to have shown what a horse he is. We shall next year."

"I wish you would promise never to ride him in a race again," she said.

"I don't think you ought to ask that," he answered sharply. "For the horse's sake, I want him to have a chance to redeem himself. Don't you?"

"Isn't it wrong to take unnecessary risks?" she replied.

He made no answer.

The rain had changed to sleet, and the ground was already white. The bare elms on the lawn were creaking dismally. They could see the stiff shrubs in the garden bend to the gusts. The storm beat on the window-panes, and in the fierce blasts the house trembled. As they stood by the window, the man brought in the lighted lamps, and they realized that the night had set in.

"Suppose we have a look at him," he said. By "him" he meant Ting-a-ling. "Won't you come? If the doctor arrives, they can send for us."

"I'd like to," she said.

On the way out, she went to the pantry and took some lumps of sugar.

The stable servants were at supper, and the stable was still except for the sound of the horses munching at their oats. As he drew the door open the grinding hushed except in the two stalls where the phaeton ponies ate stolidly on. The line of dusky heads was lifted and thrust curiously forward. From the box-stall in the corner came a low whinny, and in the dim light of the wall lamp they saw a long neck stretched out and two pointed ears cocked forward. It was Ting-a-ling.

"You beggar!" said Curtis. "You know what we've got." He went into the stall and stripped off the blankets. She followed him. "Hello!" he exclaimed. His arm was nipped gently. "You have very bad manners." The horse drew back, tossed his head, and pawed.

"Look here," Mrs. Curtis said. She held out a piece of sugar. A soft muzzle touched her hand, the lips opened and scraped across her palm, and there was a crunching sound.

"You baby!" she said, and gave him a second piece. "I'm very fond of you," she added under her breath, "in spite—" She stopped.

"He seems to be feeding well," said Curtis.

He put his hand into the manger. It touched the clean, moistened boards of the bottom.

"You're a pig!" he exclaimed. "He's put away five quarts already," he said to his wife. "Doesn't he look fit?"

They drew back and looked the horse over. The legs were clean, the great muscles stood out on forearm and quarter, the flesh was hard and spare.

"He's a great type," said Curtis, "isn't he? But if he were three-cornered I'd like him just as well. I'm ashamed to care so much for him."

"Do you remember the day we got him?" she asked.

He stepped back and put his arm around her.

"It seems yesterday, dear," he said. "How the years go by!" He put back the blankets, and stood a moment fastening the surcingle.

"Barring accidents, old horse," he muttered, "we'll have your name on the cup yet."

A swelling feeling came into his throat and he put his face against the sleek neck. He straightened up quickly as he heard the doors slide apart and somebody come in.

"Mr. Curtis," called a voice. It was Tim.

"Hello!" said Curtis.

"The doctor's come," said Tim.

"All right," answered Curtis.

He drew his wife's wraps about her, and they made their way back to the house.

The doctor met them at the door of the nursery.

"This child is sick," he said. "The temperature has gone up in a way I don't like. We've got to operate."

"Operate!" Curtis exclaimed. He put his hand upon the banister. "What do you mean?"

"Yes," said the doctor.

"When?" said Mrs. Curtis.

"Lamplight is bad," said the doctor, "but we must do the best we can. It ought to be done before ten o'clock. I should be afraid to wait longer."

Neither husband nor wife spoke. The doctor looked at his watch.

"Whom would you rather have?" he asked.

"Have?" repeated Curtis. A gust rattled the windows at the end of the hall, and as it died away he heard the tick-tick of the sleet on the pane. He looked at the doctor with a white face.

"Can't you do it?" he asked. "Suppose we couldn't get any one from town by ten o'clock?"

"We must," said the doctor, cheerfully. "I'm not a surgeon, and there is none in the village. Would you rather have Anderson, or Tate?"

"Dr. Anderson," said Mrs. Curtis.

"He must get the train that leaves town at eight o'clock," said the doctor. "There is no other until midnight."

"It's a quarter past six now," said Curtis. "That gives us an hour and three quarters. I'll telephone at once." He left the room and went to the telephone.

After some delay the village operator answered.

"You can't get the city," said the girl; "the wires are down. I have been trying to get them for an hour for the telegraph people. Their line is closed, too."

"When do you expect your wires to be repaired?" he asked.

"Can't say," the operator replied. "Not to-night, though. The linemen can't work to-night."

"Thank you," said Curtis. He hung up the receiver and stood blankly before the instrument. He was about to move away when he heard a footstep. He turned, and his wife was standing beside him.

"He'll come, won't he?" she said.

He put a cigarette in his mouth and struck a match.

"Is anything the matter?" she asked. "Won't he come?"

"He'll come," he answered. "I'm going to the station for him myself. I'll dine when I come back. You and the doctor get things ready." He went into the smoking-room and walked the length of the room and back. "Six miles, ten, fifteen, and six more down-town," he said aloud. He looked at his watch again. It was twenty minutes past six. "Start at half-past," he went on; "that's twenty-one miles in an hour and a quarter—and these roads!" He went to the wall and rang a bell. "Twenty-one miles in an hour and a quarter," he repeated. "Search-light can't do it, nor Xerxes, nor Huron, nor the roan mare."

A servant appeared.

"Tell Hobson," he said, "to saddle Ting-a-ling at once. Tell him to hurry, and send Tim here."

Tim came, and Curtis explained.

"Can he do it?" asked Curtis.

"I don't know, sir," said the boy.

"He's got to do it," said Curtis. "Do you understand?"

"Yes, sir."

They hurried to the stable, and found Hobson buckling the throat-latch.

"All ready, sir," he said.

Tim climbed into the saddle and gathered up his reins. Then Hobson threw open the door, and the horse and boy clattered out and disappeared in the storm.

Curtis looked at his watch. It was twenty-eight minutes past six. "Have the bus and a pair at the house at eight," he said, and went back to the house.

He met his wife in the hall.

"Is there any change?" he asked.

She shook her head.

"Suppose he should miss the train?" she suggested.

"He won't," said Curtis.

She sighed, and was silent for a pause. "What a wonderful thing the telephone is!" she said. "What would we have done without it?"

"That's so," said Curtis. "I'm going to the station at eight," he added.

At ten minutes of nine she was standing with her face against the window-pane, when the lights of the station bus glimmered through the storm. She went to the head of the stairway and waited breathless.

"Suppose," she thought, "he has missed the train!"

Presently there sounded the crunching of wheels on the gravel under the porte-cochere. This meant that the bus was stopping at the house. Then the door opened.

"Come along," said her husband's voice.

"Thank God!" she murmered. She sat down for a moment, and then went to the nursery, which had been made into a hospital.

There was the tramp of ascending feet on the stairs, and then the surgeon and the village doctor came in and asked her to leave the room.

It seemed a long time, but it was only half an hour, when Dr. Anderson came out.

"It's all right," he said.

"What are the chances?" she asked.

"There aren't any," he replied; "that is, perhaps only one in a million—"

She looked alarmed.

"Of anything unpleasant happening," he went on. "We got it

just in time. Your son is better off than other boys who wear their appendices. His is in a bottle."

The door-bell sounded faintly from the rear of the house, and they both listened. A moment later the front door opened, and she heard voices in the lower hall.

"They're a lot of people who've come in to play bridge. I'd forgotten about them," she said. "Will you tell them I'll be down presently?"

She went into the nursery, and Dr. Anderson went downstairs.

When she came down she found them in the dining-room, watching the surgeon and Curtis eating supper, and asking them questions about the operation.

Her eyes caught Willie's. He was quiet and white. He drew a chair for her, and she sat down next to him. She put her hand in his.

"It's all right," she said.

"It was an awfully close shave," he whispered.

"Yes, it was," she answered.

She turned to Dr. Anderson. "You were good to come," she said. "What would we have done if you hadn't been at home when Mr. Curtis telephoned?"

"Telephoned?" he repeated.

Curtis got up and went to the sideboard for a whisky-decanter.

"Yes, telephoned," she said.

The surgeon looked at Curtis.

"Mary," said Curtis, "the telephone wires were down. Tim went to town for the doctor."

She looked around in amazement.

"But we didn't know till nearly half-past six," she exclaimed. She turned to Dr. Anderson. "You caught the eight-o'clock train. How did Tim go?"

"On horseback," said Curtis.

"But that's twenty miles!" said Willie.

"Twenty-one," said Curtis; "he went in an hour and a quarter."

There was silence for a moment. Then she spoke.

"What horse did he ride?" she demanded.

"What horse have we that could have done it?" replied Curtis.

She looked at him for a moment in apprehension. "Is he all right?" she asked.

"I don't know," said Curtis. "Tim came back by train."

"Send for Tim," she said to the butler.

Tim came, and stood fumbling with his cap, which was soggy with melted snow.

"Weren't you frozen?" she asked.

"No, ma'am," the boy answered.

"Tell me about it," she said.

"Tell about it?" repeated the boy. "Why, ma'am—" he grew confused and stopped.

"But tell me"—she hesitated, and her lip trembled—"tell me how Ting-a-ling is."

The boy made no answer, but looked toward the surgeon.

She turned to Dr. Anderson. "What is it?" she demanded.

"I was starting out to dine," said the surgeon, "when a policeman came to the door and said there was a sick horse on the corner, and a boy with him who wanted to see me. I went and found them both there."

"Well?" said Mrs. Curtis.

"Well," said the doctor, "as I reached the corner the cross-town trolley-car was letting off a passenger. When the bell rang to start, the horse in the street lifted his head, scrambled to his feet, staggered a step forward, and came down again. He was dead."

There was a stillness in the room, and the crying of a sick baby sounded faintly from up-stairs. Presently it ceased. For an instant the wife's eyes met those of her husband. Then resting her elbows on the table, she hid her face in her hands.

"God forgive me!" they heard Willie murmur in a queer voice. "That was a horse!"

"A street-car horse," said Curtis, gently.

No one spoke again, but each rose and left the dining-room.

If You Like Horses

By JACQUELINE RUSSELL

I T WAS a wet day, and the going was heavy. The hounds had
found down by the river and flung themselves into it and
across. The Pony took to water like a duck, so we had passed
with a bound half a dozen horses ahead who were obstinately
refusing the plunge. I found myself directly behind the Whips.
The river was not very deep, but the Pony was small. The water
was up to my stirrup iron. Once across, the hounds checked wildly,
hunting the line in wide circles. The next instant they were away,
up a bank, into the meadow atop of it. The bank was a steep one,
and the Pony's short legs did not cover the ground as quickly as
the horses ahead. When I reached the top, the landscape was a
blank—hounds, horses, and riders had completely disappeared.
The meadow ran downhill for a way, then sloped gently upward.
On this rise was a wall. The Pony stood back to take off. As we
flung ourselves over, a most alarming sight met my eyes. Facing
me, in the middle of the field beyond, head down, nostrils dilated,
stood a bull ready to charge. A young bull, to be sure, but still
a bull and an angry one. I took one look at him, turned tail with
the Pony and fled back over the wall, as if none less than the
Devil was in pursuit.

Once back to safety, I turned to view the scene. Way at the
farther end of the field, also behind a sheltering wall, Mrs. I. J. P.,
and the Whips were in hot argument with a farmer. On the
opposite side, cosily enclosed by a wire fence, sat Jimmy the Drag
Boy on his piebald pony, surrounded by panting hounds.

J., evidently, had not seen my quick entree and exit. For now
he waved his arm and shouted, 'Don't come over!'

I galloped down toward him, still on the safe side of the wall,

From "If You Like Horses," Houghton Mifflin Company.

to see if I could jump it somewhere in a corner and join him, unnoticed by the bull. At that moment, the rest of the Field came charging for the wall, just where I had first taken it. Down in our corner, we joined in giving loud, warning cries. They did not hear. The wall was long, there was plenty of room, a dozen horses took it abreast. Pandemonium ensued. The bull, infuriated by the invasion of his territory, charged blindly, terrified horses scattering in all directions. Some riders turned as I had and took the wall backwards, others flew to join the M.F.H. Others still tore around the field, unable to control their frightened mounts, the bull in close pursuit.

I am ashamed to confess that I could not control my laughter. I laughed till the tears rolled down my face. It was the most ridiculous spectacle I have ever witnessed. We all laughed down in our corner, even Mrs. I.'s hot rage gave way to the general hilarity. I asked Jimmy the Drag Boy afterwards, what he was doing in the wire paddock.

He grinned. 'I come over the wall,' he explained, 'and there in the holler was the bull, lookin' at me with eyes like two balls of fire. I thinks to meself, "Jim, you're no matadore," so I makes for the paddock, through the gate, slams it in his face, and waits for the hounds.'

Lucky it was that there was a hound left to join him!

After a bit, order was restored, Jimmy and the hounds were rescued, the hunt resumed. On the very last wall of the run, the White Pony slipped on muddy ground at the take-off. He struck the wall with his knees. The wall was loosely built and gave way. We came lurching over. I think that I could have held him up, for he practically recovered when he landed, had not the bridle snapped at the headstrap. As it gave way in my hands, we crashed to the ground, most of the remaining wall coming with us. I was thrown clear, and not in the least hurt. But the White Pony cut both his knees wide open. I was not able to hunt him for a month, and though he is still sound, his knees have always been big since that day.

The Children's Runs had become one of the features of the countryside. They were written up in the papers, photographers from sporting sheets attended them, and took and published spirited pictures of the youngsters. Among hunting people the Chil-

dren's Runs were made much of. For they felt, as did Mrs. I.,
that the future of the sport, after all, lies with the younger gene-
ration. Mrs. I. took more pains with and put more thought in the
Children's Runs than in any of the rest of the hunting. It is no
easy task to mount children on the right pony. In the first place,
to get the right pony (for most of the ponies for the children
were club ponies) means a lot of searching and the exercise of
good judgment in purchasing. Mrs. I. supervised all Hunt Club
purchases. Then to know your child, that the timid one shall
have the docile pony, the bolder, a bit more horse; to plan the
runs over safe ground; to pick hounds who are eager, yet who
will not set too fast a pace; and last but not least, to placate and
humor nervous parents—all this means hard work, thought, and
true generalship.

A new contingency arose as the years passed. Children grew
older, yet not old enough or experienced enough to hunt with
the grown-ups. They were ambitious to progress, their enthusiasm
should not be discouraged. A great many had learned to jump,
and demanded experience in the field. Mrs. I. devised a plan. The
Children's Hunt should be divided into two sections: the jumpers
and the nonjumpers. Both sections should follow the hounds,
one led by the Master, the other by the Huntsman. The jumpers
should go over walled country, the non-jumpers to follow the
gaps as usual, all meeting at the finish. This involved more work
for the indefatigable Master. New country had to be opened,
walls had to be lowered or built up to be made safe for beginners,
ponies had to be schooled. Very soon, parents who had not hunted
for years, enticed by their children and tempted by the less difficult fencing, joined the ranks on Mondays. The Children's Runs
became as popular with a great many as the longer and more
difficult runs were with the regulars.

As both my girls were now ardent followers, I went very
regularly on the Children's Runs, and enjoyed them hugely. They
were full of incident and most amusing. One in particular I remember.

We were riding up a long narrow lane, behind the hounds,
hacking to the Meet. There were a great many children out that
day, at least twenty. It was a warm day and the ponies were lazy.
We were jogging along slowly, the children chatting with each

other, exchanging hunting experiences, I suppose. I was behind, with several other mothers, benignly smiling on the cavalcade of youthful enthusiasts, and discussing the joys in store for them, when a piercing shriek rent the air. The long line of ponies came to an abrupt stop. They halted, startled and bewildered. Another shriek followed. Ponies at the head of the line started to buck and jump, others turned in the narrow way and came pelting back. In one instant the lane seemed filled with plunging horseflesh and shrieking children. One child after another fled by me on bucking ponies, their faces varying in hue from bright red to deep purple. Some weeping without restraint, others merely bellowing in a mixture of rage and fear.

I was at a complete loss to know what on earth had happened. I kept shouting to them to stop and explain, while I tried to snatch at bridles as they sped by. The White Pony was of no help at all, as, squashed up against the wall that bound the lane, he vented his outraged feelings by kicking it, assiduously, to pieces. In another moment no explanations were necessary, the truth burst upon me with a flash—for the White Pony rose like a rocket from the ground, and leaped high in the air in a series of the most unpleasant bucks I have ever sat to. A swarm of hornets had settled upon his rump! He joined the panicked cavalcade with a rush, rearing and plunging with the rest.

That no one was hurt was extraordinary, that we finally drove the hornets off and quieted the ponies, still more. The unseated children were restored to their mounts, the runaway ponies were recaptured, several of them having adjourned to a near-by pasture for a roll in the grass; tears were dried, costumes rearranged. The Hunt proceeded, embellished by lumps from hornet stings, tear-stained faces, and torn clothing, but pluckily responding to the call of Mrs. I.'s horn sounding the 'Gone Away.'

Another time my small niece, on a visit from the South, aged eight, a stout little horsewoman for her age, but who had never yet ridden to hounds, implored me to allow her to go. I did not know how her parents would feel on the subject, but gave way to her entreaties at the last minute. Unfortunately, all of the ponies had been engaged for the run, but an obliging little boy, seeing her disappointment, very close to tears, offered to share with her. He was to ride to the check. We were to meet him there and my niece was to have his pony the rest of the way. I rode the White Pony to the check, behind the obliging little boy to size up the manners and going of the mount my young visitor was to have. He seemed docile and easy-going. Wreathed in smiles my niece met us at the appointed place, whither she had been conveyed by a motor. The hounds went away presently, and I and my young relative threw in at a round gallop. I turned to look at her. Every tooth in her head, including the gaps which are usual in the dental display of the very young, was exposed in a broad grin of pure, unalloyed joy. Head back, hair flying, she sat the bounding gait of the fat Shetland, unconscious of everything except the delirious excitement of the chase.

The White Pony at this point flicked up his heels and decided to give the Shetland an exhibition show of speed. I fought him halfway down the field, for I wanted to stay by in case of need. After a brief tussle, I persuaded him to abandon frivolous and conceited side play, and he sobered down to a conservative canter. Faint cries behind me brought me to a dead stop. I turned. The Shetland was still coming on at a smart pace, but even from the distance I could see my niece's expression of delight had changed to one of alarm and consternation. As they approached, something unfamiliar about the Pony's appearance struck my eye, a certain naked look about the head. It was not until they were almost upon me that I realized a deficit. Unaccountably, the bridle had slipped and was hanging about the Shetland's throat like a necklace. Freedom from the restraint of bit and reins had lent wings to his heels. He darted by me like an arrow from its bow. The White Pony reared, thinking it a challenge to a race, wheeled and flung after him. We pelted down the field. As we caught up to the Shetland, I leaned out of the saddle, snatched at the dangling bridle, caught it up, and brought the scamp up with a jerk. The child, unprepared for the sudden halt, flew over his head. I followed. Together we sat, ruefully, on the grass and watched the White Pony and the Shetland gallop off in unmitigated glee to finish their race in parts unknown. Provokingly, in the distance, we could hear the hounds in full cry.

'Well,' I said to her, 'I guess that's all for today.'

'Yes,' sighed my small relative sadly. 'And he was such a nice little pony!'

While the White Pony was recuperating from big knees, after the 'Bull Run' (as that hunt was known, thereafter), I rode a hireling, a big strong horse, with a Roman nose and an intense dislike for chicken-coops. Apropos of chicken-coops, a friend of mine, a lover of horses (from a safe distance), who found great enjoyment in following the Hunt (by motor) and who knew nothing of hunting terms, asked me one day where we were going to 'throw up,' and when I smilingly responded, 'Over Mr. C.'s chicken-coops,' she exclaimed, 'Well! I think it very good-natured of Mr. C. to allow you to go jumping about his henyard. I know I wouldn't!'

But then we all make such mistakes!

Once during the heat of a gallop, in the early days of struggles with Grey Eagle, I found myself jostling by a disgusted Whip, who growled at me, ' 'Ware Hounds! 'Ware Hounds!'

In my sweet ignorance I thought he was entering into conversation, and, desiring above all things to divert his attention from the distressing fact that I could not hold my horse, I answered brightly, 'Really? And what kind of hounds are they?'

But to return to my hireling of the Roman Nose. Every time we approached a chicken-coop, he would gently fade away in front of it, and stand gazing pensively at the scenery beyond as if listening to church bells ringing the curfew. Muttering incoherent anathemas, riders behind me ordered me out of the way, or, very red in the face with contained wrath rode right through regardless of my blocking the jump or their own safety, while the Roman Nose and I, surrounded by flying hoofs, continued to pose in front of the coop, individually, as Patience and Despair.

However, once I found myself sincerely grateful for this unfortunate habit of the hireling. Late one afternoon, three of us burst, simultaneously, from a wood. An Irishman, a tall stranger with eyeglasses, and myself. The Irishman schooled horses for other people to hunt and was a daring and skilful rider. That afternoon he was out on a steeplechaser which had proved too slow for the track, and whose owner desired to see if he could be converted into a hunter. It was the horse's first experience in the hunting field and he was wild at being held. Even the gag-bit with which he was bridled seemed to have very little effect on his manner of going. The tall stranger I knew nothing about, as I had never seen him before. His horse was a big, powerful brute, evidently a puller, and over which he seemed to have no control whatsoever. As I joined them, I thought to myself that I was travelling in fast company, but I had lost the hounds, and I did not know the way, so there seemed nothing to do but stay by them.

We charged along very comfortably, abreast, for a space, when off in the distance flickered the gleam of a wire fence.

'It's panelled, I know,' said the big man between grunts (his horse was giving him a horrible ride).

'But it's narrow as h——,' said the Irishman. 'Someone's got to pull out.'

I looked from one to another struggling with their mounts. Unquestionably, it was up to me. I leaned back on the reins, but to my intense and indignant surprise the Roman Nose tossed his head angrily, stretched out his neck, and took hold of the bit. The fast company had gone to his sedate head. He was going to stay by them or die in the attempt. The chicken-coop loomed into view.

'Ah!' I thought to myself, 'now will you stop, old top!'

And I pulled back again with all my might. Not at all! What was a chicken-coop to him at that moment? A bagatelle! Still abreast, we were nearing it with alarming speed.

'Pull out, Mrs. J., pull out!' shouted the Irishman. 'It's too narrow!'

The big man was speechless, his face purple with exertion. I was doing my best, but a very poor best it was. We were onto it now, all three of us helpless. The panel was very narrow, wire on both sides. The Irishman did the only thing possible at the moment. He dug his heels into the steeplechaser, shot ahead, and skyrocketed over it sideways, half over the wire. The big horse never rose to the coop, at all, that I could see, but hit it with a crash and ploughed through it, his tremendous weight carrying all before him, reducing the wooden panel to splinters. The Roman Nose took off, dropped suddenly, and wilted before the wreckage at his feet. When the other two were well out of sight, he stepped over the debris disdainfully, swished his tail, and gave me a look as much as to say, 'Now will you be good!'

Every year, after the close of the hunting season, the 'Harriers' entertained the farmers, 'over whose land the Hunt rides.' These entertainments were given in the Town Hall and consisted of a 'Variety Show,' by local talent at its best, followed by a supper. It was a gesture of thanks to the landowners for the privilege of knocking down their fences, pounding through their fields, and cutting up their gardens. Not that the Hunt was wilfully or carelessly destructive, but accidents will happen. The farmers, however, were a sporting lot and complained very seldom, and the Hunt responded by being as careful as is possible. Frequently, Mrs. I., at the Meet before a run, would favor us with a curtain lecture on the responsibility incurred by crossing other people's land, followed by special injunctions:

'We circle Mr. K.'s strawberries today. If there is so much as a hoofmark in those beds, we shall never be allowed through there again.'

Or, 'Old Mrs. T.'s cows are out. Please cross at the end of the field where it is flagged.'

Or, 'Under no circumstances ride over Miss P.'s little dogs, no matter how much they get in your way.'

To which last, a voice in the crowd (Mrs. I.'s young daughter) responded: 'You'd better muzzle the hounds, Ma!'

A great deal of rehearsing went on before the Show. Neighboring Hunt members who possessed a talent were enrolled also. The occasion was preceded by a Hunt dinner. Many and varied toasts were given and taken, and the party started with a bang. Mrs I., who in the field never, under any circumstances, showed the slightest trace of nerves, always worked herself to fever heat over these entertainments. She never tasted a morsel of food, and left for the Town Hall before dinner was half over, with a parting warning that if any of the performers were late, she would faint back-stage and have to be carried off.

The Show started with a speech of thanks, from Mrs. I.; then a hunting member, whose wit and ability as Master of Ceremonies had elected him to that responsible position, took hold and ran the Show off, to use the vernacular. There were always hitches. Curtains refused to be drawn at the crucial moment, lights went on and off in the midst of an act, artists became hysterical and forgot their parts, important and necessary stage properties were mislaid at the last minute, etc., etc. But the audience was lenient, the atmosphere one of friendly enthusiasm. The entertainment was always a success, and the supper afterwards made up for the missing professional touch in the Show.

Another event customary in the spring of the year, relative to the Hunt, was an annual Gymkhana and Horse Show. Committees made up of hunting members under the captainship of Mrs. I., arranged the details, the Club Polo Field was commandeered for the day, a band was hired from the village, and by the Grace of God and Good Weather, the affair was pulled off. Everything was home-made, as the Hunt had no wherewithal for lavish expenditure, and had to rely upon the ingenuity of its members for the necessaries. A nice little 'Outside Course' was erected by the village carpenter, consisting of a gate, a brush, a post-and-rail pen, and a chicken-coop, making a fair test for hunters. The 'ring' jumps were for the children and could be lowered or heightened at will, ground was staked off with flags for racing events, a gaudy cotton umbrella provided for the Judge, cups and ribbons were donated by popular subscription, and show numbers drawn and painted at home.

The children looked forward to the 'Horse Show' for weeks beforehand, and turned out in full force on the eventful day. There were horsemanship classes ranging from the age of five to twelve years, jumping classes for beginners, jumping classes from twelve to sixteen years (exchange of horses required), bareback jumping, pair jumping, four-foot jumping, pony races, donkey races, Parent and Child Class, and Gymkhana Events, such as ducking for apples and racing to finish, saddling and bridling and racing to finish, egg and spoon races, etc. In fact, the entire day from ten o'clock until sunset was devoted to the Annual Horse Show and Gymkhana. One judge passed on all of the classes, usually a member of some neighboring Hunt, and to say it was kind of him is putting it mildly. For of all the ticklish and difficult jobs, this was one of the most. To keep your eye alert and make conscientious decisions over a stretch of some six hours of constant concentration, is no easy matter. The classes were big and the children appealingly eager. The grassy banks along the Polo Field were thronged with parents, friends, or relatives. The situation was one that called for impartial opinion, sound knowledge, and adamant nerves. Yet every judge we ever invited, more or less apologetically, to preside at the Annual Horse Show and Gymkhana, proved not only most efficient, but seemed to enjoy the day and left with enthusiastic praise for the children, their horsemanship, and their good manners in general. Slight mishaps frequently happened. Ponies ran away, children were spilled, but, on the whole, the affair passed off most pleasantly and smoothly. Considering ponies, donkeys, and horses were tethered here and there to bushes and trees, and classes were being run off at the rate of every fifteen minutes, all ages competing, it was really a remarkably orderly performance.

The donkey races, to me, were by far the feature of the day. They were ridden bareback, these little Irish donkeys, over two-foot jumps along a straight course, the rider sitting way back on the rump, his feet almost touching the ground. Each donkey had an attendant stationed behind him at the start, who enthusiastically and painstakingly followed his progress during the race, merely to keep him in the course. The attendant's powers of persuasion were enhanced by a light switch which he plied at his discretion during the course of the race. When this method failed, he would rush up behind and tweak the donkey's tail. Apparently, a donkey's one idea in a race is to turn and run back as quickly as possible. Failing in this, he rushes off the course at a tangent, running blindly among spectators, horses, and ponies. Therefore, the attendant. No sooner were the donkeys lined up for the start than they attempted to turn. There followed desperate attempts to reorganize the line, in which attendants and riders were aided by interested spectators, numberless small boys, sometimes even the judge. The flag usually fell with half the participants stern to. From then on was a constant battle. Some of the donkeys broke into a canter, dashed headlong for the first jump, leaped it wildly, and as wildly veered to the side and rushed up the bank among the cheering crowd, followed by breathless attendants, and leaving the riders prone upon the ground, somewhere, during the flight. Others trotted to the jump, ears flapping, eyes half-closed, turned within a foot of it, and galloped back to the starting-line. This made a constant come and go of racers coming in and going out. Still others would balk completely and refuse to take a step, in spite of the roars of their riders and the tattoo of switches on their backsides. Those which had never been turned at the start ran off in the opposite direction pursued by willing and exuberant small boys, to be rounded up at some distant point and led back, if possible, in time to start again before the race was over. The entire Polo Field, at one stage of the race, was dotted with donkeys running in all directions, their riders in the process of being bucked off, or lying doubled up on the ground, or being hoisted up again by faithful followers. No one watching ever really knew who won the race or when it was over; but a prize was always awarded, usually to the donkey who, in the course of time, cleared all three obstacles either going or coming, and eventually crossed the finish line.

J. being a Whip aroused an engrossing and new interest in the family, namely, the Kennels. We learned to know the hounds by name and by sight; we studied their growth and development, their good or bad work in the field, their speed, their drive, their nose, with keenest appreciation. In fact, with all of us the hounds became as popular a topic of conversation as the horses. In the first days of hunting, one is so engrossed with the manners and performance of one's horse that the hounds are taken more or less as a matter of course. Either they give you a good run or they don't, and that's about all there is to it. Then little by little it seeps through that every hound in the pack is a personality; that 'Likely' picking up a line, represents generations of training, blood, and tradition; that a hound is an intelligent, loyal creature, with boundless affection and endless courage. Sturdy, Bounder, Banker, Belle, Blacky, Mischief, loyal and true friends, brave and sporting running mates. Even the scallawags of a pack, lovable, over-ambitious puppies, who hunt their own line—rabbits, squirrels, cats, anything that runs—who break without the slightest compunction with a trusting following at their heels, who spell despair to the Huntsman and hard work for the Whips, afford impromptu sport which at times is most diverting.

Every fall the different Hunts round and about New England, about seven in number, hold Hound Trails, a most entertaining event. Two couples of hounds are picked from each pack and are raced cross-country on a drag. It is a stirring sight.

One autumn Mrs. I. invited J. and myself to accompany her to the Trails. They were to be held in Westchester County, some two hundred and fifty miles from D. The hounds were sent on the night before by rail, in care of the Kennel Boy, and we went down over the road. We left D. promptly at half-past nine in the morning, J. at the wheel, Mrs. I. and myself ensconced with the luggage in the rear seat. It was a beautiful day, an excellent road, and a good time ahead. We were in the best of spirits. Many festivities awaited us at the other end. Besides the Trails, there were to be Hunter Trials, a Hunt dinner, a breakfast, a tea, and a ball. The County had turned out in fine form to give the visitors a royal welcome.

About fifty miles on our way, Mrs. I. remarked, conversationally: 'I say we cut some of the social activities. We shall be exhausted if we try to do everything, and personally, I'm not much for that sort of thing.'

'Good!' agreed J., with enthusiasm. 'Neither am I. Let's cut them all!'

'We can't very well do that,' said Mrs. I.; 'it wouldn't be manners. Let's go tonight to the dinner at Mr. H.'s (the resident M.F.H.) and . . .'

'Great Caesar!' interrupted J., irreverently, 'I've forgotten my suspenders!'

'Splendid!' said Mrs. I., 'but suspenders or not, you will have to appear tonight, because I have accepted for all three of us and we are expected.'

We continued in silence for another fifty miles, dismissing the suspenders as unworthy of further discussion, when Mrs. I. clapped her hands to her forehead and exclaimed:

'Marciful Heavens! I've forgotten the Horn!'

This was a more serious matter. After all, suspenders can be procured by the roadside at any village shop, but hunting horns do not grow on bushes. Particularly, when the hounds have grown accustomed to its own particular blasts, and were running in strange country with a half-dozen or more hunting horns being blown, to pack them in after the Trails. It is a risk, at best, running hounds with several other packs in unknown country, and when it's your best two couples and there is no familiar note to announce your presence at the end of a long, hard race, well . . . we were cast into gloom. So much so that J. turned a corner too sharply and ran into another motor. At least the motor ran into him, J. said, but whichever way it happened, we bumped together.

But nothing graver resulted than an exchange of cards and some paint off the mudguard.

We arrived at our destination in due time, without further incident, and repaired at once to a very nice old inn, where rooms had been reserved for us. They were a bower of flowers, a very courteous attention from Mr. H. We dressed hurriedly, for it was late, and went on to dinner, suspenderless, but well fortified with safety pins. At Mr. H.'s we found a large and gay gathering, amongst whom were many friends. It was a delightful evening, a delicious dinner, beautifully served, good music, and informal dancing afterward. Toward midnight the competing packs were auctioned off and a pool made, the winning pack and first hound to bring in a good round sum for him who held the lucky number. The auction was most amusing, a great many pleasantries were exchanged, some of them very witty. The party broke up hilariously with a general rendezvous at the Kennels early in the morning.

The next day, therefore, immediately after breakfast we donned those unlovely but most necessary garments, Kennel Coats, and adjourned to the Kennels to paint the hounds. As all the other hounds were being painted also, it was a hectic proceeding. A slight drizzle had set in, just enough to keep the paint from drying thoroughly, so no sooner were the numbers blazoned on their sides than it smeared and spread in unreadable blurs. Different-colored ribbons tied to the collars were then resorted to, but very shortly these hung limp and drab from the increasing dampness. It was a discouraging start.

After a short walk about adjoining fields to exercise the hounds, the procession started for the Meet. Mrs. I., being the only woman M.F.H., led with her pack, accompanied by Mr. H. Quite a crowd of people had assembled in spite of the bad weather, which had now settled into a fine, steady rain, and they were grouped about the starting-line and scattered over the adjoining hills. A long line of restless hounds was formed some feet back of the start; each held in leash ready to be slipped. One hound breaking before the fall of the flag disqualified the pack; therefore, the importance of holding your hound was paramount. The resident Huntsman, in colors, on a stalwart grey, bounded over the starting-line dragging the aniseed, galloped through a couple of fields and disappeared into the country. The shifting wind wafted back with each gust whiffs of the pungent drag. The swaying line of hounds caught the scent with wild cries, leaping and straining at their leashes.

'It's going to be fast!' shouted Mr. H., above the din.

'Plaze God, we can hold thim!' muttered a Kennel Boy to me.

The next few minutes seemed interminable. The Judges were chatting unconcernedly on the line, while we struggled with our panting charges. It seemed as if they would never step back to raise that flag. At length a Whipper-In, stationed on a promontory, raised his cap against the skyline and waved it, the given signal that the Drag Boy was halfway around the course. The Judges stepped back, stop-watches in hand, the flag fluttered high over the line. The starter, standing at the head of the waiting packs, counted the seconds.

'One—two—three—four—and off!'

Down came the flag. The leashes were slipped, hounds hurled themselves forward, noses to the ground, sterns waving, giving exultant, frantic tongue as they doubled their muscular, spotted bodies to the line. Simultaneously, we rushed to the nearest hill for a farther view.

Below us stretched woods and fields, a rain-soaked panorama of sloping meadows and dripping autumn foliage. In the distance, just emerging from a patch of woods and racing uphill under the proverbial tablecloth, the mottled, straining crew, blurred, flying specks, their music wafting back like chimes from some far-away, storm-tossed bell. Up the hill, over the grass, onto a wall and over it, not a sign of them left, a few spent stragglers staggering on behind.

'They're down in the hollow now! Watch the stream!' someone cried tensely.

Silence, all eyes straining for the next glimpse.

'There they are! There they are!' from a dozen throats.

They were at the stream now; the leaders had flung themselves into it and were struggling up the farther bank. The current was strong, some hounds were being carried down, others had stopped on the brink, howling dismally. On their way sped the leaders. The line stretched out, the pace was telling. Uphill once more, around a curve and into the woods.

'You won't see them again,' announced an old huntsman, 'until they come up the last stretch. It's three miles of wood they are crossing now, and bad footing. Only the best can do it!'

We raced back to the finish line. The Drag Pony came galloping in, bathed in lather, mud to his withers.

'Heavy going, but the scent's sticking like glue!' shouted the Huntsman, as he flung his bag to a Kennel Boy. Tensely we waited. At last a few faint yelps. The leaders were breaking from the woods, three couples or so, straining, straining, still uphill, around the curve, with panting, choking cries, but coming on. A last stone wall, up and over and down the home stretch, the first two running nose to nose, big black and brown hounds, tongues hanging, sides heaving. Then a white hound smeared with blood (or was it paint?), and fourth a little weed of a bitch, covered with mud and almost spent.

'Mischief!' 'Our Mischief!' 'God bless her stout little heart!'

I wept. I am not ashamed to admit it, it's just one of those times when you do.

Surrender to Youth

By NASH BUCKINGHAM

At Home—Christmas Time.

MY DEAR NOELLY—
In sending you this patched and smelly rucksack, my treasured hunting knife and a few other "Possibles" as the Mountain Men used to call such odds and ends of personal equipment, I'm thinking that such a veteran conglomeration may come in handy, now that you're beginning to ramble on your own, out-of-doors. You see, I call you "Noelly," rather than the more grown-up "Noel," because, to me, you're still the chubby, apple-cheeked youngster who romped under your Daddy's feet and mine when we spun yarns and hefted our rifles and shotguns amidst endangered lamps and bric-a-brac. It's a wonder we haven't acquired permanent squints. And those tall, cold concoctions he used to dish up; what were they called—"Flying Trapezes"? Well named they were, lad! One or two of those and you sure flew through the air with the greatest of ease. Anyhow, Boy, you'd best inherit these "Possibles" while there's a chance of their being as helpful to you as they have been to me.

Your young shoulders are squaring. Mine may begin to sag before long, but not if I can help it. My use of that word "may" shows, however, that I'm not admitting, by a darn sight, being "washed up," as today's saying goes. Your outlook on life is eagerly restive, your eyes strong with youth's keen vision straining for new horizons. You'll hear and read a lot about "last frontiers," Noelly. But maybe by the time you're able to really begin trying to look "in back of beyond," there'll be airship rockets to Mars and you can load into a covered wagon from where you land. Or

From "Ole Miss'," Derrydale Press.

maybe a conscience-stricken America will rebuild or salvage some wilderness miraculously spared. I hope you and other woods rookies can have high sky lines to quest, and drink from undefiled streams. I'm not one to sell my country short, Boy, but I've just read something that troubles me. I've thought the same thing but couldn't put it into words. A man wrote—"if personal character is on a low level, then there comes a time when no refinement of social planning and no expenditure of public wealth, however great, will create a good social order. In my opinion, life in America is approaching that point." I'm just quoting that because you're getting plenty old enough to understand what it means, and there may come a time when you'll have to make some grave decisions and back them up in the manner prescribed by War. And War, Noelly, can get extremely back to nature and down to the brassiest of tacks. But getting back to that word "may," while I don't have to shoot in glasses, something tells me that it won't be long now. There's still plenty of kick in the old horse, though. I'll probably pop away at many a quail or duck and snap a fly into some bass or salmon. That is I hope to, because, as your Daddy moans, our greatest fear is that we'll check out inbetween gunning seasons. What I mean is, that I'm getting inclined to be overly willing to look back. While you? You're looking forward, or, better, as we dog handlers say, "you're broadening your casts."

Packing the old kit bag tugged some heartstrings, I'll admit. Some day you'll understand what we silly old out-of-door sentimentalists feel about such plunder. It isn't the junk so much as what it has meant to a man. I've had this rucksack since I came out of college nearly thirty-five years ago, when your Daddy was a youngster with "stummick ache" from eating green apples. It's almost like parting from a favorite old bird dog; something I hope you'll never have to do. I don't mean because of death, but because of—well, because circumstances make it necessary—put it that way—and with a grin. To keep up your courage you say to him—"Don't worry, Old Scout, you're going to a good home with someone who'll care for you as deeply as I do—there'll be quail bevies no end, and plenty of rabbits." Noelly, I hope you heavy your sack with many a rab. I don't want you to grow up one of those hypercritical (you're a trifle young for that crack but your Daddy will explain) guys who forgets he was ever a boy. The kind who doesn't savvy the all-around fun a boy and his dog can chase up together.

This old pack and I went west to punch cattle on a Rocky Mountain ranch. It used to take me two long days teaming and sometimes longer to make our place from the railroad. Great years those, Noelly. Wandering both slopes from the Canadian border southward. Some of those "Possibles" are a lot older than the rucksack. No telling how many times its drawstrings have been replaced. You can see for yourself how it's been cobbled on. "Man-sewing," the women folks call it. But it's stout. I've used mountain sheep, goat, moose, elk, deer and steer whang. But the best lacing is made from the oiled and rolled spinal cords of the fresh-water sturgeon. Boy, are they stout and long-lasting?

I've packed this bag from ocean to ocean, and where it hasn't gone with me my dear old hunting partner Hal Howard took it, God rest his fine soul. Clean across from New Brunswick's bogs and salmon water to innermost and uppermost Alaska, British Columbia and on down into vivid Old Mexico. Since Hal passed on I've never slipped out of the pack and put on the beans and "tay" without somehow seeing the old boy squatting opposite munching his chuck. Ours were the days of the 45-70 and 30-40, iron sights, long heavy bullets and a sound stalk that socked 'em where they belonged. Oh! I'm not saying these moderns don't make long shots with their highfalutin bullets and powerful telescopes. We just had to take up a lot of slack with more hard work, that's all. But we got the meat and I recall no crippled trophies to amount to anything.

Boy, we've sure packed some fine fresh liver and tenderloins back to camps in this old grub-toter. I can smell it frying right now, kinder strong-like if the grease was inclined to age a bit, and even with spuds and a red onion in competition. It has filled our bellies with hot victuals after many a tough day and half a night's scramble over bruising, snow-clad rim rocks and down-timber. Its medicine kit has healed many a trail jab for man or beast. It has burned out a long and honorable line of tea buckets and fry pans. Emptied and stuffed with ferns or browse it has pillowed me when only saddle blankets and a push-log made campfire contact. It always goes along on quail or duck and goose hunts. I'll bet you can dig feathers from its seams right now. You can shoot from it, with ease. I've even swum with it on my back. In a tight place I'd say to myself, "Well, you're not alone, you've got the old sack." It's an ally that'll stick by you, boy! A real friend! Remember that. And now, just a little something about the other odds and ends.

This hunting knife. My dear Mother had a favorite uncle, Noelly. He sailed the seven seas in the King's "Navee," and his hobby was collecting swords and weapons from all countries at ports of call. He gave Mother a pair of these Chinese dirks when I was just a tot. As I recall her story of them they were a present to Great-Uncle Tommy from some mandarin. So you can get an idea how old this soft steel, hand-forged frog-sticker may be. Its mate was lost and so was the ivory sheath to this one. So it has been with me longer than the rucksack. It takes an ideal cutting edge, but the temper isn't so hot. You have to keep up with it pretty close—that's what the hone is for. It has helped dress out practically every species of North American big game, and sliced enough steaks, bacon and bread to keep half the country off relief rolls. You'll find a flint and steel in the sheath's side pocket. Get yourself some punk and grass straw or a hover of lint and some raf with powder rubbed into it and learn to spark 'em ablaze. That arrowhead I picked up on the Laramie plains of Wyoming, the same morning I found the buffalo skull. I was sneaking some teal I saw pitch into a plains trickle, and stumbled over something. I examined the sharp, black point and began to dig. Before long I uncovered a mammoth "buffler" head, in fact the whole carcass was there, or rather skeleton. I forgot the teal and finally worried off the mud and cleaned the trophy up pretty well. This same rucksack backpacked it to the ranch. And before I forget it, if you don't know how to sharpen an axe or this hunting knife, why go to some butcher or grinder and get yourself taught. One of the most pathetic of all half-baked alleged outdoorsmen is the chap who don't know the first principles of edging up his most important tools.

At our old E-Bar-X ranch there used to come an early heavy snow. When it had melted off, the weather invariably faired into a run of sparkling, winey days and frosty nights. Then was when we figured on getting in most of our winter meat, and old John Dunlap and I usually rustled the assignment. John was a card, and a trump one, too. Born of seafaring folk down Taunton Way. But the Civil War fouled his compass and he dragged anchor west. Turned his hand to black-smithing and prospecting until mountains lured him to a homestead away back in our valley. At well past sixty John's was a still powerful frame and a clean, keen, kindly mind. Somewhere, I've got a pair of silver mounted spurs old "Jawn" turned out for me in the ranch smithy.

Well, John and I'd clap the diamond hitch on a light pack and with a couple of extra nags, usually old "Blue" and "Sailor," hit for that big country in between Sheep Peak and Lost Solar. There was a monstrous draw in between the heads of Ripple and Fawn cricks that we particularly favored. We'd throw a quick snug camp an hour of the sun, picket the ponies and separate for a look around afoot. Sleeping bags weren't much use in those times so we used a big double tarp and some thick Navajo blankets. And would they keep you snug atop a jag of spruce feathers! The first night we'd grub on sow-belly and beans because we disliked shooting up the country while getting the lay of things. I can see old John now, sitting tailor fashion by the embers while doing his dishes—he was a great hand to keep a clean camp. That's another thing you'd best remember, too, Buddy. Keep a clean camp; it helps out in later everyday life, sort of "habit-forming" if you get what I mean. Then we'd build up the blaze and lay back while John smoked a couple of pipes. He loved to talk about his young days in staid New England; about tall ships and high seas; and if you'd ever been there as I had you could smell the clam flats and fresh sweet marsh grasses and feel the sting of cutting east winds. The last thing John used to do before we rolled in was to slip his stubby, ivory-sighted carbine under his alongside bedding and shove his boots down under the tarp. Then he'd sit up and wrap a big bandanna round his shiny bald head. His dry wood for next morning's touch-off went under the cover, too, for John just naturally believed in preparedness and labor saving. Those are good camp rules, too, Noelly. Of course we always camped close to water but bedded down just beyond the reach of blow-down trees in case of a storm. Long before the pine squirrels turned on their alarms, John and I would be outside some hot Java and a crust. He'd have his route spotted, and I mine, so we'd be off through the frosted elk weeds and begin stalking the timber edges around the parks. What we liked best to hear was a bull elk bugling the evening before. When we'd killed, we did just a quick job of butchering and went on back to camp. Figuring we had the panniers full, we'd pack up and horse to the first load, then to the next and so on back to the ranch. I have watched and helped a lot of meat skinners and carvers in my time, but John was the best I ever saw. He had a skinning outfit of two knives he'd made himself out of files. John told me he "got learned" by the buffalo hunters, and the way he could walk around a carcass and lift the hide after a few slashes and rips, was a work of art in venery. Old Bill Gibson who did the ranch tanning used to say that fleshing and graining skins behind John was a pleasure. But John always said (and here's another thing you can remember, Noelly) that after you'd learned the proper cuts even that wouldn't do you much good unless you worked with sharp tools. John's knives and axe were razor sharp, and kept that way, too. Those were great days, Buddy. To ride out on some hog-back away up eleven or twelve thousand feet, and look out across a world of blue shadows, sun-shot with dark spruce belts and wide ribands of deep lemoned aspens. Or to stalk silently through the lower ridges after sun-down and see deer feeding out and up the hillsides like so many cattle. Heigh-ho!

The old rucksack reminds me, too, of Arthur Pringle and his gorgeous moose country spreading far and wide off "Baldy" and crisscrossed with grilse and salmon pools of Sevogle and Miramichi waters. A wonderful man, Arthur Pringle. He'd lost a fine son in France and the blow shook him to his heels. I remember one day he and I had boiled the kettle and were munching sandwiches on a little shrubby point overlooking the lower end of Nash Lake. A fat beaver was having the time of his life playing on his slippery slide just across from us. There were snow flurries but a brilliant sun broke through and routed them. The beaver went off home up the lake. Arthur stirred his "tay" and told me about his lad and how he had so hoped Donald would be spared to take over things. You could tell from the shadows in his fine eyes that he bled inwardly. But, like many another Canadian father, he gave without a whimper for God and Country and for King. That afternoon we sat back to back with the summit of old Baldy and searched a miniature world far below with our binoculars. The packs had gotten a mite heavy after that steep climb. Then Arthur spotted a big bull splashing across some beaver water. We slipped out of harness and lit out down to timberline. There was just a rime of light across Baldy when we finished butchering and hung the heavy cuts onto sprung trees until we could return with the horse. Then we had to reclimb Baldy, get under the packs and hit for home. The shack looked good about midnight.

One afternoon, Noelly, I knocked a yearling bull elk two hundred feet down a snowy sidehill. I did a thorough job of butchering and hung the meat until I could get back for it several days later. When Sam and I rode into the spruce opening where I'd skinned out the bull, it was deep dusk. I said, "Sam, someone's been here since I was; look how that carcass has been dragged through the snow." I'd hardly spoken when out of a bush at my elbow jumped two grotesque croaking dwarfs! Scared? Boy, we were so frightened we couldn't move or speak. Our visitors proved to be two gigantic eagles so gorged with meat they couldn't get air borne. I never did hear Sam cuss better and it was all I could do to keep him from laying them out with a club. He would have, too, if his eye hadn't happened to catch sight of their nest, on top of a tall dead pine down in a burn just over the gulch. That was the night I probably ate more meat than at any other one sitting. Minnie Frost sliced ropes of succulent tenderloin into thick filets and grilled 'em rare. With spuds and cornbread and chokecherry wine Sam and I did a noble job. Another time, I got down the best sheep I ever took. I managed to get the caped skull into and on top of this sack and tried a short cut around the ledge and down to my horse, far below. I came to a slide not over forty feet wide but so straight up and down it was shuddery. Turning back meant a two-mile detour and bumping some black timber in the dark. It took me ten minutes to screw up courage for the tackle. Just as I made the last stomach-turning stop the slope underfoot caved and down I plunged. At the first bounce that sheep head slipped and a horn point caught a rock just in time to hold me long enough to claw a hand and foot hold and roll over once to a shelf of rock. And there I lay until my "tummy" settled. Do you wonder I feel close to this old side-kick of a pack?

You'll find a battered Army mess kit in the pack, Noelly.

There are two or three extra knives, forks and spoons with the original tools. Maybe my chatting along with you about the mess kit smacks of mere sentiment; but, by the time you're as old as your Daddy, and have bucked Life's line as hard as he has, you'll find sentiment an amiable companion due a warm spot in your "Possibles" sack. And that web snap-pocket that holds two clips of .45 auto cartridges is the mess kit's matey. The latter was issue stuff back in '16 when Uncle Sam decided Pancho Villa had become too annoying. Shortly thereafter, the Kaiser knocked a chip off History's shoulder and started a fine free-for-all.

My younger brother came home to say good-bye, and, meanwhile, I'd been using the mess kit on goose and duck shooting ventures. In order to reach France faster, Henry transferred to another outfit and had to surrender his sergeant's status. He walked aboard the transport a "buck" private. I don't know why, but I asked him to pack that old mess kit along, just for luck. Nor can I explain, Noelly, the deep, tender silence that came over two brothers who had been mighty close, when the time came to —well—perhaps call Life a day. Henry got knocked pretty well to pieces, Noelly, like your Daddy did, but he lugged this piece of junk along home with a lieutenant's trappings, a field promotion for gallantry, and no end of souvenirs "Francaises" for the nieces and nephews. That .45 pocket-clip was his, too, and makes a grand belt holder for hunting licences, medicine gadgets, or fish hooks. Peace and war make strange bedfellows! Like bird nests in cannon mouths, or flower pots out of French 75 cases. And was I glad to see that old shot up, gassed doughboy? As glad as I used to be back in the stone age of professional football when we'd go down under punts together.

So, back went the mess kit into my pack, Noelly. How deeply Henry and I enjoyed the duck hunt we made that first winter he was home from the hospital. Our honored father had passed on and willed me his certificate in a great wild-fowling club. The Boy and I shot together at our favorite family stand—the head of Long Pond. Shrapnel and gas hadn't left him overly strong, and how he drank in every breath of that glorious day. When snack time came, we waded ashore and broiled ham and eggs over a bed of coals. He related war experiences, and remember, your Daddy was doing his bit right over there while this mess kit was being packed around by an engineer of the Blue Ridge gang. So, in a way, it's just changing homes.

But I recall one day when lack of this pack and the mess kit played the wild with your Daddy and me. We were improving our conversational calibers by gunning ducks in an Arkansas pin-oak flat. Figuring the flight would be fast and our "limits" soon acquired, we left the pack at home and waded far out into the over-flowed forest. But ducks, as Horace puts it, were "scaice," and by noon, with a four-thirty a.m. breakfast behind us, the pangs of appetite gnawed upon and reproached us bitterly. So, there we sat, bowling over an occasional mallard and sustaining each other by guesses as to what toothsome dish would best satisfy the moment's craving. Starting with continental offerings, we had worked our way through practically every worthwhile American restaurant down to New Orleans, and were all but drooling at the mouth, when Clarence LaCotts arrived with a paper-sack full of roast pork sandwiches. Your Daddy said—"Like the Prodigal Son, I saw Clarence while he was yet a great way off and ran to him and fell on my knees."

Many a good hunter has dipped his fingers in this old mess kit's stews. It last fed Ira Richards and "Dick" Bishop in that same mallard woods where your parent and I so narrowly escaped starvation. I told Ira and Dick how one meal from the kit reminded me of another story. The gunning season previous, I shot with a party of men who had their wives along—including a very lovely Chicago debutante. And a jolly good sport that youngster was, too. One icy forenoon, after a midnight breakfast, she, too, waxed "hongry." So, I waded ashore, set some Java to dripping and rummaged a can of hot tamales into the pan. The youngster had never seen a hot tamale, and she sniffed the red-peppered, corn-husked concoction with visible trepidation. But one bite, and did she tear into them?

Her expression had me remembering a long ago afternoon at our old ranch when I came in with a mess of big trout to clean and hand to Grandma Carpenter, the cook. Grandma's pet, a bright-eyed, precocious grandchild and close pal of mine, went along to watch the operation. Kneeling and working fast, with the five-year-old alongside like a pert wren, I became conscious of someone else standing over me. Looking up, I discovered a very aloof and high-nosed Boston woman, who, with her husband, had stopped off at the ranch to study rural characters and atmosphere for a book she was writing. One glance assured me, however, that trout cleaning offended not only her olfactory and pictorial senses of atmosphere, but, in fact, her very being. Just then little Edna piped up—

"Do you know what THEM is, lady?"

"W-h-a-a-a-t?"

"Them's guts, lady—fish guts."

Tableau.

So, Noelly, let's hope the mess kit endures and that someday you and I and your Daddy will have a duck shoot together and while we two old fellows wheeze and lounge against a log, you can rustle up what my sweet lady always refers to as a mess of "Buckingham U-g-h-s!" And maybe, out of the fire's haze will emerge reminders of what good men like your Daddy and Henry went through with that you might live to carry on—and have a darned old tin fry platter. Don't ever low rate a mess kit, Boy. Nobody has ever yet produced a satisfactory explanation as to what causes wars. And what's more, after they arrive, a lot of guys like your Daddy and Henry extract considerable secret enjoyment from them. For why do we have Memorial days? Why do we walk among monuments raised to countless believers in and upholders of our now imperiled Liberty? Nobody in particular hunts up a War, Noelly, but write off a lot of this radio crooning by craven idealists that they "hate war." That sort of clap-trap gets votes, too. The story of the "Three Little Pigs" is the best answer to all that sort of chatter. Just build your house of brick, and when War comes to your door, Noelly—you may get a break. But the boys will all pack mess kits, just the same.

I can see you smile, Noelly, as you prowl through the jumbled contents you're examining. As years go by you'll replace them one by one with fancies of your own. You can carry a sight of useful stuff this way. But the two things I want most of all for you to have along, Boy, are your ideals and your independence. Make them your shield and sword, and when the going gets toughest why, damn it, keep 'em up with your guard and your God and lam back at the enemy. Sometimes that enemy is just yourself, and at others he can slip up on you with all the pictured disguises of the Big Bad Wolf. The habit of eternal vigilance out-of-doors, Noelly, will help teach you to take nature apart.

Jot this down, too, in your memory book. If you like to fight, for fun or otherwise (a failing of your Daddy's and mine), don't ever figure that you will skip taking some punishment. You'll get yours all right enough. We all do, from life and the rest of the ants running around loose in it. But let me tell you this much, definitely. The hurt of the hardest battering, or the stiffest, rocking punches you may be called upon to absorb, are as nothing compared to the shame of knowing you turned up afraid to risk taking them. Hell, Boy, even a clean knockout is just a jarring bump and flash of light, and then they tell you how it happened. And even while you're stopping punches why remember that the other guy has a chin and a belly, so make it your business to keep firing away. Maybe he is worse off than you are. Maybe he can't take it. I tell you, lad, the only thing the floor is good for is to get up off it when you have to stick. Keep your head and take a "nine count," but get up. I remember one piece of advice good old Patsy Hogan gave me years ago, just a whispered admonition as we waited to be called out to the center of the ring for instructions. "Kid," he gurgled, "hit d' Ref'ree, hit d' ring posts, hit d' water buckets, but f' Pete's sake, hit sump'n."

Noelly, you won't find a compass among all these "Possibles." Mine got lost. You can get lost in life, though, just like men do in the wilds. Sometimes its sky is so overcast that every crick mouth and drawhead looks bafflingly the same. Just blind alleys every way you turn. That's the time to keep cool and sit down for some steady thinking. But any compass isn't worth a farthing unless you learn to use one correctly. A compass, after all, is just mechanical presence-of-mind out-of-doors. And while I'm on the subject of compasses, study your stars and planets and where they hang out at all hours of night, winter and summer. The Mountain Men had no compasses, but could they navigate? Nor were they astronomers, except by eyes or ears. They journeyed by the sun in daytime, and if they didn't know the stars by name, they knew them by sight. And they swore and steered by them. They got to be old friends and once they clapped an eye on a certain twinkler, the route was as good as won. And in tramping the out-of-doors, I want you to learn to "read sign." Trails, creek bottoms and gully sides are clue-bearers, so keep your eyes on the ground aplenty. Watch the bushes for browse lines. Hawks and owls are invariably up to something, and changes in the wind have meanings all their own. Learn the trees and wildflowers by name; not to know is like being a stranger at the feast. And if you ever doubt your MAKER'S sense of justice, remember HE gave animals their wonderful sense of smell and hearing, and to birds their supersight.

Unpacking and repacking the old rucksack, I came onto the little dog-eared, all-but-worn-out tract of St. John. I started to keep it, but something said, "No, send it on with its comrades to Noelly, and tell him why you do so." Well, I'm a more or less doggy old sinner, good as was my raising in the Church. I'm afraid we backsliders are worse off than most. I've lived among rough fellows a lot, but some years ago I began to notice that around campfires or long, snowed-in winter evenings the he-men who stood out as most worthwhile in memory knew their Bibles and took delight and not shame in studying the Word in His sight. Then an experience in faith came to me through an old negro who believed that prayer during a hunting ordeal we endured brought us out alive. Ever since that night the Gospel of St. John has had a home in this rucksack. So, let it abide now, with you. It's a grand compass, when you're fixing to lose your wits, or worse, your "guts."

About all a fellow like I am can do is believe in ONE CAMP and its COMMANDER. It isn't just a hunch, or nigger superstition. It is deep conviction. Writing this, there may come a day when you'll have to back me up with this old rucksack and the Gospel of St. John. I may be lucky enough to crash Gabe's Gate and wangle an interview with Saint Peter. About all I could claim is what I've been trying to tell you here, Noelly. Everything would hinge on whether I was telling the TRUTH. Peter might say, "How can you prove it?" And, standing first on one foot and then the other, I'd probably reply, "Well, suh, I sho' lef' my Witness in an old pack bag I gave to a young fellow named Noel Sheldon." And Saint Peter would tell Gabriel, "Check on that, Gabe." So, if you lose the rucksack, much less the Gospel of St. John, why, Boy, I'll be in one Hell of a fix.

Merry Christmas, Noelly, good luck, and God bless you all.

Thomas Doggett's Coat and Badge

By ROBERT F. KELLEY

O N THE MORNING of August 1, 1716, the early light on the river Thames illumined a cluster of boats about one of the piles of London Bridge. Here and there in the craft, a boatsman stood up to peer across the others; an occasional shout stopped a passing oarsman and brought him over to join the group. Their voices filtered up through the morning air in approval of the message flapping against the bridge. Its wording was repeated every now and then by those who could read for the benefit of those who could not.

"This being the day of His Majesty's happy accession to the throne," it read, "there will be given by Mr. Doggett an Orange Colour Livery with a Badge representing Liberty to be rowed for by Six Watermen that are out of their time within the past year. They are to row from London Bridge to Chelsea. It will be continued annually on the same day for ever."

Kings and people have changed; colonies have grown to foreign empires; wars, famine and pestilence have raged over the face of the earth; the river Thames threatens to disappear under a coating of bridges, but for more than two centuries the magnificent confidence of the last line of that proclamation has been undisturbed.

Thomas Doggett was an Irishman who had first conquered the stage of Dublin and then crossed to England to invade the great world of London toward the end of the seventeenth century. It was in 1689-90 that he first began to be heard of in London with a traveling company. For a time he appeared at Bartholomew Fair and picked up what he could in odd places, but early in the next century his success became assured when he formed a friendship

From "American Rowing," G. P. Putnam's Sons.

with Congreve and began appearing in his comedies, playing with the beloved Mrs. Anne Bracegirdle among others. In time he rose to the eminence of actor-manager at the Drury Lane and from this height dipped into politics as a violent Whig. The son of a small tradesman in Dublin, Doggett was born there somewhere between 1650 and 1670, the exact date being in dispute. He died childless in 1721. During his lifetime he had been a real and vivid member of the intellectual company of London, his name being mentioned in connection with those of Swift, Addison, Gay, Steele, Pope and Handel in what must have been a sort of round table at the famous Swan Inn by the bridge. Among the legends clustered about the race for the Coat and Badge is one that Handel's Water Music was inspired by it.

In the face of this, there is the odd fact that today the place of his grave is unknown, the vast majority of his race have never heard of him. Of the minority who have, most have done so because of a prize which he left for a race among watermen.

It would be, of course, absurd to call this the first race of the world. There were probably boat races soon after the first craft had been fashioned. With the exception of polo, archery, jousting and running, racing in man-propelled boats is very likely the oldest form of competition. There are signs of racing among the ancient galleys, though it is not likely the oarsmen themselves thought them very sporting. The first indications of boat racing in which the rowers themselves were willing competitors are found in England, and this a good many years previous to Doggett's prize.

But these were sporadic and disorganized, often started on the spur of the moment. Those who have followed Thomas Doggett, actor-manager and patron of rowing, have built the oldest tradition of organized sport in the world. There has been only one break in the pattern of the race, and then it was merely an interruption. After sticking out the first year of the great war in 1914, the holders of the race gave up in 1915. But careful records were kept and in 1920, six races were rowed, for the six years from 1915 to 1920, inclusive. In each race the competitors chosen were those who had qualified during the year in question.

It may be that there are semi-sporting events connected with ancient religious festivals which own a longer unbroken ancestry, but the Doggett race is older by more than a century than the second oldest aquatic event, the university boat race between Oxford and Cambridge which started in 1829, and antedates by more than fifty years the St. Leger, which started in 1776, and is older than both the Derby and The Oaks in British turf history.

In Samuel Pepys' time there were several thousand licensed watermen on the Thames and it was quite the thing for young bloods in search of amusement to stop and offer purses for impromptu brushes. Some of these races must have been more or less formally arranged, for in 1661, Pepys' Diary speaks of his plan to watch a race which had been arranged for the day in question. But there can be no doubt of the fact that the Doggett race, by reason of its tenacious regularity, rightfully belongs to history as the legitimate ancestor of boat racing, in America and abroad.

The reason for the gift of Doggett is discovered in the close connection of the watermen and the theater of the day in London, a relationship in evidence before Doggett and which endured for some time afterward. The river was the main artery of travel and the watermen of the day were the taximen of London. As early as the year 850 A.D. there was toll-taking on the river during a Viking raid; and in 1514, Henry VIII passed a statute regulating watermen and their fares, thus founding the Waterman's Company which has since governed traffic on the Thames. Even before the Army and Navy had adopted any uniformity of garb, the watermen were distinguished by their pleated coat, knee breeches, stockings and badge, like a serving dish, on their left arm, denoting the fact they were licensed to take passengers. They were, then, the first uniformed service in England.

In 1593 one of the hideous plagues settled on London and resulted, among other things, in the closing of the theaters. There has been handed down a petition of that day from the watermen asking that the theaters be reopened, for the closing was working a hardship on the watermen and their families. Much of the life of London which depended on any transient trade was built with the river in mind and architects of the theaters of the day were always careful to have in their plans a good boat landing, which was afterwards advertised in the handbill of the theaters.

In the time of Pepys there were as many as 10,000 watermen. The hardships of their lot were obvious. A hard frost, with a

frozen river, meant no business at all. They must serve six years
of apprenticeship before taking a license to ply for themselves.
The younger men were constantly in danger of the press gangs
from the Navy; so much so that they frequently abandoned con-
voys from the country before reaching London and permitted old
men, in whom the Navy could have no interest, to carry the boats
on to their destination. When they had finished their apprenticeship, it was often a real hardship for them to find the money for
the purchase of the customary livery and badge, without which
no waterman could hope to compete with his fellows. Hence the
prize of Thomas Doggett was a real one, doubly so as time passed
and it came to be recognized as the mark of high skill.

The most robust legend of the founding of the race has it that
Doggett, after an evening of good talk and wine at the Swan
Tavern, came out on the landing stage to find the night cool,
rainy and unpleasant and the wind and tide against his direction.
Much as moderns find their troubles in reaching the sanctuary
of a taxicab on rainy nights, Doggett found it difficult to induce
a boatman to take him aboard for the trip home. Finally a young
chap, just out of his apprentice work, volunteered and took him.
On the way he pointed out to the famous Doggett the hardships
and worries of the young waterman. Doggett rewarded him handsomely and then, thinking it over, established his race as a means
of encouraging the younger men of the river.

It was not many years later that Doggett died, but he had
made careful provisions in his will for the continuance of the
race. Edward Burt of the Admiralty office was charged with the
responsibility of administering the funds, which were to result
from the purchase of lands to yield an annual income of ten
pounds. Five pounds were to be spent for a badge of silver weighing about twelve ounces and representing Liberty; eighteen shillings were for cloth for a livery; one and twenty shillings for
making up the cloth and thirty shillings to the clerk of the
Waterman's Hall. Edward Burt eventually turned over to the
Fishmongers Company the handling of the will; and the unfailing
faith of this great guild has kept the race alive.

In the beginning it was the rule that the starters were to row
at the time when the tide was strongest against them, the course
being from the Old Swan at London Bridge to the White Swan

at Chelsea, a bit less than five miles. In 1769 the Fishmongers Company took over supervision of the boats to prevent abuses and the six men were drawn by lot from the entrants, so that it appears likely the best were overlooked in some years. In 1873 the practice of choosing the starters by means of preliminary heats was begun.

Today the race is rowed with the tide, but through a river in which the competitor is called upon to pass under eleven bridges and a river which pays no attention whatsoever to the competitors so far as suspension of traffic is concerned. It is a terrific test of watermanship and endurance. Originally the men rowed in their regular boats, big and heavy and capable of carrying passengers. Gradually they began to improve on these, and some, able to afford it, built craft for racing only. But it was not until the race of 1907 that the modern racing shell was used. Wooden outriggers, which were little more than built-out sides, were used as late as the race of 1906. Today the regular metal outriggers are in place, but the boat, obviously, must be sturdy and seaworthy, for the going is never smooth and often very rough.

When the list of winners is approached there arises a question as to whether the race was started in 1715 or 1716. The evidence would indicate the possibility of some sort of race as part of a pageant in 1715, but that the Doggett race, as formally so named, occurred first in 1716.

The name of the first winner has been lost, but there remains a portrait of him still hanging in the Waterman's Hall in London. In it a chap sits at the ready somewhat forward of the waist of a high sided boat shaped, very nearly, like the modern Cape Cod fisherman's dory. The oars rested in grooves cut in the gunwales, and the oarsman wears a full-sleeved, white shirt, his head bound in a bandanna tied in the back like those of storied pirates.

After him has followed a long line of river men, several of them famous figures in rowing. On several occasions the records note that the race was held more than once in a year. This is undoubtedly due to the fact that Doggett's regulations provided that an affidavit to the effect that the race had been unfairly won would mean holding it again. This clause still exists, but in modern years there has been no fouling. The earlier oarsmen were apparently as rugged as the race they rowed in.

At the beginning, as now, the various competitors were followed on the river by their friends in other craft. But in the early days it was apparently considered proper for the followers to take a more active part in the proceedings. London Bridge was the only one near the course in the old days, but if a competitor happened to be coming to the race from up river, he often found friends of his rivals on the bridge, ready to drop water and stones into his craft. In 1752 the race was rowed over when a competitor had his wherry filled with water before the start. The quaint practice of hurling bottles was also indulged in in 1736 with nearly fatal results to the head of one Evans, a competitor of that year. In 1720 another had his bows stove in by a big craft crossing too close, and this practice, chiefly designed to stir up waves, persisted until quite modern times. In allotting the credit for keeping the race alive, some share might be reserved for the courage of these early oarsmen who braved not only the river itself but the crude mischief of its inhabitants. As for the natural hazard of the race, there are frequent records of upsets and swampings, with at least two instances where the rowers clambered back into their tippy craft and continued to finish as high as fourth place.

Of the winners there have been several who went on to become leaders of the sculling of their day, among them C. R. Harding, who won in 1888, and W. A. Barry, who won in 1891. Harding's son won the race of 1931. Of interest to rowing men in this country was the victory of Richard John Pocock in 1910. Pocock, boat builder at Yale since the advent of Ed Leader as head coach, has with him in his post what is believed to be the only Doggett Badge at present in the United States.

Perhaps the best known of the winners was John Broughton, afterward to become an immortal of prize fighting. Soon after winning the badge in 1730, Broughton took to boxing and became the champion of England in 1734. In 1743 he promulgated a new set of boxing rules which endured until 1838, and he has been called the father of English boxing. He was the man to introduce gloves to the sport and to change the rules so that some science replaced the brutality of the old style.

It is, of course, obvious that the waterman of old no longer exists as such in London. For one thing, the uniforms have disappeared and the badge winner today usually wears it only to be photographed and then lays it away among treasured souvenirs. The rivermen of today are for the most part no longer ferrymen. They are lightermen and bargemen; river pilots, etc. The Waterman's Company still binds apprentices, now for five years, and still grants freedom to contestants for Doggett's Coat and Badge. In addition the company now measures all barges and pleasure craft for hire, in order to see that proper safety is provided for as regards numbers allowed aboard and equipment.

The Fishmongers Company govern and arrange the race, with the competitors decided on through trial heats rowed from Putney to Hammersmith three weeks or so before the date of the race. The date is shifted occasionally, as when it falls on a Sunday, and the race is rowed up with the full tide. The start and finish are almost the same as in the first race, though the Old Swan and the Swan Tavern have long since disappeared. Ten pounds has been added to the prize for the competitors.

The big, rugged boats of the founders of this tradition have been replaced by slim, trim-built racing boats, sometimes weighing less than thirty pounds all told. The followers no longer scramble along in galley boats, wherrys and oar barges, but hire for the occasion steamers, towboats and launches, each bedecked with the colors of their favorite.

Even with its modern setting the race still is one of the most picturesque events that sport has to offer. Each of the contestants wears his colors. The start is made from stakeboats stretched across the river, and then, as the scullers shoot away, splashing, into the rough water, the fleet of paddle wheel steamers and launches swings into line behind, like hens convoying a brood of chickens, and the strange fleet heads up the river, oblivious to the ordinary river life which in turn pays no attention. Dodging strings of barges and various other river traffic, winding back and forth to take full advantage of the wind and tide, the contestants survive, when they do, probably the greatest test of watermanship the world has to offer. The new boats, of course, make it possible to cover the distance in an hour less than the beginners did it in. But still it is no mild ramble. The winner of 1931 covered the distance of slightly more than $4\frac{3}{4}$ miles in about twenty-nine minutes, almost a solid half hour of steady, hard work.

The start is still made by the barge master of the Fishmongers

Company, resplendent in great cocked hat and gold-braided livery; the finishing poles flaunt the crowned fishes of the Company on their flags; and the red-coated finish judge still raises his hat in gallant tribute as the first man crosses the line. Then the contestants are pulled aboard their following craft, boat and all, and taken below for a rub and refreshment. The officials and guests return to the historic basement of the Waterman's Company, there to sit for a while, to break bread together and to complete one more of the long line of chapters in this most ancient story of rowing.

"By how slight an occurrence may man's memory be fixed in the hearts of posterity!" wrote that very famous British sportsman and author, the late Sir Theodore A. Cook, in the pages of the special volume which he and Guy Nickalls prepared on Thomas Doggett, and which Constable & Company published in 1918. "Alas, poor Doggett! 'Where be your gibes now, your gambols, your songs, your flashes of merriment that were wont to set the table in a roar? Not one now to mock your own grinning? Quite chopfallen?' I can end no better than by quoting those lines, written only sixteen years after his death on a window pane at Lambeth, by some young sculler, belike, with more of muscle than of meter in his composition—

> " 'Tom Doggett, the greatest sly droll in his parts,
> In Acting was certain a master of arts;
> A monument left—no herald is fuller—
> His praise is sung yearly by many a sculler.
> Ten thousand years hence, if the world last so long,
> Tom Doggett will still be the theme of their song.
> When Old Noll with Lewis and Bourbon are forgot,
> And when numberless Kings in oblivion shall rot.' "

There is no known grave of Thomas Doggett, but here in these lines is the perfect epitaph.

Vicarious Adventure

By BRIAN MEREDITH

WHEN I TRAVEL I am greedy. I pitch not only into food, but into people, settings and situations. I am sensually hungry; I feed eagerly upon everything that comes; I see and absorb and remember; and after a few days I am glutted to the point of listlessness—and I realize that I have probably been very naive and childish in my enthusiasm.

But in time the confusion is adjusted. My memories become orderly and from among them certain people and places, certain moments of fear and ecstasy are outstanding. They are inward realities to which I can turn when outward realities are too much for me. They justify the whole nerve-racking business.

Skoki ski camp supplies a background for several memories. It is a collection of log-cabins in a wooded valley, walled about by mountain giants, and at the junction of other tributary valleys giving access deeper into the titanic alpine fastness.

It is the one human outpost north of the transcontinental line of the Canadian Pacific Railway in the Rockies until you reach the line of the Canadian National at Jasper. And then the mountains continue north of that for a thousand miles on into the Arctic Circle. To the east are several ranges before the foot-hills and the prairies; to the west is the Continental Divide, the Selkirks, and a jumble of ranges terminating in the coastal bulwark indented by the deep fjords of the Pacific. South of the railway are two more ski camps, and then again untracked snows until the mountains lose height in their reaches beyond the American border.

Fifty Switzerlands in one, this land is called, and in winter,

From "Escape on Skis."

and in terms of skiing, this is particularly so. In place of the crowded resorts of Switzerland and Austria, however, with their hotels and funiculars, there are here only a few organized ski centres, two main lines of railway, a few scattered park rangers living the life of hermits in winter; and then great areas of unexplored snow-fields.

At Skoki I met some of the men who live in this limitless landscape, and I found they were beginning to live in it on skis with the same ease and enjoyment that they did on horses in summer. Since white men first penetrated the Rockies they have saddled their mountain ponies and pack-horses and disappeared for weeks and months at a time. It has been to hunt, fish, to trap, to prospect, to aid in surveys, to take "dudes" on tours, or it has been just for the fun of the thing. And the terrain that is theirs is usually not "discovered" until they guide someone else there.

The youngsters, I gathered, had begun to wander on skis, to guide "pioneers" and to use their skis in the same free way they used their ponies. They back-packed their grub and "flea bags"; they slept out under Arctic conditions in "brush camps"; they crossed passes that had never been traversed before in winter, and in some cases they penetrated into country never before visited.

The ski camp where I met some of them was typical of others I should see and characterized by an atmosphere found nowhere else in the world. It lacked the comforts, the plumbing, the service of Switzerland; but it had a charm of its own. It was in many ways a Dude Ranch with the ski complex. In the main cabin the log walls displayed the skin of a grizzly bear (Come now, Meredith: Was there a skin of a grizzly bear on the wall? . . . Well, I think there was; and if there wasn't, it would be nice if there had been), an old lariat, a climbing rope and an ice-axe, a First Aid cabinet, some broken ski points, a western saddle, a skull of a horse, ski posters and maps, a pair of antlers, and some huge roweled western spurs.

The stove was of the air-tight type, a large drum set horizontally, and above it was festooned an amazing collection of ski gear: mittens, socks, boots, skins, headbands, moccasins, wind-breakers, and a shameless set of milady's long woolly underwear.

Reached by a series of radiating paths tramped deep in the

snow were smaller bunk-houses and, luxury of luxuries, a bath house with a water heater, tank and shower. The whole place was sheltered among the trees and hard to find, for it was half-buried beneath the snow.

This picture was animated by several interesting people. There was Jim Boyce, who was a fascinated spectator of my skiing during the first two or three pages of this book. He had worn skis for the first time in his life a couple of seasons back, but now he managed very well. There was a chubby little American from Minneapolis who kept up a delightful line of banter, and his wife who was about the nicest thing I've met in a long time; there was a pretty girl from Calgary, and a thin, red-haired, pleasant young man from the same city named Art.

We sprawled along the long dining-table at one end of the room and gossiped—about the ski-races at Banff, about the weather, and about what we might do the next day; and Dan, the cook, clambered over us and set the table in complete calm and good humour. At last he'd announce: "Grub's ready, folks, come and get it." And then we'd banquet, western style.

On the evening of the second day others arrived. There was Victor Kutchera, an Austrian ski and climbing guide who trained many of the Banff boys to ski; a pleasant couple from Vancouver, and two pretty girls who had been on the ski-car east-bound; and Rupert Edwards, "one of the boys from Banff."

He was an unobtrusive young man, this "Rupe" Edwards, and he said little. It was a pity, for he had a story to tell. I think it illustrates my ideas on ski-pioneering. He had been on skis to the Columbia ice-fields.

Straddling the Continental Divide in the Rockies, this is the largest mass of ice in the world south of the Arctic Circle, and from it flow waters that find their way into the Pacific, the Arctic, the Atlantic, Hudson's Bay, and, I think, the Gulf of Mexico. I've glimpsed it myself from the Castleguard meadows when I was lucky enough to join with the Rt. Hon. L. S. Amery in making the first ascent of Mount Amery in that neighbourhood.

To reach it in summer is child's play. Pack-horses carry all the equipment and food. But "Rube" had been there in winter.

He was one of three, Clifford White and A. L. Weaver of Banff were the others, who skied from Lake Louise station to the ice-fields and back in March, 1933. The trip was not epic, not the first of its kind; the three-hundred-mile trek on skis between Jasper and Louise had been made a couple of times already by westerners; the ice-fields had been visited twice in winter. The point to me is that they did it for fun, and without the backing of any outside "pioneer."

The account of it I've picked up in a back number of the Canadian Ski Year Book, written by Weaver. There are bits that should interest you. I'll quote them.

As only a small quantity of food was cached en route, each skier had to back-pack about fifty pounds to start with. This included a light tent and ground-sheet, a glacier rope and axe, sleeping-bags, a spirit-stove and fuel, and ninety pounds of food between them. They started north from Lake Louise by way of Skoki because part of the route by that much longer detour had never been traversed on skis.

"Cutting across to the Pipestone River, we jumped a large bull moose. Packs were dropped and Edwards and I (Weaver) pushed in to corner it, while White set his camera. The advantage was all with the skiers for the moose had heavy going in the belly-deep snow. Within five minutes the animal was cornered—and on the fight. Backed under the protection of a big tree he defied the three humans who ran on top of the snow and snorted his contempt of them. In his efforts to get within good camera range White nearly came to grief when the moose charged, and being without ski-poles could barely out-distance the infuriated beast. However, the moose wouldn't leave his fort very far and, after putting White to flight, returned to get his wind. Several exposures were taken and the party proceeded, leaving the moose with the feeling that he had won the day."

They made the first crossing of dangerous Molar Pass from the Pipestone back into the upper Bow Valley, spent the nights in empty park rangers' cabins where possible, and in six days they had plodded over Bow summit, descended to the Saskatchewan at its junction with the Alexandra, and followed the North Fork round the flank of Mount Saskatchewan. The distance was over ninety miles from their starting-point. The snow amongst the trees was heavy, but in the open it was better. The temperatures ranged from thirty-two below zero Fahrenheit to a few degrees above. At last they reached the final ridge on the threshold of the ice-fields.

"Below us was the tongue of the great Saskatchewan glacier which, rising steadily, was silhouetted against an angry cloud-banked sky that the setting sun shot with yellow and orange light. Between Mounts Castleguard and Athabaska the wind was whipping the snow down on to the glacier where it was carried along like dust before a great giant's broom. Beyond that sun-shot horizon lay our goal, a desert of snow and ice, devoid of shelter; a place of sudden storm and burning brightness; a high valley of ice built up for centuries between two magnificent mountain ranges, with mighty glaciers escaping from the awful pressure, projecting forth between the mountains . . . a magic place, but little known and only touched in winter; a beckoning area of mystery for which we had toiled so many miles. . . ."

They camped that night near the edge of the glacier. It was then fourteen below zero. "A wind was blowing and getting into bed unfrozen was accomplished by numerous twists and turns which left no portions exposed to the mercy of the cold for many seconds. The night's sleep was more a nightmare than a sleep as we spent most of the night trying to keep our feet from freezing, though White, being wiser, kept his moccasins on and stood the ordeal in fairly good shape."

It was twenty-four below the next morning, "but after an hour we were all thoroughly warmed up. . . . About eleven o'clock a high wind was funnelled over the glacier and came whooping along, carrying snow with it, and we faced into it with parka hoods up and extra mittens on, the wind cutting our faces like a knife." Late in the afternoon they reached a ridge, 11,000 feet in altitude, that gave them a splendid view over the fields.

"The shifting winds exposed to view a mountain panorama of this vast, icy desert. Off to the south, perhaps six miles away, but seemingly a stone's throw, Mount Bryce (11,507) stood out, one of the most glorious of all these gorgeous peaks. Mount Castle-guard (10,096), closer still, but still at least a mile away, seemed dwarfed by the high altitude from which it was viewed; while Mount Athabaska (11,452) seemed not a mountain at all, but a pile of snow.

"To the north and close, in fact we were nearly at its summit, sprawled the Snow Dome (11,340), topographical centre of the fields. And looking west the monarch of all these peaks, Mount Columbia (12,294), the second highest peak in the Canadian Rockies, stood boldly out against the setting sun. To the southwest ran a range of mountains, the names of which none of us could call to mind, and it was far too cold to handle maps."

But conditions were unfavourable and unpromising and they decided to forgo a longer stay on the inviting ice-fields. It was necessary to cross several dangerous crevasses in the dusk in returning.

"White was in the lead, Edwards next and I last. White's ski-tail broke through the snow and Edwards, close behind, turned aside from the broken snow. Suddenly the snow gave way and he was suspended from his elbows, his skis dangling in space and looking down for many feet into a huge crevasse. No time was lost in rescuing him, and we all took a few minutes off to get back to normal, while to add to the eeriness of the situation a huge ice-fall came roaring and plunging down the Snow Dome to land with a shattering crash on the glacier.

"Decidedly the glacier was unsafe, so to choose the lesser of the two evils we went along the wall of Athabaska. Here ice-falls had landed and the crushed ice was filled with drifted snow, making a rough but safe path so far as crevasses were concerned. But overhead hung suspended tons upon hundreds of tons of ice. For nearly half a mile this dangerous route was followed, and no time was lost as we sped under the overhanging menace. . . ."

By three in the morning they had reached the cabin they sought for shelter, had cooked a meal and crawled into their bags.

After breakfast at nine they had a cupful of porridge left. There could be no waiting to rest up. They had to continue on to where they had cached supplies and equipment at Graveyard Flats.

From there on, however, the last sixty or seventy miles, wrote Weaver, were pretty much of a picnic. They made a return traverse over Molar Pass, thus crossing it in both directions, just to drop in on their friends at Skoki camp, and then hit the home trail towards Louise.

I wish I could remember more of Edwards, and I wish I had known of the trip he made, just for the fun of it. It is always interesting to see a man who has hung over a crevasse with only two friends to help him, and 150 odd miles between them and civilization.

At Skoki my anxious alter ego was established as my constant companion. He had been psychologically resurrected when I was frightened on skis for the first time in several years at Norquay above Banff; but as I followed my new friends at Skoki up into the grey uncertainty of my first morning of high alpine skiing, he fell into pace beside me, and followed me thereafter like a shadow.

"Look how high those mountains are," he'd be pointing out unnecessarily to me as I toiled up the track broken by Jim Boyce in the deep snow. "This is a very steep slope," he'd remark comfortingly as we traversed a shoulder high above the tree-line. Then, after an hour's climbing: "See how high you are now. It makes you dizzy, doesn't it?"

But if he was diabolical when I climbed, if he taunted me into hysterical falls and plunges when, as Jim also said, I'd reappear fifty feet farther on, he was also generous in his praise if I succeeded.

"That was marvellous, wasn't it?" he'd agree with me at the end of a long run, just as if he'd done it all himself. "You did well, your knees are knocking together now, but you did well. In fact you are wonderful."

And as he'd pat me invisibly on the back I'd do a round-about jump on my skis and head enthusiastically back up the slope.

I was introduced to what I call the High Country by easy stages visually as well as physically. My first morning of skiing was in a flat, grey light, broken by moments of brightness. A heavy sky slid by, dusting the heavily laden trees by the camp with still more snow, but showing gaps between the clouds that gave promise of better weather to come.

When we had climbed towards Deception Pass, over which I had come the night before, and had made a partial ascent up the flank of a small summit by the pass, the visibility across Skoki Valley was poor. The falling snow obscured the scenery like mist, but when there came a pause it would dissipate, and there would be glimpses of the giants about me and of the ranges bordering the valley that were almost more thrilling than an unobstructed view could have been of the whole panorama.

I was making my acquaintance with a world I should learn to love passionately, a world with which I was already infatuated in anticipation. It was a world of simple elements: the sky, the mountains and the snow. Trees dropped away until they were a confused blur that filled the floor of the valleys; then came the open sweeps, the towering cliffs, and the jagged horizons of this sublime Upper World. When man was discovered in it he seemed like an insect interloper.

As I watched the figure of Art, my red-haired friend from Calgary, climb enterprisingly high above me on the afternoon of that first day, the insignificance of man seemed to be thrown into relief.

"That gives me the willies," I said to the chubby little man from Minneapolis who was near me as I looked up at the speck that stood out against the sky on the crest of a ridge.

My neighbour was a cautious skier, and he climbed slowly. I found later that he had an injured knee, that he was alive, thanks to modern medical treatment and would be finished if it were stopped, and that he had made the two hundred odd mile trip into the wilderness from Jasper to the Columbia ice-fields and back. But none of that information came from him. He would just chuckle and pull the legs of the guides, and produce things for which he said he had no need. For instance, my ears had been cold and he gave me a black head-band that I still have. He had dozens of them, he said, dozens.

As I was speaking he was looking up at Art speculatively. "I'll just stick round a bit and get my wind," he remarked, as I panted and puffed beside him, leaning on my ski-poles. "You must be tired now. You've done a lot for the first day. If you follow our tracks you'll run back to camp in a few minutes. . . ."

So after a pause I headed gingerly down-grade towards camp, and the little man stayed behind, to get his breath—and to keep an eye on Art.

That evening in the main cabin our numbers were increased by Victor Kutchera the guide, by the four people from Vancouver, and Rupert Edwards. Vic arrived with his boots frozen. The leather sounded like hardwood when he rapped it with his knuckles, and he said it helped insulate his feet. There was talk about the ski-races at Banff, a later stage of which the new-comers had seen, and about avalanches, which were apparently something that should be avoided in the mountains.

I wondered, as I crawled into my sleeping-bag that night, just what they were and whether I would ever be lucky enough to see one.

In the morning Vic, Art and my friend from Minneapolis started up through the big timber behind the camp to make a morning tour along the slope of Skoki mountain. I was late in getting ready, but impatient to follow, and I hit their trail after they had been gone about a quarter of an hour. Jim Boyce and one of the girls from Vancouver started after me a few minutes later.

The trail zigzagged up through the deep snow for several hundred feet, and then began a long ascending traverse towards the tree-line. At first the trees were lofty and heavy-trunked. It was virgin timber here, never damaged by lumbering or fire, and the great pines that marched triumphantly up the steep slope were almost as overpowering as the mountains themselves. Then the pines gave way to spruce and junipers, and the skeletons of larch, and after three-quarters of an hour I had followed the ski-tracks of my friends to far above the trees. I could look down into Skoki Valley, where the camp was completely hidden, and towards Deception Pass and Fossil and Ptarmigan peaks in the neighbourhood I had visited the day before.

There was a steady breeze blowing in my face, and as my route climbed higher along the slope of the mountain and rounded a shoulder it was uncomfortably cold. The snow higher up was no longer deep, but hard under my skis and blown into a wave-marked surface. At one point the wind had exposed the jagged rock and debris that slipped down in the summer from the cliffs above, and I took off my skis and carried them over this portion as I observed from the trail the others in the lead had done. When their footsteps led back on to the snow again, it was hard to see the marks at first, so firm was the surface, and I continued on foot round a shoulder of the slope.

I was feeling lonely now for I had seen no one for an hour, had not been able to catch up to those in front nor yet had been overtaken. The landscape began so very far below me and swept up the slope to cliffs so very far above. The valleys and ranges, that were aligned in vast vistas converging towards me, were designed on such a grand scale. It would be a relief to see someone.

My skis were cutting into my collar-bone as I carried them. . . . I would put them down and wait for the two behind. I thrust them into the hard snow so they stood upright and looked about me. If I continued a little I should see more of the foreground of the landscape, perhaps catch sight of the skiers ahead. So I tramped ahead on foot and topped the sloping crest ahead.

Then I stopped amazed. There was a broad open sweep of snow slope slanting gently down to the forest far below at the left. A hundred yards ahead of me the surface of the snow was broken. A great area seemed to have dropped away and slid down upon itself. I could see where the upper crust of the snow had slumped and was patterned by a series of jagged horizontal cracks. Below it the snow was jumbled in a great mass of blocks and fragments that spread out until it had come to rest.

This was very interesting. This must be one of the forms of avalanche that had been discussed in camp the night before. Had the others seen it, I wondered?

Then I noticed the tracks. They separated from being a single track, where they followed the leader in climbing and broke up into three distinct tracks as they headed downward. Here was a fine open slope of hard snow ideal for turning; and each skier would choose his own course, and swing back and forth across the slope as often as he wished.

But the tracks as they divided disappeared into the area of broken snow. Then the slide must have occurred after they passed.

If they had gone on, however, where were they? I looked quickly over the landscape ahead. I could see for several miles, and there were no figures in sight above the tree-line. Moreover, their tracks did not emerge at the far side.

My heart jumped suddenly inside me. Had they been caught in the avalanche? It was said they were dangerous. I remembered people got killed by them.

I put my hands to my mouth and called.

"Hul . . .l . . . l . . . oooo." The sound seemed to lose itself in space. There was no echo back, no answering cry, no sign of movement.

Then I gasped with relief for I saw, to the left far down the slope, where the ski-tracks emerged from the area of broken snow. The avalanche then must have happened after they had gone.

But I looked sharply. There were only two ski-tracks. They converged into a single trail and headed back in the direction from which I had come.

I called again, and still there was no answer. Then I began a frantic scramble back along my route. I passed my skis and left them untouched. I was due to see Jim Boyce who was following me any minute. I could have wept with joy when I saw him making his way with the Vancouver girl across the rocky shoulder.

I shouted to him: had he seen the others: there was something funny in the snow ahead: it looked like an avalanche.

He hurried forward, carrying his skis. Then he stopped, looked down the slope, called and waved. Yes, he could see the others: Kutchera and one other. They were far down the slope, but not out of ear-shot.

Had they seen a snow slide? No? Where was the third man? Where was Art?

Faintly the reply came: he was just behind them somewhere. He had gone back to take another down-hill run.

But I knew better. I had seen from above the trail behind them. And there had been no sign of Art, only the snow slide.

Kutchera started running back over the hard snow and occasionally plunging through with one foot. If there is danger of avalanche, I was to learn later, and you must cross a slope, it is less dangerous if you traverse it on foot.

Boyce and I ran back to the crest overlooking the avalanche. We shouted with relief. There was Art fixing his skis or something at the edge of the broken snow far below.

He waved to us. He was safe.

Boyce went back to take the others back to camp, and I skied down and joined Kutchera. The slope was hard and curiously hollow in its sound as I slewed across it; but it was a gentle enough incline, and it seemed queer that it should slide or be dangerous.

Together Kutchera and I reached Art where he was poking about among the blocks of snow.

What had happened? Was he all right?

Art looked white and subdued. He was looking for one of his ski-poles, he said. It had disappeared. He turned over a few of the big blocks of snow with an effort and fished about with his remaining stick, but there was nothing to be found.

Oh, yes, he said, he had been caught in the avalanche. See, his trousers had been torn badly where he was dragged down against some out-cropping rocks.

Gradually the story took shape.

He had decided to go back for a second run over the slope the three had found so interesting, and the two others had gone ahead. Then, the one minute that morning that the party was separated and he was alone, the accident had happened.

He had been tramping diagonally upward when he felt the snow give slightly. "Going Wooff," they called it. Cracks appeared across the slope above him and beneath his feet, tiny cracks, but he knew what had happened. He remembered in a flash what Kutchera had told him to do if he got caught in an avalanche: loosen your bindings.

He reached down and plucked one binding loose. It was an arrangement with a catch on the ski ahead of the toe-iron, and one gesture would do it. There was not time for him to reach the other.

Then he didn't know what was happening. He seemed to be engulfed, smothered by the snow, turned, tumbled and twisted this way and that. The snow crushed down upon him and he felt himself being dragged against some rocks. He speculated then as to how long it would be before he was found; he knew he was lost, and yet he was detached.

In a few seconds that seemed an eternity the snow came to a rest. His head was at the surface and one arm was free. He lay still for a time.

Then I had appeared on the sky-line far above him and had called. He waved one arm, but I did not see him. Then I had disappeared. He worked himself free and found one ski and a ski-stick. The other ski was still clamped to his boot, and he had to undo the binding to get it clear.

Kutchera scrambled about the snow, weighing the blocks in his arms, looking up the slope from whence it had come, questioning, explaining, scolding, comforting and gradually easing some of the tension that must have existed in Art's mind.

He said that it was a wind slab avalanche, and that the summer slope or natural slope of the mountain at that point must have been concave and quite steep higher up. Then the snow had been driven against it by the prevailing wind, and a new and almost convex surface had been formed during the winter.

Sliding down it on skis might not jar the structure, but the weight and movement of the climbing skier had been enough to break the slight arch and tension of the snow. The sustaining balance was broken, the snow dropped down the steeper internal slope, and the whole mass slid down and piled up upon itself at the bottom.

He drew little diagrams in the snow to illustrate his point, said this was the most dangerous of all forms of avalanche and the most difficult to detect because the visible slope mattered little. He pointed out the proper points to probe first for a body; observed that had Art been buried it might have taken many hours to find him.

He was philosophical: "You must think of this as another birthday. You have been born again. Five minutes ago, and you might have been finished. Your life begins again."

As he talked I remembered a little of other forms of avalanche discussed the night before. There were some things a skier in the east would never see. To me, they had been something abstract and as unlikely as an earthquake . . . until I had this vicarious adventure with one.

I know them now as a danger that need never prevent one from skiing in alpine country, but only a danger that must be guarded against when you are there. They are predictable as much as weather is predictable; but whereas you don't have to take shelter until it starts to rain heavily, you must be well out of reach before a slope starts to avalanche.

There were, Kutchera had told us, avalanches of wet snow and of dry snow. They are the surface or even the whole body of snow slipping down a slope when a change in temperature, a movement or even a sound will break the structure supporting the snow. It may only be an inch, a fraction of an inch over the surface; but when it covers a few acres, funnels down a gully and pours like a waterfall onto another slope below, the ultimate and cumulative effect can be devastating. A wind is sometimes set up by the cascading, sliding snow that lays waste trees by the side of the avalanche as it carves its way into the forests of the lower slope. Sometimes the snow will push its way across the flat and up the opposite slope.

It was this variety of snow-slide that made the early days of the railway in the Rockies so hazardous, but that was now less threatening with tunnels and snow-sheds, and steel equipment.

As we started skiing back towards camp, Kutchera recounted several anecdotes about avalanches. I could hear the shaken Art commenting in monosyllables.

"Yes," he would say occasionally, or, "No." The yarns didn't call for much else.

Vic was an Austrian and one of the most expert skiers and most experienced guides in the Rockies. He had seen a lot of avalanches and told us how they wiped out alpine villages, how people were buried by them but how they sometimes lived, how they were found with rods, and how some had lucky escapes.

He told the story of the man who was buried deep in a light snow-avalanche and who was able to work in the darkness with his arms and to clear a space before his face so he could breathe properly. But he couldn't tell whether he was upside down or, if he was to dig, in what direction he should begin. He got his watch from his pocket and hung it by the chain. He then discovered by this plumb-line that he was on his side, and he knew which way he should dig to escape. He worked his way to the surface and was saved.

But his yarns, as we skied along, Art with one pole, were not all as encouraging. He explained how he had dug many bodies out from avalanches. There had been nineteen in all, I think he said.

Some of them had been in a terrible state. They would be twisted and broken by the snow . . . particularly with windslab avalanches like the one Art was in . . . which showed how important it was to get free of one's skis so they couldn't twist one's legs. He had seen porters with their necks broken by their pack-boards.

"The pressure of the snow usually made them vomit," said Victor. "It was horrible."

I could hear Art grunting occasionally.

"Oh," was all he replied to that anecdote.

Men Against McKinley

By BRIAN MEREDITH

FOR A WRITER I have a most unsatisfactory memory. Time and again I am faced by a situation when I think: I must remember every word of this, every inflexion, every detail: this is history, this is tremendous. But thus excited my mind folds up into a tight resisting mass, and only a few irrelevant pictures are left upon the surface of it.

At least that is so with phrases and dialogue, which makes me chary of quoting conversations unless I am very sure. But I do remember, selfishly and egotistically, the impressions that the event or the conversation I hear conjures up in my own mind, I remember the emotions invoked; and however inadequate, my recollection of Strom's account of the climb of Mount McKinley is a jumble of irrelevant fragments I shall never forget.

Mount McKinley in Alaska is the highest peak on the North American continent, twenty thousand odd feet. In its altitude above sea-level it is not the highest in the world; but in magnitude, in the height of the summit from the base and surrounding terrain, it is one of the giants.

The greatest mountain in the world, the biggest, is probably adjacent Mount Logan that forms the corner-post between Alaska and Canada's Yukon. The latter towers head and shoulders up above the St. Elias range, which is in itself roughly equal to Switzerland in extent.

So McKinley is a giant in a land of giants, an inaccessible mountain not far on the map from the Arctic Circle, a challenge to every mountaineer. Its fascination, its drawing power, is difficult to explain to those who have never climbed and who never want to climb. To attempt to reach its summit, to reach the

From "Escape on Skis."

summit of any high mountain, seems madness—and it is. Climbers try and explain away their fixation on an artistic or scientific or physical basis; but the truth is that they are just a little queer about mountains, and they climb them just for the fun of it.

If you've never done much on your own two feet you couldn't understand. But you don't need to. The men fling themselves against the heights, that some of them reach their objective, and some of them disappear, never to return. There's a world of mystery and adventure in that alone. What happens to them? What happens to the aeroplanes that head out to sea and are never seen again? There must be a special heaven set aside for souls with this kind of courage.

What happened to Irving and Mallory on Everest, to others like them on other peaks? It's nice to think of them plugging always onwards towards their goal, always young and fair as the snow and the cold will keep them, always fighting through the blizzard, just for fun.

When climbers disappear or are killed, it is, of course, tragic; but I don't think many of them would want to finish any other way. They belong to a breed that wants to die with its boots on, and death, if they are daring climbers, has been their companion so long that they are not likely afraid when it strikes for the last time. It's a tragic comedy, and I must confess I am always susceptible enough to be moved by it.

McKinley was first seen by Captain Cook in his explorations of the coast in the eighteenth century, first named forty years ago, first climbed in 1913 by a party led by Archdeacon Stuck. By a coincidence interesting to me I had met Belmore Brown who aided in the early attempts on the peak, and whose book gave inspiration and data sufficient for the second climb in which Strom was involved in 1932. The former is an artist who, to me, has led an almost ideal life. He has been able to live and paint with his family in the heart of the mountains he loved so well; and his summers are spent trekking through them with his own pack-train.

Browne describes the mountain as "formed by a gigantic mass of granite forced upwards through the stratum of slate that overlaid it. On many of the lower peaks close to the mountain this stratum of slate is still in position, giving them a strange, black-capped appearance. The granite is of a light tan colour, and at a distance its grim cliffs take on a pinkish hue which gives the mountain a delicate atmospheric appearance that differentiates it from all others, and stamps it with a beauty and grandeur of its own."

He must have come to know it intimately for he took part in expeditions to it in 1906, '10 and '12. He shared over a hundred camps on the glaciers of the mountain with his friend Professor Parker. He went in summer and in winter with pack-horse and dog-sled: he and his companions, after failure and disappointment and many narrow escapes, deserved to win. But their victory fell short of the final summit by five minutes; the weather that last time defeated them twice. To their successors the next year went the technical victory.

The latter deserve great credit because their route was barred by a new hazard in the form of a ridge broken by a cataclysm a few days after the descent of Browne's party, and they had to cut their way through a maze of ice-blocks.

Browne's description of the earthquake provides an interesting background. Resting in their base camp on the Clearwater one evening Brown observed that ". . . the sky was a sickly green colour, and that the air seemed heavy and lifeless. . . . It reminded me of sinister skies that I had seen on the eastern sea-coast before heavy storms and I turned to Aten and said, that if I were on a boat I would overhaul the ground tackle and see that everything was snug because it looked like 'dirty weather.'

"The words were scarcely out of my mouth before a deep rumbling came from the Alaskan Range. I can only compare its sound to thunder, but it had a deep hollow quality that was unlike thunder, a sinister suggestion of overwhelming power that was terrifying. I remember as I looked the Alaskan Range melted into mist, and that the mountains were bellowing, that Aten was yelling something I could not understand, and that the valley above us had turned white.

"And then the earth began to heave and roll, and I forgot everything but the desire to stay upright. In front of me a boulder . . . turned, broke loose from the earth and moved several feet . . . then came the crash of our falling caches, followed by another muffled crash as the front of our hill slid into the creek, and a lake nearby boiled as if it were hot. The mossy surfaces on the hills were opening all around us, and the cracks filled with liquid mud.

"Then suddenly everything was still.

"We stood up, dazed, and looked about. The Alaskan Range was still wrapped in a haze of avalanche dust, and the country far and near was scarred, and stripped of vegetation where the earth had slid. Our dogs had fled at the beginning of the quake, and we could hear them whimpering and running about the willows. . . .

"While we were restoring order out of chaos an awe-inspiring sight met our eyes. Just east of Mount McKinley stood a magnificent 12,000-foot peak. It was somewhat like the Matterhorn in shape, and formed the culminating pinnacle in a range some six miles in length . . . and we saw that the whole extent of its western flank was avalanching.

"I have never seen a sight of such overpowering grandeur. The avalanche seemed to stretch along the range for a distance of several miles, like a huge wave; and like a huge wave it seemed to poise for an instant before it plunged downward on to the ice-fields thousands of feet below. The mountain was about ten miles away and we waited breathlessly until the terrific thunder of the falling mass boomed and rumbled among the mountains.

"Beyond the range that rimmed our valley a great white cloud began to rise. As it came into view and began to obscure the range we could almost check off its growth as it billowed upward with startling rapidity—two—three—four thousand feet—until it hung like a huge opaque wall against the main range. And then it fell, the range that rimmed our valley was blotted out and the grave wave of avalanche debris came rushing down our valley.

"We were already at work, strengthening our tent in frantic haste. We knew that the cloud was advancing at a rate close to sixty miles an hour and that we did not have much time to spare. With boulders to hold the bottom and tautened guy-ropes we made the tent as solid as possible and got inside before the cloud struck us. The tent held fast, but after the 'wullies' passed, the ground was spangled with ice-dust that only a few minutes before had formed the icy covering of a peak ten miles away. . . ."

Remember this earthquake, and the avalanches. Their thunder makes a macabre accompaniment for the tale that follows, though they are not the villains of the piece. The greatest and most relentless enemy was the cold, the bitter cold of the latitude and the altitude, cold that made each achievement heroic, each risk the greater.

The history of the district is brightened by an ancient controversy over a claim made by a doctor, who subsequently discovered the North Pole—to his own satisfaction—that he had climbed Mount McKinley. The resourceful doctor had been on the 1906 Expedition, but had remained behind with one other, and claimed to have made the climb in circumstances that his former companions knew to be physically impossible. The 1910 Expedition did some amusing detective work and were able to duplicate fake photographs taken by the famous doctor, and prove him unquestionably to be wrong.

Another climb over which some argument continues was made in 1910 by four "sourdoughs"—old-timers—one of whom had the delightful name of McGonigle, who carried a flag-pole with them and are supposed to have set it up on the North Peak. It was not found by Strom's friends.

But stranger things have happened. I remember a yarn told at the annual camp of the Canadian Alpine Club at Roger's Pass in '29, of the "first ascent" of Mount Sir Donald nearby. The climbers rejoiced over their victory until one of them happened to lean back and place his hand for support in a shallow pool of water. It fell on a railway spike.

Years later he told of the incident in a lecture, and a man present said he had been one of a party of railway workers who had made the climb one Sunday during the construction of the railway over Roger's Pass.

Strom's story begins with his first sight of McKinley on a visit to Alaska, and of his description of it to his friend Alfred Lindley, a Minneapolis lawyer, who had been with him skiing two seasons at Assiniboine and once on a visit to the Columbia ice-fields. Lindley sounded like a good fellow to me, and from his accounts of the trip I read subsequently in alpine journals the impression is strengthened. Certainly he was enterprising, for he visited Alaska himself to investigate, and took a plane to fly around the mountain to have a proper look at it.

The idea was that, though their experience of high-alpine climbing was relatively limited or conventional, their knowledge of skiing was considerable; and that skis should be a great aid in attempting that particular ascent. They were. They facilitated the downhill parts of relaying of equipment, and speeded reconnaissance work; and I am surprised that ski-journals have not taken greater note, for, as the first ascent of North America's great mountain in which skis were used, it is of historic significance.

There are quaint jealousies among older and more conservative climbers against admitting skiing into the sacred precincts, and there have been schisms comparable to the divisions of religions over details of dogma and over arguments as to the number of angels that could be balanced on the point of a needle. Skis from a purely mountaineering viewpoint have made much possible. They have shortened the time interval in descending retreats over snows and glaciers; they have provided safer means of crossing dangerous snow-bridges; they have made climbing a year-round sport and added hundreds of exciting winter ascents and first ascents to the annals of the sport; they have given it new life and new blood.

Strom went on to tell of the co-operation of the Alaska Park authorities, of the preparations for the climb, and of the addition of the park superintendent, Harry Leik, and an experienced ranger, Grant Pearson, to the party.

The latter stood out as a personality from the narrative. He seemed to be a sort of Donald Duck to the outfit; swearing, humorous, plucky to the last and taking the most terrific punishment as a matter of course.

He fell on the summit, slid down five hundred feet over the glazed slanting surface of the mountain, and was just saved by loose snow from continuing on into eternity. He wounded his arm with his ice-axe, lost his mitts, his hands were badly frost-bitten, his nose was smashed, and his face lacerated.

But later Lindley's account mentions Pearson, philosophically remarking that they had had no hardships yet, for had they not always had enough to eat and a sleeping-bag at night. He had never done such climbing before, but he took it all in his stride. Towards the end, at a time of great strain and anxiety, he slipped and fell into a crevasse and was hauled out with difficulty. He suffered most of the hard luck, and seemed to have grit enough for the lot of them. He had "guts," though there must have been a lot of them in the neighbourhood at that time.

Starting on April 1st they packed in about two thousand pounds of equipment by dog-sled from a point on the Alaska railroad one hundred miles to their base camp on the Clearwater, within a few yards of the camp site used by Browne and from which he had watched the earthquake. Three-fifths of the load was their own, two-fifths represented cosmic ray apparatus being taken in to be cached at the head of the Muldrow Glacier, part way up the mountain. This latter equipment was for another expedition, whose leader, Carpe, had been invited previously to join their party, which was to combine scientific observations with mountaineering. Cosmic rays are something I can no more comprehend than the rotation of the galaxy; but they are emanations supposed to be more frequent at that altitude and at that proximity to the earth's magnetic pole than elsewhere; though what that proves I know not.

Part of this other party was being brought in by aeroplane; and Strom's had the queer experience later of looking down from 15,000 feet upon an aeroplane buzzing above the surface of a glacier at about 6,000 feet, and seeming to be an angry red hornet crawling up on the very surface of the snow itself. It was then dropping supplies to two men, Carpe and Koven, who had already been landed, and who had set up camp on the glacier, preparatory to relaying supplies to a higher camp.

Little pictures suggested by his story stand out clearly in my mind, and the sight and sound of this aeroplane is one of them.

Another was the moment when the old thermometer was found. This recorded the maximum and minimum temperatures reached during the last nineteen years since the instrument had been left there by Stuck's party. It was in a wooden case wedged between two rocks kept clear by the wind. The minimum needle had sunk into the bulb, past the 95 degree below zero (Fahrenheit) mark on the scale. It must have fallen to a hundred degrees or more at that point, 15,000 feet in altitude. The instrument was later tested and found to function accurately.

But to achieve McKinley they had to work their dog-teams up over the Muldrow Glacier, a dangerous adventure. There were many hidden traps, and the dogs or the sled or the men were constantly breaking through and hanging suspended over crevasses in the ice that may have been hundreds of feet deep. A few of these were visible and could be detoured, but for the most part the route had to be marked by upright willow-wands so it could be followed on the return. To forget, to lose the way back over this treacherous area, would mean almost certain death.

When on the return over this part, blinded by driving snow, exhausted by forty hours of tramping under sixty-pound packs with no sleep, Strom put out his hand in the grey murk and felt one of these slender willow-wands, the gesture seemed miraculous. Almost by instinct he had picked up the thread that would lead them through the deadly labyrinth; and it probably saved the lives of the party. But life and death depend on so many small elements at such times that only unfaltering courage, an experienced wisdom, and a great store of good luck can bring men through. There was luck abroad on McKinley that week. Good luck and bad: theirs was the good.

They cached the cosmic ray recording equipment, where it was found safely soon after by Carpe and his friend Koven, sent back the dog-teams, and continued on up their mountain. From here everything had to be back-packed, and the narrative becomes bewildering to the layman in the maze of Camp I—Camp II, in the strange geography of the mountain, and in the uncertainty of unfamiliar alpine phrases.

Skis that had helped much in traversing the dangerous glacier, speeded the relay of supplies from one camp to another. The party had to consolidate itself stage by stage, like an army advancing into an enemy country, always having food and shelter with them to tide over days of storm, always having a known line of retreat and extra supplies to fall back on. They would tramp slowly up, but, on their skis, they would go like hell on the return relay. Skis helped in reconnaissance, and after an hour or more in winning a ridge or col from which they could observe the lay of the land ahead, they would return to camp in a minute. Skiing is like that.

But skis after a point became useless. The snow was too hard and bumpy. They changed to oversized Alaskan moccasins, with many layers of socks, in-soles and felt slippers within, and iron crampons, which are long-pronged creepers giving a foothold on hard snow or rough ice. They had to cut steps, thousands of steps, some in the hard snow of the lower portion, some in the ice; and when the time came to return, weakened and close to exhaustion, there was the heartbreak of finding them obliterated by fresh wind-blown snow.

They worked up, inch by inch almost, in altitude, and established themselves between the twin peaks of McKinley. Packing as much as sixty pounds at that height was slow work, and the intense cold seemed to parch and further rarefy the air. It was twenty-five and thirty degrees below zero Fahrenheit most of the time, which at fifteen or twenty thousand feet is bitter cold indeed.

It was exhausting to climb, tiring to do the simplest things in camp. To turn over in their sleeping-bags sent their hearts pounding and gave them a sense of suffocation. " 'Pass me a knife,' the man beside you would say," Strom told us, "and you'd think: Damn you, you . . . ! And you'd reach slowly out for it and hand it to him as if it weighed pounds."

The climax did not come when they ascended the South Peak, struggling unsuccessfully to take photographs and got badly frostbitten hands in doing so, for it was over thirty below and a wind was blasting over the summit. Nor yet when plucky Pearson slipped and went plunging to what seemed, as they watched helpless, to be sure death. They did not use a rope for climbing the ridges to the peaks, for it would have hopelessly delayed the relaying of supplies: it was every man for himself.

Nor yet was the moment of triumph when they stood upon the top of the slightly lower North Peak. Perhaps to their story there is no fine climax, for the whole episode was too intense to allow for many peaks of excitement. Perhaps it is the knowledge of alarums without, of menacing thunder on the left, lingering on perhaps from the earthquake of twenty years before, that makes it impossible to provide a dramatic curtain to the sequence. Realities seldom arrange themselves in good theatrical sequence.

After a night's rest in the camp between the two peaks the party set out on the gruelling return journey in weather well below zero and in the teeth of a merciless gale. They made good progress during the day and decided to push on during the night without stopping. They knew the route and worked their way through the dim light, shovelling new steps where they found the old ones buried, and reaching Muldrow Glacier at dawn.

There they found the tents of the two climbers who had been dropped by plane to take observations with the cosmic ray apparatus and who were awaiting the rest of their party to join them from below. One of these men was Allen Carpe, thirty-seven, one of the most experienced and ablest of American climbers, perhaps the best, and Theodore Kovan, twenty-eight, of Jersey City.

The tents had been occupied, but were now deserted. Two days' snow-fall had accumulated. Strom had snaps and they seemed pathetic and lonely in the midst of the white waste of the glacier. The little camp, and the cosmic ray apparatus that was ticking mysteriously, was in good order. The diaries of the two men showed that they had been expecting their friends and had become anxious over their non-appearance. The last entry was two days before.

Worried over the whereabouts of the men, Strom's party continued down. After they had gone about a mile and a half over the glacier, and had descended about a thousand feet, they came upon the body of a man frozen in the snow. Lindley knew Carpe personally, and when they turned the figure over they knew it must be Koven. He had been injured, had started to struggle back towards camp, and had perished.

Nearby was a hole in the snow showing where the snow over a crevasse had given way. There were marks of skis side-stepping beside it, and a confusion of tracks that would indicate they had both fallen in, perhaps one in trying to rescue the other. The snow was too treacherous to permit them to examine the place closely, and they lacked the numbers and the strength and the ropes to allow for any risks being taken at that stage.

They called, but there was no sound in reply. The accident must have happened over forty-eight hours before.

They tried to move Koven's body on a sledge, but gave up after a time. The snow-bridges were too dangerous. Pearson had abandoned skis and, like a proper sourdough, resorted to his beloved snow-shoes; but he fell through despite them, and was wedged by his pack after he had fallen forty feet into a crevasse. He was recovered with difficulty; and soon Koven's body was wrapped in a tent and cached beside the upright sledge.

They had been driving on under sixty-pound packs for over thirty hours, remember, and this new turn to affairs threatened them with a like fate.

They went on, that afternoon and through the night, and because he could sometimes feel the hardness of their old track through the newly fallen blanket of snow, and because his instincts were good and luck was with them, Strom put out his hand and found the first of the willow wands. And so in storm and darkness they continued along the treacherous labyrinth over which they had so painstakingly picked their way a few days before.

At three in the morning they came upon the tent of the men whose arrival Carpe and Koven had awaited. There they found one man ill and another nursing him. A third had been sent back to find a non-existent telephone and to have an aeroplane sent in to help them, and was apparently lost.

They broke the news to them about their friends; but there was nothing more that could be done. They undertook to have a plane sent in when they reached Fairbanks. Then they skied on to their base camp, which they reached a couple of hours later.

Strom's yarn ended there. They were safe . . . they only had another hundred miles of ordinary skiing ahead of them.

And so the account of the second ascent of Mount McKinley is overshadowed by another tragic story. It would perhaps not be kind to set it out at great length here, though there has been much written about it in various journals; and not wise to speculate about it without being more intimately acquainted with the many facts.

There are so many ifs; and one of them of course is the fact that if an aeroplane had not been used, the accident might not have happened. It was because the two skiers, Carpe and Koven, had not become familiar with the dangerous detail of the glacier below them through having to achieve a route up it themselves, that they were trapped.

And yet, for all that, the aeroplanes brought out another bit of matter-of-fact courage that warms the heart. The pilots battled with danger and death as much as the climbers. The first machine landed on the upper glacier and dropped its passengers and their supplies. It was a risky business. The skis of the plane might sink deep in the snow or be caught and cause it to crash. The very snow might give way and reveal a crevasse. Landing and taking off at that altitude with lighter air had to be done at a hundred miles an hour. The first take-off attempt was a failure, and the pilot philosophically left his machine stranded, after folding back the wings single-handed so it wouldn't be damaged by the driving wind, and tramped back on his snow-shoes to get the help of his passengers to start up again. Mountains rose on every hand ten and fifteen thousand feet higher, winds and air currents were treacherous, clouds materialized in a few minutes, snow would fill the air. They rocked the machine so the skis broke loose from the snow, where they were frozen, and the pilot and one of the trio took off safely. Carpe and Koven remained.

"We don't often have a job like that to do," remarked the pilot when it was all over.

Subsequently, on the lower glacier a plane aided in transport and rescue work, twice axles were broken and the machine stranded. It all had to be done at a season when the spring break up was hitting the rivers about Fairbanks, and skis were useless. They seemed to be able to switch their machines from pontoons to skis and to wheels in short order. They would have to take off from snowless regions and land on glaciers where broad skis were the only means of support. They managed it by the fire department hosing the air-field at Fairbanks and making it so muddy that the skis would slither across it. They must have worked like beavers.

If McKinley belongs in the annals of skiing this other business is an honour to flying. But in Alaska and Northern Canada aeroplanes have been doing the most fantastically dangerous things for years, and getting away with it. It's been all in a day's work, and never for fame. There are some grand yarns to be told.

The end to this secondary story is, I think, in the dairies of the two men who died. Photographs they had taken were found and developed, and together with their notes they give an interesting impression of their last days. They did not live, as did Scott, with any premonition of death; and their memoranda is a human jumble of scientific data and homely detail.

Carpe, who wrote a delightful account of his climb of Mount Logan in 1925 that was published after his death, stuck pretty much to record of cosmic ray readings. His last note mentioned a ". . . soup made of chicken and thickened with oatmeal and boullion cubes. . . ."

Koven's was fuller. Five days before his death he wrote: "Had the finest ski run of my life back to camp, a continuous 25-minute slide through powder snow, interrupted by two sitzmarks in the least excusable places . . ."

He draws a picture of their little tent at four-thirty the next morning. . . . "Awoke very early as it began to blow badly. A. had to get up and prop the cosmic ray tent as it was sagging. From then on it kept getting worse by the minute. Soon we had to take both poles down. It seemed as though every moment everything would go roaring down the glacier. Then there would be brief intervals of calm, and we could hear the wind pounding over the ridges like a locomotive blowing steam. We lay in our sleeping-bags and held down the tent."

And the next day: "The wind had cut the snow away from everything hard. Ski-tracks were elevated several inches in the air. I wonder where the others are? Percy and Spad?"

And the next: "Skied down a ways to look for the boys but they are not yet past the ice fall." The last entry still speculated: "No sign of P. & S. yet."

In full his diary gave a nice glimpse of the man. He mentions being shown the mysteries of making cosmic ray readings by his friend, and of the temperature recorded by "Max and Minnie."

But I like that line: "Had the finest ski run of my life." They must have been happy there.

Perhaps the epitaph for the two should be: "We've just . . . skied down a ways to look for the boys. . . ."

Bobsleds Are Like That

By GEORGE CARROLL

NOT MANY MEN had ever beaten Kurt Borden at a game he really cared about—and especially at racing bobsleds.

Kurt had what Stephen Grant could only term, inadequately, a feeling for the sport. Uncanny judgment on the great curving ice walls; split-second control flashing around the hairpin turns; the ability to know what he was up to at all times—even when blinded by singing clouds of snow, and gasping for breath in a rush of wintry wind.

And now Kurt Borden was gone. Finished.

The news caught up with Stephen Grant in California where his law business had taken him briefly. It was one of those things for which he had been prepared—in a way. And yet it had all the force of a sudden blow when it finally came.

"AMERICAN SPORTSMAN LOST IN ACTION WITH RAF" was the headline that first riveted Stephen's attention. What followed was scant enough, and obviously censored under its London date-line.

That was about all they were willing to tell. Of course the local editor had dug into his files to supplement the brief cable with some notes on Borden's career. Socially prominent. Internationally known sportsman. Leading amateur golfer. Olympic bob-sled champion—

After a time when the sudden numbness had left his limbs, Stephen Grant threw the paper aside and took himself down to the quiet bar off the lobby of his hotel. There, confronting his favorite whisky, he let his mind flow back over the days that had

Permission from The Chicago Tribune-N. Y. News Syndicate, Inc.

been; over the places that he and Kurt Borden, and Tom Lang, too, had known together.

Chamonix—St. Moritz—Davos. There they were again as if it had been yesterday. Alpine sunlight streamed down on colorful little houses half-buried in the snow. Now the cheering crowds line the great breakneck run of Lake Placid. Now again, bands blare and the evil sign of the swastika fills the snow-laden skies above a place called Garmisch.

All these places—and others too—Kurt Borden had ruled in his day. If the big four-man sleds were racing, it was a safe bet that Kurt Borden was in it for all he was worth. Cutting the corners; risking his neck for a half second's advantage; using every bit of his uncanny skill to jockey five hundred pounds of bouncing, swaying wood and metal down a frozen mountain side.

And in those days it was a safe bet that Stephen Grant and Tom Lang were somewhere nearby, too. For most of what either of them knew about this maddest of all mad Winter sports, he had learned from Kurt. Most, not quite all. For the rest they had picked up on their own, the hard way. Stephen Grant, crouching low over the steering wheel; Tom Lang, bouncing around at the tail end of the sled, gloved hands glued to the brake handles. Finding the rest of their four-man crew wherever they could. But training them well.

Could it possibly be six—closer to seven—years since they had said good-by to all that? Since the day when he and Tom Lang had decided it was time to stop roaming around the world, time to buckle down to the real business of life?

In Stephen's case, when they had sold their sled, hung up their helmets, and carefully placed the last silver cup in the trophy case, the real business of life already included something more than the practice of law. It included Cynthia, Cynthia Gordon, who had been Mrs. Stephen Grant through a year of growing disillusionment.

So far as Cynthia was concerned, Stephen knew there were those who said he had put off the settling down process much too long. Fatally long. Well, time might still prove them right. Perhaps, Stephen reflected, these recurring misunderstandings, this almost chronic coolness that never quite flared into open hostility had had its beginnings in those days.

Was he fundamentally as stubborn, as set in his ways as Tom Lang hinted? Was that really the root of the trouble? Stephen Grant found it impossible to think so. Certainly he was firm and determined, once his mind was made up; a man who prided himself on arriving at his decisions by virtue of logic, rather than sentiment. Strange that Cynthia couldn't seem to understand it.

As for Tom Lang, obviously Tom was one of those soft men who could never say no to any woman; who made a point of humoring them. So it followed that, if his marriage to Cynthia seemed headed for the rocks, Stephen could look for little sympathy even from his closest friend. With Kurt Borden it might have been otherwise.

Two weeks later Stephen was back in his New York office. There was, among other things, a message from Tom Lang marked important. Stephen got him on the wire and they arranged to meet for lunch the following day.

When they had given their orders, Tom Lang could wait no longer.

"About Kurt," he began, his round, smooth-shaven face seeming older, more serious than Stephen had thought possible. "Maybe you've heard? The Olympic committee and the Lake Placid crowd are planning a memorial—gold cup or something. . . ." He hesitated.

"I'm on the committee."

He was eyeing Stephen closely. The latter nodded.

"Good. I'm all for it. Want my check now?"

But Tom Lang shook his head impatiently.

"That can wait. To tell the truth . . ." Again he seemed oddly hesitant. "To tell the truth, Steve, I've got something else in mind. A different kind of memorial. From you and me alone. The only kind Kurt would give a damn about. . . ." Tom Lang fussed with his cigaret.

Stephen Grant's long handsome face was noncommittal. "All right," he said. "Let's have it."

But after he had listened for long moments the narrow line of his lips grew tighter. He must not, he told himself, say yes to this wildest of wild schemes. Tom Lang was mad. But he, Stephen, must refuse to join him in his madness. Must not let this appeal to sentiment blind him to reality.

"It's an idea, Tom," Stephen Grant admitted finally, choosing his words carefully. "A great idea. But that's where it stops as far as I'm concerned."

And then seeing the sudden look of hurt that clouded Tom Lang's face: "Be reasonable, man. You know I haven't touched a bob-sled in over five years. I doubt if you have either. We'd be laughed off the mountain. And the Nationals—of all races."

This was Stephen Grant again, coldly, clearly logical. Fighting down an idea that simply failed to make sense. Thinking up all the sound reasons against it.

"Can you imagine how tickled Kurt would be? 'The old men,' as he used to call us, the Old Men coming back to win another one —for him? Not telling anybody else, the real reason. Keeping it to ourselves—"

"The time element alone makes it impossible." Stephen Grant was still arguing. But a new note, something akin to doubt seemed to have come into his voice. "That race is only four or five weeks away."

Tom Lang's voice dropped, took on a new note of intensity. "Look, Steve. All over Europe, all over the world, maybe, the young fellows, the kids like Kurt are going out to fight. Giving up everything they have. Putting their lives on the line, up there above the clouds—on the ocean—in the jungles. While you and I, and others like us sit behind our desks—go smugly about our business. . . ."

"I don't quite see . . ." Stephen Grant began, uncertainty in his voice. Yet, even as he said it, something deep down within him was accepting Tom Lang's idea. More than accepting it. Welcoming it; rationalizing it; working on it.

You've seen it in the news-reels without doubt. And perhaps you've been there, too. Stood in the snow and watched the big gaily painted sleds come thundering down the great icy slide at Placid, each with its quartet of madmen.

Figure five hundred pounds for the sleds—add something more for the crew of four. Half a ton of streamlined wood and metal, flesh and bones. Down they come. Roaring through the long steep straight-aways; rocketing up the high curving ice-walls; zooming around the hair-pin turns. Down they come. Down and down, in a welter of flying snow, gleaming metal, hunch-backed figures looking hardly human in their helmets and goggles; bouncing, swaying, slithering in a one long sustained flirtation with frozen disaster.

Bobsled galleries are like sports crowds the world over. They like to be in at the finish—the kill. Always you'll find the biggest crowds milling around the foot of the mountain. There they can watch the sleds come whipping around the ultimate perpendicular wall of ice above the finish-line. There the billowing plumes of snow explode skyward as the brakesman jams mightily on his saw-toothed gear to kill the wild, swaying momentum of eighty miles an hour. And there, finally, amid the blare of music, the crackle of flags, the calculations of the electric timer are posted high on the huge scoreboard. Quickly; indisputably; to the last hundredth of a second.

This is the bottom—the finish.

But far up the mountain, at the starting-line, things are different. Here the excitement, the suspense of a big race seem hidden beneath the surface, curtained over by the age-old silence of the high places. In this silence the crackling of a frost-tortured tree rings out like a rifle shot. A sudden burst of nervous laughter echoes across the intervening valleys.

Someone ploughed past Stephen Grant where he stood ankle deep in snow against an angle of the starter's shack.

"Nice going on that first heat, Steve. Not bad—for an old man!" This was Monahan, the wiry little Irishman who headed the local committee.

Stephen forced an answering grin.

"You'll eat those words yet," he promised over his shoulder.

Stephen Grant did not have any illusions about that first heat.

The trouble lay precisely where it had lain through weeks of practice. In the "Glacier." Even in the old days, this great curving wall of ice had been bad medicine for him. Now he couldn't seem to fathom it at all. Of course they had changed the thing since he had seen it last. "Re-engineered it," the officials said. Well, whatever they had done, it had been enough to throw him off badly.

It was that way in other places, too. Every bob-run he had ever driven had something of the sort. Some spot, a curve, an S-turn, even a stretch of straight-away which remained a puzzle forever.

Mental hazard, mostly. But one that could take disastrous toll of your driving if you let it.

The loudspeaker above Stephen's head sputtered into sudden articulateness. The second of the four racing heats was about to begin. The Number One sled was being called to the line.

Number One. That, Stephen told himself, would be the Frenchman, Charmoz. No one he needed to fear, judging by what he had seen so far. Nevertheless he watched the starting procedure with genuine interest. One thing about racing the big bob-sleds: you never knew when you might pick up something worthwhile even from the novices.

An official appeared from somewhere, climbed down into the trough at the head of the run. Stephen knew, without seeing, exactly what the man was about. He was bridging the run with a slender string whose breaking would start the electric timer at the foot of the mountain.

Stephen stamped his heavily-booted feet for added warmth, leaned his long frame against the starter's house. The Frenchman and his crew have eased their sled into the top of the run. Quickly they take their places beside it.

Slowly at first, but with increasing tempo, they bring their combined weight to bear against the sled's inertia. Now the sled moves—a little. Forward. Now back. Now forward again. Faster, and still faster.

Now a final push, harder, more sustained than anything yet. The big sled comes to life. It begins to move down the slope, picking up speed. On that instant it is hidden under an avalanche of flying helmets, parkas, heavy boots. Four husky men fling themselves into position on the thin cushions inches removed from the ice. The driver settles himself behind the black circle of the steering-wheel; the brakeman takes a firm grip on the iron handles on either side of him; the loudspeaker sets the echoes ringing across the mountains:

"They're off!—Charmoz driving."

To Stephen Grant, fighting to keep a grip on himself, refusing to admit a growing case of racing nerves, it seemed an interminable time before he heard his own name being called for the second heat.

But when the moment came and he went ploughing over to

join Tom Lang and the others he felt surer of himself than he had all morning. Poised. Ready to go. Only far back in his mind the "Glacier" was still flaunting its unanswerable challenge. But he would not think of that now. Not yet. Not until he had to.

A final checkup as he lined up beside the sled. Rangy Bill Albert grinning at his shoulder. Okay for that. Fenn, his number three man, a step behind. Then, finally, Tom Lang nodding encouragement from his place at the tail.

"All set? Let's go!"

And he took them down for the second time that day.

Took them snaking down the first steep straightaway; roaring around the slanting snowbank that was "shady"; pounding off at a tangent to take the punishing whip-lash of the "Pigstail."

Faster, faster, faster. Weaving, pounding, jolting down the tortuous mile-long course. Until nothing mattered but the whining song of the long steel runners, the gasping struggle for breath, the relentless, stabbing attack of the upflung ice.

It was a good run. And when that second heat was finished Stephen Grant was in undisputed possession of fourth place—no more than a shade away from the third.

But Tom Lang was obviously troubled as they piled into the truck waiting to haul them and their sled back to the mountain top.

"If it hadn't been for that skid in the 'Glacier'—" He left the remark hanging in mid-air.

There was so much he wanted to say. To begin with, Stephen was too keyed up for his own good. Of course it had been a honey of a run. But it could have been better. Take that skid, for instance. Inexcusable in a driver of Stephen Grant's experience.

The trouble was, Tom Lang told himself, Stephen was fighting the "Glacier." Trying to bull his way through it. Tackling it his own way. When every one had told him for days the secret of the big murderous curve was to ease in and out of it. Let the sled do most of the work. After all, the curve had been designed just that way—

They were grinding up the steep road that paralleled the bob-run.

Time was, he thought ruefully, when he wouldn't have hesitated to tell Stephen Grant what was on his mind. Now it wasn't so easy. True, the whole idea of the race had been his. But now that he was committed to it, Stephen seemed intent on running it his own way.

"It's his nature," Tom Lang muttered, staring off at the snowy landscape. "Something fundamental within him."

Chances were, he reflected further, this same stubbornness was at the root of Stephen's present difficulties with Cynthia. Stephen insisting on running their little show his way. Cynthia resenting it. Fighting down her resentment most of the time because she really loved him—

Now the truck labored around the final snowbank and stopped with a loud grinding of gears. The familiar scene of the starting-line lay spread out before them. The handful of spectators; a news-reel crew fussing over their equipment; the helter-skelter line-up of the sleds. And finally, the racers themselves. Big, burly fellows for the most part, looking bigger than that in their heavy woolen parkas, their gaily daubed football helmets.

"Watch that rear runner!" Stephen cautioned irritably as Bill Albert and Fenn prepared to ease the big sled out of the truck.

Later, kicking his way through loose snow to his favorite vantage point, he was silent, taken up with his own thoughts.

He was searching for something that persisted in eluding him. Something that had to do with Kurt Borden—and the "Glacier." Only this much was certain: there had been a formula of a sort. And it would fit this damnable curve, too, if only he could think what it was. Kurt had been full of such things. Tag-ends of racing wisdom. This wouldn't be much, perhaps. Something he once heard Kurt toss into a conversation casually enough. With that characteristic laugh of his.

It went against his grain to have to lean on any one for help, including the memory of Kurt Borden. Yet anything was better than the growing sense of defeat that seemed closing in on him.

Stephen Grant stirred uneasily, cocked a weather-wise eye at the Adirondack skies. The sun had disappeared behind a bank of clouds. The air was definitely colder. That meant the run would tighten up now; become even faster than it had been.

A number of things happened on that third heat. To begin with, Bob Curtis, who was pacing Stephen Grant in third place, made the mistake of trying too hard and came to grief in "Zig-Zag."

Up at the top they knew something was wrong when the loud-speakers froze into sudden dumbness. Then for long anxious moments men stood frozen in their tracks.

Yet, when the word came up to them at last it was better than anyone had dared to hope. A battered sled; a badly wrenched shoulder for Curtis; a twisted ankle for his brakesman; an assortment of bruises for the rest of the crew. But, of course, automatic disqualification.

Then, moments later, Fox, who was in second place, went down again, followed soon afterwards by Wells who had led the pack all morning.

Shortly it became evident that neither of them had done much more than hold his own in the aggregate-time standings. The lines above Stephen Grant's mouth relaxed noticeably. The first glimmerings of hope flowed through his limbs. His strong hands flexed and unflexed inside their heavy racing gauntlets.

Tom Lang moved over to stand beside Stephen.

"Looks like we get a break," he said quietly, his eyes riveted on Stephen Grant's face.

Stephen Grant nodded. He flicked away his half-smoked cigaret.

"Hang onto your hat this trip," he warned. "Maybe you'll see something."

It was coming back to him now. Coming back for the first time. The old feeling; the feeling that you knew precisely what must be done; exactly how to do it. This was it. This was the veteran in him, the champion who had been. Seasoned, self-controlled, clear-headed. Surer of himself than at any time since they had first embarked on this wild endeavor.

So they thought he was finished? Too old for their gruelling and reckless sport? Well, he'd show these kids a thing or two yet.

And he did just that.

Then suddenly the atmosphere of the finish-line was charged with new excitement. Who was this bob-sledder who had come roaring down the run so fast that he had eclipsed the Number Two man Fox? So fast that now only the favorite, Tippy Wells, stood between him and the national title? What were these rumors about winning for a dead man? For the great Kurt Borden? No matter. He was giving them a race fit for the national championships. The kind of slam-bang running they had come a long way to see. Of course he didn't stand a chance of beating Wells. Still—anything could happen in a bob-sled race, and frequently did. Better not miss this fourth and final heat—

Interminably the truck rumbled up the mountain. Crowded into a corner, Tom Lang pulled on his cigaret, staring moodily at a cake of ice clinging to one heavy boot.

Seeing him thus, all the rising tide of elation drained out of Stephen Grant. At length he could keep silent no longer.

"Well," he said, making an effort to keep his voice free from irritation, "what was wrong with that ride, if I may ask?"

But even as he said it he could have bitten his tongue. For there had been something wrong with it. Notwithstanding the scoreboard; in spite of the excitement down below. And Stephen knew that Tom Lang would not have missed it.

"I was just wondering," Tom Lang was speaking slowly, deliberately. "I was just wondering what you were waiting for back there on the 'Glacier'?"

After that, of course, they did not speak again through the long, jolting climb. When they reached the top, Stephen Grant jumped from the truck and strode away.

"Let some one else worry about unloading the sled," he muttered under his breath.

The sharp unreasoning resentment that had flared within him at Tom Lang's sarcasm needed to be dissipated. He would go off somewhere by himself until he had cooled down. Until his nerves stopped their infernal jumping about.

He was longer coming out of it than was good for him. The loud-speaker was calling another sled to the line. Tippy Wells? It couldn't be. Not so soon. But it was, nevertheless.

And getting away beautifully, too, Stephen noted glumly. If only he and Tom Lang had been able to bring their own starting technique to such a point of perfection. But that took time. Long weeks of gruelling practice.

There. Wells is on his way.

Now the loudspeaker is blaring again. Again and yet again.

Telling the whole mountainside that Wells is on his way. Following him down. Reporting his progress through all the tortuous windings of the icy track.

Confound them, down below! Stephen Grant fumed inwardly. Why must they be so infernally slow. Now, here it comes? Wells is down. Over the line. Now, hold your breath—here comes his time. Fast, no question of that.

But when the official announcement rang out in the winter's air, Stephen's shoulders sagged appreciably. Tippy Wells had rocketed down the twisting, curving, mile long descent in the startling time of 1:06 flat. Now on the basis of their aggregate times he led his nearest rival by nearly two full seconds. Two full seconds! A lifetime when the big four-man sleds are tearing themselves apart. A margin for victory that would call for little short of a miracle to overcome.

Stephen Grant groaned inwardly. He simply must not quit now. Whatever else he might be, he wasn't one to quit until he was finally, definitely beaten.

Even Cynthia would admit that, he told himself. Cynthia— odd that she should be in his mind at this point. If only things had been different, it would have been pleasant having her here. But bob-sledding had been one interest of his which she had made no pretense of sharing. Any form of Winter Sports bored Cynthia. And that was one thing on which he had not insisted. Let Tom Lang think him stubborn, domineering, if he would. This was one point on which Cynthia had had her own way from the start. Her own way—

All of a sudden Stephen Grant stood as though transfixed. Then, almost immediately one gloved fist was drumming against its mate, and he was laughing—short, mirthless laughter, oblivious of the curious stares about him.

Her own way. "But, of course, of course!" he muttered half-aloud. "Such a simple thing. Such an unbelievably simple thing. And I couldn't get it. . . . It wouldn't come to me until now. . . ."

Up there in the Adirondacks you can still find people eager to tell you about Stephen Grant and how he drove his bob-sled in the final, blasting heat of the National championships. They cling more firmly than ever to such memories now. For the war is closing in on the Winter sportsmen, as it is on all of us. Racing days come less frequently. New sleds are out of the question. And, one by one, the husky young men who have never known the meaning of fear are lost to their old haunts.

But there it was that February day.

First there is Stephen Grant adjusting his helmet, ploughing slowly over to the top of the run; taking his place alongside the sled. Afterwards he recalled thinking that Tom Lang's nose was frost-bitten. That tell-tale whitish look.

But now their eyes meet. And Tom Lang's are filled with something that is at once a question and a plea.

Stephen Grant allows a faint reassuring smile to play around the corners of his mouth. It's all right now, he seems to say. It's all right with the race; all right with us, too.

"One thing." His voice is low, confident. "Leave your brakes alone on the 'Glacier.' Understand? No matter what happens."

Then they were off.

Now the long, rocking descent of the starting straight-away flows beneath their runners. The high curving loom of "Shady" takes them to its icy clasp, spews them forth beyond like a wind-tossed leaf. . . . Now brace yourself again! This time it's the stinging whip-lash of the "Little-S"—Easy does it. There, you're done with that. And still you're roaring along, picking up speed, speed, more speed.

Stephen Grant plays the big red-white-and-blue sled as a jockey plays a thoroughbred. His long frame is bent far over the steering wheel; his eyes strain through the snow-filled blast that assails them. His mind races on, picturing each sweeping wall of ice, each spine-rattling turn that lies ahead of them.

Hang on tight! Keep your head down! Here comes—"Zig-Zag" —devil's own invention. A skid now would spell disaster. Take it high if you want speed. Up—up—up! Slam! Bang!—Wow, you're out of it. Cleanly, with no sign of a skid. With more speed than you've handled before.

What next? The long tricky loop of the "Pigstail." Easy enough. Oh yes?—Perhaps, but not at this speed. Not now. Nothing in this interminable tunnel of raging wind and upflung snow can be easy today. Not when you're draining yourself of all you've got. All you ever had. Digging deep into your aging body; bringing forth every last ounce of stamina, skill, craftiness. For what? For

Kurt. To win another one—a final one—for Kurt Borden—remember?

Wonder what Tom Lang is thinking now. Hang on back there, fellow. Grit your teeth. Dig your chin into Bill Albert's shoulder. Close your eyes. Gasp for breath against the drumming tide of freezing air that engulfs you. Call this fast, Tom Lang? This is nothing. The calm before the storm. Wait a minute. Wait till we hit the "Glacier"! Wait—Wait—

And then they are roaring down upon it. A ghastly gray blur. Solid wall of steel-blue ice rising up and up to dispute their progress. Seemingly designed for one thing—and that only; to send them and their sled hurtling end over end into the dark blur of forest that haunts them all the way.

Now, miraculously, at the last, ultimate split-second, the solid wall of ice curves away beneath them. Steel runners bite into its frozen surface. They soar upward in a long, slithering arc.

Up—up and up. Tom Lang can wait no longer. His mouth opens wide to fling futile soundless words into the arctic blast. "Steve—Steve! Pull her down, you fool!—Pull her down. She'll never hold—she'll never . . . !"

But even as the words were torn from him the big sled shivered at the upward limit of its flight; trembled violently on the knife-edge of disaster. Then, without a break in the smooth continuity of Stephen Grant's driving they had turned their backs on trouble, were looping downward and forward in a blinding flow of speed.

And in that instant Tom Lang knew they had won.

He knew it as surely as if the figures were already posted before his eyes. Knew it with all the certainty born of years of experience at this very thing.

Afterward, when it was all over—when they had posed endlessly for the newsreels, flung breathless words at the microphone somebody shoved in their faces—they were hurried back to the big clubhouse by the shore of the frozen lake. There, for the better part of an hour the new champions found themselves caught up in a swift sequence of events celebrating their achievement.

But at long last it was possible to seek sanctuary in Stephen's rooms and close the doors behind them. Quickly Stephen produced a bottle and poured the drinks they had waited for.

"You name it," he said. "It was your idea—remember?"

Tom Lang grinned. "Okay, 'Champ.'" Then his round, red face grew serious. "To Kurt," he said simply. "To Kurt Borden . . . Peace." Together they raised their glasses.

After that, so far as Tom Lang was concerned, only one little matter remained to be cleared up, the "Glacier." He put the question to Stephen Grant with characteristic bluntness.

At first it seemed the only answer he would get was laughter. But soon Stephen Grant was saying: "Up there at the top of the mountain, just before we started down for the last time, I had been thinking of Cynthia." He smiled a little wryly, flicked at his cigaret before continuing:

"Then, suddenly, it came to me. The thing I had been trying to remember. The thing that Kurt Borden had said sometime, somewhere. It was so obvious—almost commonplace if you will— that I almost let it go again. But somehow I didn't. All it was is this: 'Sometimes'—I remembered him telling me—'Sometimes, bob-sleds are like women. You can't drive them . . . You have to let them go their own way.'"

He paused, enjoying the look on Tom Lang's face.

"Simple, isn't it? And not very profound when you come to think of it. Yet up there it seemed a revelation to me. At least it solved the 'Glacier' as far as I'm concerned."

Tom Lang was staring at Stephen Grant curiously. Not thinking of what he had just said especially. But seeing something else. Seeing it dimly, and not quite sure that he was seeing anything at all.

But now Stephen Grant had swung to his feet, was crossing the room to the telephone.

". . . Want to see if I can get out of Lake Placid tonight," he explained over his shoulder. "Cynthia is due back in New York from Palm Beach tomorrow." He hesitated, the lines of his face softened. "I—I was thinking I'd like to be there when she arrives."

The Battle of the Fastnet

By ALFRED F. LOOMIS

OR A WEEK it has been blowing half a gale in the English Channel. On the evening of August 12 toasts to the King and the President have been drunk in the banquet hall of the Royal London Yacht Club at Cowes, and the chairman has the floor. "If it is very stormy tomorrow," says he, "the letter S will be flown from the Royal Yacht Squadron staff and the Fastnet race will be postponed."

The seventy-odd members of the crews of fifteen competing boats look at one another knowingly and nod seeming agreement. But each man knows that the stop signal will not be flown. Since its inception in 1925, the Fastnet ocean race for cruising yachts has achieved a world-wide reputation as a sea-going event. Pride overcoming caution, nothing short of a hurricane will cause postponement of the third battle for the classic cup. The crews leave the club to board their vessels this night satisfied that the amenities have been observed—and relishing the thought of their coming struggle with the sea.

But in the night the wind pipes down, and on the morning of August 13 fifteen cruising yachts drift across the starting line at the discharge of the gun. Through the pouring rain of that dreary morning in the Solent let us look at them, not in the order of their start—for that matters little in a race down Channel and across the Irish Sea and back to Plymouth—but in the degree of their potentiality.

First there is the forty-four-ton cutter Jolie Brise. Under command of George Martin she won the Fastnet race of 1925,

From the Sportsman Magazine.

255

sailed across the ocean in 1926 to take part in our Bermuda race, and returned to England to compete in that year's Fastnet. She is under new ownership now and the Viking Martin is not aboard, but she is still the most dangerous of the contestants.

Next to her comes Ilex, a twenty-ton yawl owned by the Royal Engineers Yacht Club. She is small by comparison with Jolie Brise, but she is last year's winner and is sailed by a hard-battling crew who, according to tradition, are untroubled by the victualing problem because they eat nothing but beer and marmalade.

After her, the Nicanor. Hats off, Americans, to her owner, Daniel Simonds, and the others of her Harvard crew who sailed Nicanor across the ocean for a try at the Fastnet Cup. She is a thirty-six ton Alden schooner, and so would classify as a possible winner even without her valiant crew. With them, and with two Ratseys and another Englishman aboard to outwit local conditions, she is almost as much to be respected as Jolie Brise.

La Goleta—she is another schooner, as her name declares, built to Alden's Malabar VIII design. Six tons smaller than Nicanor, she is of heavier construction and sturdier rigging, and we who are aboard her feel that she has a possible chance. Built in England by Ralph St. L. Peverley, an American citizen, she is not allowed to fly the blue ensign and has had great difficulty in obtaining permission from Washington to fly the Stars and Stripes. But fly them she does, and she is manned by five Americans and two Scots.

Then there is Saoirse,—pronounce it as you will,—a square-rigged staysail ketch owned by the reboubtable Conor O'Brien from the Irish Free State. She is only a twenty-tonner, but if she gets her weather she will run like a scared rabbit, and it is worth remembering that O'Brien has already sailed her around the world—from east to west!

Aboard La Goleta we have not thought much about the cutter Tally Ho. She is a twenty-nine ton modified Falmouth quay punt, which means that she is a windward worker, under-canvased, and at her best in a blow. She is owned by Lord Stalbridge who, although new to yachting, has this year won important cups and sailed to Spain and back for recreation. We have to allow her approximately five hours over the course of 615 miles, but we are a faster boat under average conditions. Ilex gives us an hour and ten minutes, Nicanor better than three hours and a half, and Jolie Brise, the scratch vessel, allows us nearly four hours.

Although their time allowances are high, the other contenders —Spica, Shira, Content, Thalassa, Altair, Maitenes, Morwenna, Penboch, and Nellie—are small and cannot win except by freak of circumstances. More honor to them for starting in the Fastnet.

Did I say that the southwest wind had died? Halfway to Nomans Fort it piped up again, and under main, fore, jumbo, reaching jib, and two topsails we tore along, our lee deck almost awash, ahead of us the Jolie Brise reaching out like a race horse. Next her the Nicanor, and then the Ilex. And Tally Ho on our port quarter. Perhaps, we thought as we eyed them in the pouring rain, this would be the order of the finish. We did not yet know what the weather had in store for us.

We rounded the fort close to, and Marshall Rawle, our bowsprit specialist, put his 175 pounds of brawn to the job and doused the reaching jib. Up went the ordinary jib, and in the shift of canvas we worked ahead of Ilex. Down toward Nab Rock we beat, taking in the kites before we tacked, and as we left the lee of the Wight the sea made up and we ate lunch—a necessary and yet unwise procedure.

The weather thickened and the wind increased and in the first two hours of sailing we came to know the discomfort of racing in the English Channel. Dunnose showed its blunt head momentarily through the drizzle, and we figured that we could carry the port tack around St. Catherine's. But now a cutter flashed out of the murk, cutting across us on the starboard tack. Peverley, at the wheel, held on to the last moment, hoping against hope, and then we were forced about. Tally Ho, sailing like the Flying Dutchman, had come to grips and drawn first blood. We did not forget her when we tacked again toward St. Cat's and parted company.

There was a sea off the point—a bad one with the west-going tide fighting the sou'west wind—and we took it over green. Peverley had built La Goleta under a myriad of difficulties which would have been insurmountable to many another man, and she was finished only the day before the start. Despite everything, her decks leaked and we were wet below. But we had not thought of the Fastnet as a midsummer holiday, and we were comforted in the way La Goleta sailed into the wind and blithely took her punishment. Our competitors drew out of sight—some ahead and some astern—and we plunged on.

The next brush was with Nicanor. East of Swanage at nine-thirty that evening she cut across our bows when we were on the starboard tack beating out to clear St. Albans Race. In eleven hours we had thrashed fifty wet miles to windward, and here were the two American schooners a hundred yards apart. We waved mutual encouragement as our courses diverged. Again in the night she crossed us—this time well in the lead—but in the morning in Lyme Bay, beating up toward Teignmouth, she was astern.

That day, the second of the race, was one of pleasant—and bitter—memory. Although the sky was overcast, the wind had moderated to a mere twenty miles an hour, and until noon we carried in addition to our four lowers the main topsail and the fisherman. The sea more quiet, we made good going on the port tack, and when we came about and stood out from land we had the better of Nicanor. Working out under the shelter of Berry Head we saw Jolie Brise and down to leeward the Ilex, and, everything considered, we thought ourselves in good position. But here the bitterness in our cup of satisfaction. By standing on the port tack Nicanor gained a swifter tide and at five in the afternoon was around Start Point and out of sight ahead of us. Tally Ho fought with us the battle of rounding the Start, and, as one or the other felt more benefit from the tide, drew ahead or dropped astern. By nightfull the wind was blowing hard and we knew without peradventure that the Fastnet race was going to be a hard one—but how hard, we were yet to learn.

At two in the morning of the fifteenth, when off the Eddystone, the wind came ripping out of the west, and for the first time we shortened down to less than working canvas. With the foresail handed, the ship rode more easily and the watch on deck found it possible to enjoy the cold moonlight and the flying spray. The hours washed around, and at noon, tacking out to clear the Lizard, we once more saw Nicanor—and saw her under a rig which meant that the wind was really blowing. Ocean-going schooner though she is, she was hove to under her foresail. Jolie Brise, which we had watched during the morning fighting up toward Falmouth, had disappeared, and the only other contestant in sight was Tally Ho, working toward the Lizard under reefed

main and spitfire jib. High though the seas rose, she seemed as
steady as a church, and we watched her in silent admiration. Here
indeed was a competitor.

As we came out from under the lee of the land we doused our
jib—young Rawle going under with the bowsprit as she dipped to
them—and double-reefed the main. On we stood, riding more
easily now, with no water coming aboard, and the coke fire going
below to dry things out. We had been thrashing into it and we
were wet and tired. The change from that to storm rig was exhilarating, and the sun which shone on the green combers of the
Channel seemed almost warm and cheerful.

The glass fell steadily and the wind had more in store. By mid-
afternoon we were hove to under reefed foresail, standing on the
port tack toward the lee of the Lizard. Lieutenant Commander
Boyd, of the Royal Navy, who navigated with me, said that in all
his experience he had never seen a heavier sea off the Lizard.
And it was heavy. Spray was not yet flying diagonally upward from
the cresting combers, but we knew that the wind was blowing.
Force 8, we entered it in the log—a summer's gale and a little more.

I slept that afternoon in my wet clothes and my wet blankets,
and when Rawle hastily awoke me, a change had come over the
ship. The reefed mainsail was going up and we were running off
the wind. Why? Falmouth for shelter.

On deck there was discussion and then agreement. In America,
perhaps, we could run for port because the sea was high—but what
would the English say? What, in fact, did Boyd say? He said it
would look bad to put in. What did McOnie say? In his Scottish
burr he agreed with Boyd. What did all of us say? That in an
ocean race we mustn't avail ourselves of shelter merely because
shelter happened to be available.

The mainsail was furled again, La Goleta was jibbed over,
and under our double-reefed fore we jogged her off the land.
Jogged her off because the coke stove would burn only on the
starboard tack and we were dripping wet below. So sailed, La
Goleta made some leeway, but fore-reached, and the west-going
tide, striking her lee bow for six hours, held us up to windward.

By morning we had weathered the hardest of the blow, and
at four, the galley range having burned itself out, we jibbed to
the port tack. The wind had moderated now to a force of thirty-

five miles, and we once more set the jumbo and the double-reefed main. But the slant came from the northwest, and, fighting a rushing tide, it was ten o'clock before we could say that we were definitely past the craggy Lizard. Then the wind softened to a force of 5, and we shook out our reefs and set the jib. Beating into smoother water in the lee of Land's End, we lowered sail and took up the slack in the rigging, handed hastily scribbled letters to a fisherman, and sailed on. At this juncture I had time to find from the chart what we had done and what we had to do.

In three days of the hardest kind of sailing, we had made good less than two hundred miles. The wind was northwest. From Longships Light, our point of departure off Land's End, our course would lie northwest across the Irish Sea, 170 miles to the Fastnet Light. By the time we had rounded that, the wind which had been westerly for a month must certainly swing to the east and give us another 240 miles of beating back to the finish line at Plymouth.

The prospect was anything but cheerful. To discourage us still more, not one of our larger competitors was in sight; and as we rounded the Runnelstone we could see the red sails of the cutter Content—one of the smaller fry—working in from the Lizard not ten miles astern. So our period of heaving to had put us out of the winning class and given the others chance to catch us up.

Nearing the Longships we entered a savage lop, and, as the wind here failed us and we slatted about doing nothing but curse, I am going to leave La Goleta in spirit as I wished I could have left her in person. Let us piece together, from the telegrams received at Plymouth after the event, what sea and wind had done to some of the contestants.

Altair, sailed by a valiant woman, had suffered a split mainsail, put in to Weymouth, and abandoned the race.

Norwenna, a twenty-six-ton schooner, had put back to Ryde on the day after the start, with a man badly injured.

Shira, an able twenty-one-ton cutter of the Luch Fyne type, had been forced in to Gosport with a bad leak.

Penboch, a twelve-tonner, had put in to Dartmouth and abandoned on the fifteenth.

Thalassa, a forty-six-foot yawl, had blown a jib out of its bolt-ropes, split a staysail, and limped into Dartmouth.

Saoirse, the square-rigged staysail—or Irish—ketch, had returned to Cowes.

And Nellie, a lovely little twelve-ton cutter, forty years old but sound as a chip, had struggled unavailingly until she was within sixteen miles of Cherbourg and was now running snugly back to Cowes.

Having disposed of seven of the fifteen contestants in the first three days, the elements refused for three hours to vouchsafe an inkling of their further intentions. The barometer, to be sure, moved meaningly, but as there happened at that time to be more lows over Ireland than there are potatoes in an Irish stew, we could not diagnose its movements.

Yet at nine-thirty the air came gently out of the west, which permitted us almost to lay our course for the Fastnet, and by two in the morning of the seventeenth we were sailing on the port tack and having the satisfaction of watching the wind slowly haul to the southwest. The sea, under the influence of the tide flowing down the Bristol Channel, was confused, but the breeze was enough to fill our sails, and we moved easily. An hour later there was another change for the better, and without calling the sleeping half of the crew the watch on deck set the reaching jib, lowered the fore, and hoisted the balloon fisherman. This sail, more correctly called a balloon topmast staysail, is a huge piece of light canvas which completely fills the gap between the two masts from truck to truck and almost down to the water's edge. Under its urge La Goleta woke to new life, and our patent log, streamed at the Longships and listless for forty-four miles, began to realize that it was in for a spell of violent revolutions.

At seven and at ten Boyd and I took sights, found our fixes five miles apart, accepted the mean of the two positions, and laid a course of northwest by north to get to weather of the Fastnet. The wind, as if tiring of its opposition, hauled still more to south'ard, and by noon we were boiling at nine knots on a broad reach, every stitch set and drawing.

And now for the first time in four days we felt that we were racing. A cutter, first mistaken for the schooner Nicanor, hove in sight on our weather bow and was rapidly overhauled. A lovely thing she was, flying under full mainsail, topsail, square sail, and headsails, alternately throwing her bowsprit high in air and sinking her hull behind intervening combers. Though the Jolie Brise might be miles ahead, fighting it out with Nicanor and Ilex, we had our own unknown competitor, and we were both out to make the best of it we could.

In mid-afternoon our hearts sank. The wind now had easting in it, and, blowing on our quarter, failed to get the most out of our fore-and-aft sails. But the cutter with her square sail slipped faster still toward the Irish coast and began to overhaul us. Bad though the southeasterly was for us on a run, it would be still worse on a beat when we had rounded the Fastnet and the cutter would be knifing into it, half a point better than we could sail.

And then, as if that were not enough, gradually we found further cause for shattered hopes. For the day thickened as evening came, and in drenching rain we overran our reckoned distance to the Fastnet. What to do then? Fastnet Light stands on a detached rock three miles southwest of Cape Clear. If we had really run beyond the light we should soon find ourselves embayed on a rocky, hostile coast. If the wind increased and caught us on a lee shore, what then? Should we break the seal of our motor, and in saving our skins throw away the race after all?

But if we were to miss the Fastnet, so was our ghostlike competitor, for she led us by now, and we had determined that we would not split tacks with her as we had done to our cost with Nicanor. The cutter changed course four points to starboard and we did the same. She jibed suddenly to the other tack and we followed suit as Boyd's happy voice sang out, "Light ho, dead ahead." So at last we had found the Fastnet.

And lost the wind. A fierce gust from the southwest was followed by nothing, and in the blackness of late evening we drifted nearer to the cutter and spoke to her. She was the Tally Ho, which had put us about four days ago off St. Catherine's, had fought with us off the Start, and beaten us around the Lizard. And we had to allow her four hours, fifty-seven minutes, and thirty-five seconds.

Had she any news? Yes. To the thunderous accompaniment of slatting sails and banging blocks we picked it up. Ilex had last been seen running before the wind under headsails alone. We learned later that she had split her mainsail and sprung a leak. Nicanor and Jolie Brise had put in to Falmouth for shelter in the gale, and Tally Ho herself had anchored for twelve hours in Newlin, near Penzance.

The slight air drifted Tally Ho ahead and we called good-night. Now ensued a period which might be called a weather prophet's paradise. Becalmed in the center of a low, any guess as to the direction of the new wind was good. Within twelve hours it blew east, southeast, southwest, north, northeast, northwest, and intervening points. But first, since we were south of the Fastnet, it came out of the north, and we had to beat to round the light.

At one-thirty-five in the morning of the eighteenth, in pouring rain and refreshing wind, we considered ourselves around and signaled our name and letter to the lightkeeper. Ahead of us the Tally Ho's flare had burned a few minutes previously, and when we asked how many ships had passed and learned that we were the only two our spirits bounded upward. We had held Tally Ho to windward, and now if we could get a reaching wind instead of this northeaster that was commencing to blow the cold of the Arctic down our way, we felt that we had a chance to save our time.

But the northeaster was undeniably there. Boyd said that a comforting thing about a northeaster in Irish waters was that it never blew at gale force. Two hours later when it was blowing a gale from that quarter he admitted his error and, with McOnie and seventeen-year-old David Parsons, lowered the fisherman stay-sail, waist-deep in water in the lee rigging. When the kite was in and he considered that his sin of making an unqualified prophecy had been expiated, he called all hands and we doused the main and took in the jib.

Under foresail and jumbo we staggered along, logging six knots across a whole gale, dipping solid water aboard, wet to the skin and frozen to the marrow. For days our bunks had been wet. Now our changes of clothes and the clothes we wore were drenched, and there was little joy in ocean racing. Tally Ho, carrying on longer than we did, disappeared in the darkness, and we had other things to wish for than a reaching wind.

Rawle and I, alternating at the wheel and beside the fireless range, wished particularly for hot food, and when the hour was seven we called the cook and he, crouching over a Primus stove, fried bacon and eggs for all hands. God bless Allan, the Liverpool cook, veteran of the second retreat from Mons, and jack of all trades! Each day, as he continued to turn out hot meals under the most stupendous difficulties, we rated him higher and higher in the degrees of cookdom until on that morning of the eighteenth we gave him five out of a possible four, Navy system of marking.

There was another bright spot in that dismal morning watch. Ten minutes before we turned the deck over to Boyd and his crew of diving devils, we had the satisfaction of seeing the wind haul to northward. When at noon he turned it back to the starboard watch, the gale had gone into the north-northwest and moderated to a force of 6. Slowly it softened while the sun came out and sextants were brandished and dozens of wet garments came up for an airing. At four in the afternoon we entered upon the last phase of the Fastnet race.

At that time Tally Ho was in sight again on our weather beam. The topsail was set, and the balloon fisherman, and the reaching jib, and then La Goleta began to travel. Who, we asked one another, had said that ocean racing was a virulent form of idiocy? It was, in point of fact, the most glorious of sports. Log turning nine and then ten knots, and for one hour when it underwent a spasm of joyous delirium, eleven and a quarter knots! Bright, warm sunshine. Marvelous rolling sea—and Tally Ho dropping astern like a disappearing gun in recoil.

But there was danger, too, and for a brief instant tragedy reared its ugly head. Bill Tallman, who had come all the way from Pittsburgh to take part in the race, soon discovered that he was not cut out to be a sailor. Yet, though he hated it, he was game to the last ounce of his 190 pounds, and he pumped bilges and put his weight to halyards and smoked his cigars and smiled his cheerful smile until we all realized what true nerve is. And as he stumbled about the deck in his heavy boots we caught our breath time and again, and continually warned him, "Hold on, Bill."

Then, when we were batting out nine knots and our rail was dipping under a mill race of spume, he lost his balance and fell. His hands clutched and caught nothing. The sea tugged at his legs and he slipped, lurching, clutching, under the life line.

"Man overboard!" Boyd's curiously choked voice roused me

from my bunk and I jumped up the ladder. But it was all over
by the time I reached the deck. Bill had his hands around a life-
rail stanchion. Mac held him by the shoulders, Allan by the
waist, and two others by the legs. The helmsman luffed and they
heaved his 200 wet pounds aboard—minus one foot, but still
puffing an extinct cigar and plus the broadest smile he had ever
worn. As Bill changed into dry clothes we heard him bawling
himself out for being a clumsy fool. Hold on, Bill. You're running
down a good man.

Another good man was Peverley, the owner of La Goleta.
All my racing days—they're not many, but they're very poignant—
I've longed to sail with a skipper who would carry on. All crews
of all ocean racers have the same longing. It isn't our boat we're
racing, we haven't the responsibility of deciding when to shorten,
and it doesn't cost us anything if the spars give way. So we all say,
"Give us a skipper who will carry on." And in Ralph Peverley
we of La Goleta found him.

At sundown black clouds in the northwest heralded the wind's
increase to gale strength, and steering became a job for really
expert helmsmen. Only the skipper, Rawle, and Boyd touched
the wheel that night. So that we might carry on to the last minute
a reinforced watch of six men kept the deck, and at ten o'clock
the word came to hand the balloon fisherman.

In response, men trained in a week's hard school grasped the
halyards in the dark, stood by the sheet, and at the tack. "Down
fisherman!" came the order, and as Peverley blanketed it with the
main the tremendous sail came down like a sulky lioness—knowing its strength but momentarily overpowered.

For another hour the reaching jib—not so big as a balloon jib,
but big enough in all conscience—was carried, and then by eleven
the wind had hauled so far aft that it no longer earned its way.
During part of this hour I had watched Rawle at the wheel and
had seen that despite his strength and skill the vessel, caught on
a wave, yawed two points to windward, steadied, staggered, and
oscillated a point to leeward. One more point by the lee and she
would have jibbed, but Rawle, working like a demon, had held
her there.

And now Peverley, relieving the wheel, purposed to hold her
dead before while Rawle scrambled out to the end of the bow-

sprit and doused the reaching jib. By so doing Peverley would blanket the jib and make her possible to handle. But there would be a time—three minutes at the least—when the jib was mastered and being unhanked from the stay, that he would have to hold her without a stitch of headsail. In that time almost anything might happen.

When at last the word came to furl the jib I confess that, for me, at least, the race had reached its zero hour. Boyd and I made protesting Rawle tie a line under his arms, and as he hunched out along the bowsprit and I wrapped my legs around its middle, I thought of the two major possibilities. If Peverley, steering a gambler's course, let her yaw half a point too much to leeward, he would jib and take the sticks out of La Goleta. If she got away from him in the other direction when there was no headsail on her, she would come on the wind like a bat out of hell, plunge into green water, and perhaps sweep Rawle, Boyd, and me into the night.

But there was little time for such gloomy reflections. "Down jib!" I called. Boyd let go the halyard and passed the word. Mac, awash in the lee scuppers, loosened the sheet, and the sail went flying, dissipating its strength in resonant shaking. Down it flopped and in it came,—Boyd least secure of all of us as he staggered about on deck receiving the sail as Rawle unhanked it,—and in less than three minutes we were back on board again. The jumbo went up, two men to the halyards, and the zero hour was past.

I thought then that I had witnessed a feat of steering, but there was better still to come. At two in the morning of the nineteenth, the wind blowing harder than it had blown throughout the race, we picked up the Longships dead ahead, and Peverley was called from his bunk to make a decision.

To avoid the risk of jibbing we were running constantly to windward of our course. In twelve miles of running we should work up to weather of the light and in the boiling lop off Land's End be obliged to pass through stays and sail the other tack to clear the Runnelstone. Did the skipper want to do that?

"No," said he. He would try to work past both the Longships and the Runnelstone on the starboard jib. And work it he did, in a sea made mountainous by a weather-going tide, gaining a mile by the lee in ten miles of running dead before. I was asleep at the time, and can't say how he did it, but my dreams were synchronized with the rolling of the ship. Down she rolled to starboard and I dreamed sweetly, knowing that we were started on a luff. Then down to port, slowly, farther, and yet a little farther, and I started awake, expecting next the ghastly thunder of the mainsail, and wondering what it would be like to be dismasted off Land's End.

But at four the broken water of the Runnelstone flashed abaft the beam and we came to a point on the wind for the Lizard and all danger was past. Then as the watch changed our hopes were high that we had outrun the Tally Ho and saved our time. At five we set the reaching jib again and boiled along. At five-thirty the visibility improved astern, and there, where we had last seen her when darkness closed in, we saw the Tally Ho.

So we had failed to shake her off, and now in only six miles of running there was no hope of beating her. But we could still sail La Goleta, and sail her we did, covering the forty-four miles from the Laxard to Plymouth entrance in a few minutes less than five hours.

Now that we were on a broad reach I could once more take the wheel with safety to the crew, and of all the phases of the race, the good times and the bad ones, there is none that will stay by me like that romp across West Bay. . . . The wind blowing a moderate gale and whipping up the spray . . . the sun trying its best to dry our saturated gear . . . the white river in the lee deck curling up at times to fill the cockpit and soak me to the waist . . . the main sheet starting to wash adrift and its end caught in the nick of time . . . and the heavenly sustained susurration of the water as the fleet hull rode down the waves. It was payment a thousandfold for the weary days of beating to windward—and the final fillip that makes the spirit yearn toward ocean racing.

There were other rewards of the Fastnet, come to think of it. We crossed the line first, which was something, and when Tally Ho crossed forty-two minutes later, beating us by better than four hours on corrected time, we knew that we had bowed to a magnificent boat, superbly sailed. It was something to learn that Nicanor, our American competitor, had kept on short-handed when the three of her local crew had jumped ship at Falmouth, and had only withdrawn when a gaff snapped in the Irish Sea.

And it was satisfying to hear that Tally Ho and La Goleta were the only two of fifteen starters to finish—all the thirteen reaching port in safety.

I liked it, too, when George Martin, originator of the Ocean Racing Club and present vice commodore of its sixty members, told us at the club dinner that Tally Ho and La Goleta had made history and that never before had such a race been run.

Most of all I liked it when the Ocean Racing Club—but stand by a moment for a word of explanation. This club is at once exclusive and democratic. Nothing could be simpler than its rule of eligibility. Those, and those only, who have raced around the Fastnet may belong. So most of all I liked it when the Ocean Racing Club in a *viva voce* vote elected owners and crews of Tally Ho and La Goleta to membership. What price the fleeting hardships of ocean racing when this is the reward?

Handley Cross

By R. S. SURTEES

A S IF MR. JORROCKS'S hunting appetite grew by what it fed upon, he passed a very restless, feverish night, dreaming of all sorts of hunting casualties, and greatly disturbing Mrs. Jorrocks's repose by his evolutions. At length, thinking he was throwing down a stone wall, to pick up his fox, he set his feet against her with such force as sent her flying out of bed, and so finished the performance. Mrs. J. went off to Belinda's room, and our master got up, though it was only five o'clock. Early as he was, however, Pigg, who had not gone to bed at all, was before him, and when Mr. Jorrocks got downstairs, he found him at a sumptuous breakfast with Betsey in the back kitchen. Setting Pigg off to the stable, Mr. Jorrocks took his place at the table, and rated Betsey soundly for encouraging a man of Pigg's "unsteady 'abits."

Betsey justified herself on the score of promoting her master's sport. "Pigg," she was "sure was nothin' to her." She didn't want to be Mrs. Pigg. Not she, indeed! She could do better than that any day, she 'oped! "Pigg, forsooth!" and she bounced about and banged the butter upon the muffins and toast, as if her feelings were outraged in the extreme. How the dispute might have ended is doubtful, for in the midst of it Betsey gave Mr. Jorrocks a kidney so hot off the fire, that he burnt his mouth, and as he danced about the kitchen floor, unable to retain it, yet unwilling to give it up, she took advantage of the opportunity and slipped quietly away, to have a cry in her own room. Our master then finished his breakfast with a blistered mouth, as best he could, and then followed Pigg to the stable.

From "Handley Cross."

269

It was so dark when Pigg gave Mr. Jorrocks his horse, that our master was obliged to feel along his back to his tail, to be sure that he hadn't got hold of Xerxes instead of Arterxerxes; for though if our friend had been selling him, he would have sworn that Xerxes was far the best of the two—finest 'oss wot ever was seen, in fact—yet an inconvenient jerk he had with his hind-quarters in his jumps, more than counterbalanced any little additional speed he had over Arterxerxes. It took Mr. Jorrocks more time to get shuffled back into his saddle after a leap on Xerxes, than Arterxerxes would have lost by his steady laborious plodding, to say nothing of the inconvenience of riding on a horse's neck, instead of on his back. But to our story. Pigg, like a prudent man, had coupled the strange hounds with some of their own, or they would have been all over the town in no time. Master and man spurred briskly on, Jorrocks acting whipper-in, and Pigg yoicking and coaxing the hounds to him as best he could. They cleared the town, and got to the Whickenby Gate before the 'pike-man was up; and violent was the clattering, and dread the denunciations that Jorrocks hurled at his white cotton night-capped head, when at length he popped it out to inquire the cause of the row.

Our friends didn't get much use of the hard road for their money, for Pinch-me-near Forest being quite a back-slum sort of place, that nobody ever wanted to see, the roads all seemed to shun it, and it was only by very vague conjectures and speculative cuts that our friends managed to steer towards it at all. Not that the forest itself was worse than any of its Royal brethren; indeed, it was better than some, for Prettyfat neither stole the wood himself, nor knowingly suffered others to steal it, his being the easy do-nothing style of management, that let the trees grow if they liked, or if they didn't like, let them stand still and die, or be blown down and rot at their leisure. He made his reports regularly and fairly, and so long as he got as much money as paid his own salary and the wages of his labourers, he felt he fulfilled all the duties of a faithful servant of the Crown, and did all that a grateful nation could require.

A very rubicund sun at length began to struggle through the dull leaden clouds, gradually revealing hill and dale, fields, fences, and enclosures, the whole paraphernalia of a landscape, just like a child's puzzle-map getting put together.

"Yon's it!" exclaimed Mr. Jorrocks after a careful survey of the now developed scene. "Yon's it!" repeated he, pointing with his ponderous whip towards a dark mass in the distance.

"Ar's warn'd ye is't," replied Pigg, replenishing his mouth with tobacco. "Ar's warn'd ye is't. It's a gay bit off though."

"Trot on!" retorted Mr. Jorrocks anxiously, spurring Arterxerxes vehemently, an insult that the animal resented by a duck of his head and a hoist of his heels.

Bump, bump, trot, trot, squash, splash, swosh, they went through the open fields, over the commons and heaths of a wet, sterile, Pewitey country, which gradually got worse as they neared the stunted brushwood of the straggling forest. At length they came upon a nest of forest squatters, with their wretched mud cabins and rolling fences, by whom they were directed to a smart, well-hung green gate, with a cattle-gap on either side, as the commencement of Mr. Prettyfat's inattentions. Some well-used horse trods, converging towards a gently rising hill on the right, from whence a curl of clear smoke was now rising, favoured the supposition that the representative of Royalty was not far off. Though the morning was in its pride, yet when our friends got to the front of the neat rose-entwined house,—the windows were as white as the rough cast walls—there were no signs of animation of any sort. "The beggar's not hup yet I do believe," observed Mr. Jorrocks, spurring the great splayfooted Arterxerxes right on to the trimly shaven grass-plot in the centre of the carriage ring. Rising in his stirrups, and clearing his throat with a prolonged y-e-a-u-u-p! as he prepared his big whip for execution, he gave such a cannonade of a crack, as sounded through the house and reverberated in the forest.

"Sink, but that's a good 'un!" grinned Pigg, listening to the oft-repeated echoes.

Scarcely were the words out of his mouth, before, bang, went a lattice window up above, and a rival of the red-faced sun appeared beneath the night-capped head of the Deputy-surveyor.

"What are you doin' here?" roared a stentorian voice.

"Rum, ar say! rum!" exclaimed Pigg, thinking he was asking what he would have to drink.

"Doin' 'ere!" replied Mr. Jorrocks, whose ears had served him better. "Doin' 'ere! vy I be come to 'unt the foxes to be sure!"

"Hunt the foxes," retorted Prettyfat, indignantly—"Is this a time to come and hunt foxes—none but chimney-sweeps would disturb one at this hour."

"Sink, gin ye'll had mar hus ar'll get off and fight 'im!" exclaimed Pigg, furious at the comparison.

"Hush!" said Mr. Jorrocks, "let me talk to 'im."

"Vy, didn't I tell ye I'd come hearly?" asked our master, rising in his stirrups and speaking in a conciliatory tone.

"Come early," repeated Prettyfat recollecting the wide-margined official, "come early, yes, but you don't call tramplin' on a gen'lman's grass-plot comin' early, do ye? You don't 'spect to find a fox there."

"Hoot, thou 'ard feul, what's thou grumblin' 'bout thy grass plat for?" demanded Pigg, in a tone of derision.

"Treasonous, traitrous rogues," exclaimed Prettyfat. "I'll hand you over to the law officers of the Crown."

"Let's off!" ejaculated Jorrocks, catching Arterxerxes short round by the head—"Let's off!—I've no relish for law, still less for hornamentin' the top of Temple Bar with my 'ead;" so saying our master spurred through the pack, and treading on a couple of hounds, raised such a clamour as drowned the further observations of the Sylvan Viceroy. Down they dived into the wood again. They had not gone very far before they met Prettyfat's perspiring drab-turned-up-with-grease flunkey, panting along with a pitchfork in his hand, who exclaimed, on seeing them—"Oh gen'l'men! gen'l'men! you should ha' been here a bit sooner (puff), that tarnation fox has been at the (puff), poultry again."

"You don't say so!" grinned Mr. Jorrocks, pulling short up and standing erect in his stirrups. "You don't say so! Show us the way on 'im and I'll starve 'im out. Off with the couples, Pigg," added he, turning to James, who was already on the ground disengaging the draft. Away they tear in all directions, howling and towling like mad. A shrill blast of the horn gets them into a smaller compass, and Mr. Jorrocks trots on preceded by the man, to show him where he last saw the fox. Old Ravager first drops his stern-feathers, but speaks not, when one of the new noisy ones immediately gives tongue, and the sage taking a fling in advance, gave something between a squeak and a note, which being immediately endorsed by the rest, they drive with an echoing crash into the thick of the forest. Now our friend's misfortunes commence, for the further they get from the seat of government, the worse the riding becomes. Impervious thickets, through which hounds meuse, but horses can make no way, soon separate them from the pack, whose music falls fainter and fainter on the ear; our anxious master pushes on, through the wet sterile sand, or slobby quagmires, impeded ever and anon by a fallen tree—in hopes that a favourable turn may again land him with the pack— "Dash my vig," says he, shortening his hold of Arterxerxes, who all but falls over a fern-concealed log—"Dash my vig, I wish I mayn't brick my neck in this terrible desert—most outlandish place I ever was in."

"It is a rum place," observed Pigg, doing the like.

" 'Ark! where are they?" asked Mr. Jorrocks, pulling short up, with his hand to his ear.

"They seem arle oour," replied Pigg; "wish these Quorn dogs may be quite what they oout."

"It's the confouded hecho," observed Mr. Jorrocks, still listening attentively.

"Ar tell ye, they're divided," asserted Pigg.

"Then turn them," rejoined Mr. Jorrocks.

"Torn them thysel'," retorted Pigg, dropping his elbows and starting off at a canter.

"Now where's the man goin' to!" exclaimed Mr. Jorrocks, eyeing his fast receding huntsman diving into the thicket—"Wot's he a leavin' me 'ere for?" continued he, feeling the desolation of his position. "Wish I may ever find my way out," continued he, looking around on the grey unhealthy scene of stunted desolation.

Thinking to stick to Pigg, at all events, our master set Arterxerxes agoing again, and blobbed on in his deep, black imprints. Sorry work it was for old Arterxerxes, who was no great hand at going through deep. Jorrocks spurred him, and jagged him, and copped him, and call him all the great lumberin' henterpriseless beggars he could think of. In the excess of his energy, he overshot the mark, and kept right on, instead of turning short up a track on the left. The one he kept, from a uniformly rotten surface, now became alternately soft and hard, the water standing in the hollows like baths, and these, Arterxerxes, as if suspicious of treachery, commenced leaping, but possibly finding the trouble greater than he expected, he soon took to blundering through them, squirting the muddy water about in all directions. The forest still continued the same forlorn, unprosperous-looking place; where the wet stood, moss grey, aguish-looking trees were dying by the middle, while higher up, the oaks battled with the briars and other smothering rubbish. Our master, however, was too busy to observe anything of the sort—all he knew was, that it was werry bad riding. The sound of the horn on the left first caused him to pause and ponder whether he was on the track of Pigg. There were footmarks, but not so fresh as his should be. Another unmistakable twang, and Mr. Jorrocks determined to alter his course. Where all was so bad, there was nothing to choose. Accordingly, he swung Arterxerxes short round, and turned him up another rushy, waterlogged track, that seemed to lead in the direction of the horn. Desperately bad the riding was. The nature of the ground seemed to change, and from hop-pole-like ash and alder, to be stocked with nothing but stunted birch. The soil was black and peaty, with here and there the outline of a long-subsided drain.

"Blow me tight," muttered Mr. Jorrocks, shortening his hold of his horse, "I wish I mayn't be gettin' bogged," and scarcely were the words out of his mouth ere Arterxerxes floundered up to the shoulders in a moss hag, shooting our friend softly over his head on to his side.

"W-o-a-y 'oss! W-o-a-a-y!" roared our master, now kicking on his back like a lively turtle, expecting to have the struggling animal atop of him every moment.

"W-o-a-y 'oss! W-o-a-a-y!" repeated Jorrocks, jerking himself off to the side. The horse beat and plunged, and groaned and heaved, still stemming the black slough of despond, until he got fairly through, when, after standing a second or two to shake himself, he set off at an unprovoked trot, leaving our master in a most unhappy state of bewilderment as to how he should ever catch him, or get home without him.

"Dash the beggar," groaned Jorrocks, as he saw him rolling his great hind-quarters away in the distance—"Dash the beggar, but I wish I was atop on 'im, I'd give 'im summut to run for;" so saying, our master gathered himself together, and skirting the moss hag, commenced the unpleasant performance of running in

top-boots. Squish, squash, splash, he floundered, now over the
insteps, now up to the ankles, now almost up to the knees. He
soon began to sob and sigh—"Oh dear! oh dear," groaned he, "did
ever mortal man see sich a road—might as well try to run in a
river. And that confounded quad," continued he, eyeing Arterxerxes still on the move. "Dash my vig, but I'd give ye summut
to run for if I had 'old on ye—I'd make ye cry 'Capevi!' my frind.
Drot the road!" exclaimed he, as he plunged into a rush-concealed
rut, and squirted the dirty water up into his face. "Well this is a
pretty performance," continued he, mopping himself with a great
crimson bandana—"Beats all others into fits. Con-found these bye-
days. They're always gettin' on me into grief. And now the brute's
gone altogether," as the vista closed without Arterxerxes on the
scene. "'Ark! I 'ear 'ounds. No, they're crows. Well, if this isn't
a sickener, I don't know wot is—might as well try to run i' the
mud off 'Ungerford stairs, as in this sludge. Shouldn't like to
clean these bouts I know," continued he, looking down on his
black, and all black, tops. A bit of sound ground again tempted
him into a trot, and at length brought him to the rising ground
up which great Arterxerxes had disappeared. "Oh dear! oh dear!"
groaned Mr. Jorrocks as a stitch in his side suddenly stopped him.
"Oh dear! oh dear! I'm regularly floored. Might as well try to
follow Halbert Smith hup Mont Blanc as Arterxerxes hup this
incorrigible mountain;" so saying our heavily perspiring master
sought the support of a fallen willow, and distributing himself
equitably among its branches, sofa fashion, proceeded to bewail
his lamentable condition. "Oh dear! oh dear!" groaned he, "was
there ever sich an misfortunit indiwidual as John Jorrocks! was
there ever an independent British grocer made sich a football on
by fortin? Tossed about the world like an old 'at. Tempted from
the 'olesomest, the plisantest, the most salubrisome street i' London to take these 'ounds, and then be drawn into this unpardonable wilderness. Nothin' but rushes, and grass that Nebuchad-
nezzar 'imself would turn up his nose at. Oh dear! oh dear!"
continued he, as his thoughts reverted to home and Handley
Cross, "shall never see my dinner this day. Torbay soles with
Budle cockle sauce, Dartmoor forest mutton, puddin', and taturs
under the meat, 'stead of starvin' in a dreary desert—happed up
by cock robins or other benevolent birds;" a thought that so

distracted our master as to cause him to start and turn in his couch, when the rotten main prop to his back giving way, he came crashing and smashing to the ground.

"There!" ejaculated Mr. Jorrocks, "there!" repeated he, as he lay among the rotten fragments. "Fallen a 'underd feet from the grund! Broke every bone in my skin, I do believe. Bet a guinea 'at to a 'alf-crown gossamer I 'aven't a 'ole bone i' my body." So saying our master having carefully shaken first one limb and then another, to ascertain the amount of the mischief, rose slowly from the wet ground, and after anathematising the deceptive unfriendly tree, resumed the tracking of his horse up the hill. His boots were now well "salivated," as he would say, and the cold bog-water poached and churned as he went. But if his feet were cold, his temper was warm, and various were the recreations he promised Arterxerxes. He would ride "his tail off," then recollecting how little he had, he "would ride him till he dropped." Then he would "skin him alive, and make his hide into a hair trunk"—then he would cut it into whip thongs—next into shoe-strings—finally he would give him "to the first mugger he met."

As Mrs. Glasse would say, however, "first catch your horse," and this seemed a remote possibility, for though our master in the course of a two miles' tramp, which he called ten, did get a view of him once, the grass was of too coarse and uninviting a character to induce the animal to take more than a passing snatch as he went, which he did at a pace that seemed well calculted to last for ever. At length our master was fairly exhausted, and coming to a part of the forest that ran out into rocks and sandy heathery hills, he threw himself upon his back on a large flat stone, and kicking up first one leg and then the other, to let the bog-water out of his boots, moaned and groaned audibly. Beginning at a guinea, he bid up to a hundred and twenty, to be back to Handley Cross, and two hundred and fifty to be back in Great Coram Street, clear of the 'ounds and all belonging to them. And he vowed tha if Diana would only 'ave the kindness to come to his assistance that once, he would never trouble her with any more of his vagaries. No, indeed he wouldn't, he would sell his 'ounds and his 'osses, burn his boots and his Beckford, and drive about in a pill-box the rest of his life.

Our master was interrupted in the midst of his groans and lamentations by a low voice dropping down upon him with a "Are you hurt, sir?" and starting up, he encountered the sinister gaze of a haggard-looking man, dressed in a cap and complete suit of dirty grey tweed.

"Are you hurt, sir?" repeated the man, not getting an answer to his former inquiry.

"Hut, sir!" replied Mr. Jorrocks, eyeing him as though he expected an immediate stand and deliver; "Hurt, sir! No, sir!" clutching his formidable hammer-headed whip, "I've lost my 'oss."

"Oh, that's all, is it?" sneered the man.

"D'ye call that nothin'?" retorted Mr. Jorrocks, bridling up.

"My little gal said she thought you'd broke your back by the noise you were makin'," replied the man.

"Did she?" rejoined Mr. Jorrocks, feeling he had been making a great fool of himself. "Did she? Then tell your little gal she'd made a mistake."

"Then I can't do nothin' for you?" observed the man, after a pause.

"In course you can," replied Mr. Jorrocks; "you can catch my 'oss for me."

"Is he near at hand?" asked the man.

Mr. Jorrocks.—"That I don't know. Far or near, I'll give ye 'alf-a-crown for bringin' 'im to me."

"Doubt I darcn't ventur," replied the man reluctantly.

Mr. Jorrocks.—"Huts, there's nobody to 'urt ye."

"Can't go so far from home," rejoined the man.

Mr. Jorrocks (brightening up).—"Wot! you live near 'ere do ye?"

"Not far off," replied the man, with a jerk of his head, as much as to say, "I'm not going to tell you."

Mr. Jorrocks.—"Well, but p'raps you could get me summut to drink, for my 'oss has run away with my monkey, and I'm fit to die of habsolute unquenchable thirst."

The man eyed him suspiciously, and at length drawled out, "What, you've been hunting, have you?"

" 'Deed, 'ave I," replied our master; "started afore daylight

"It 'll be Mr. Jorrocks, I dessay," observed the man, with an air of enlightenment.

"Wot, you knows me, do ye!" exclaimed our master, brightening up.

"Yes, sir—no, sir—that's to say, sir, I know your huntsman, sir —Mr. Pigg, sir."

"Indeed," mused Mr. Jorrocks.

"Mr. Pigg and I are very old friends, sir," continued the man, "very old friends, indeed—most respectable man, Mr. Pigg, sir— most fortunate in having such a servant."

"Humph," grunted Mr. Jorrocks, not being quite so sure of that.

"Finest sportsman in the world, sir—can do a'most anything— sing a song, dance a jig, grin for baccy, play dominoes, prick i' the belt, or thimblerig. If that man could have got a spirit licence he'd ha' made a fortin. He'd ha' bin the first man o' the day."

"In-deed," mused our master.

"Most accomplished gentleman," continued the speaker—"most accomplished gentleman. I'd rayther have James Pigg for a partner than any man I ever saw."

"And pray may I ax your name?" inquired our master, curious to know something more of his huntsman's friend.

"Oh, my name's Turveylow, Tom Turveylow, but he won't know me by that name. Whiskey Jim," added he, dropping his voice with a knowing leer, "is the name he'll know me by."

"I twig," winked our master. "You 'aven't a drop o' the cretur with ye, 'ave ye?"

"Hard-bye," replied the man, "hard-bye," jerking his thumb over his shoulder.

"Let's at it," said Mr. Jorrocks, brightening up.

"You're safe, I s'pose," hesitated the man.

"Honour bright," replied Mr. Jorrocks; "wouldn't peach if it was ever so—"

"Well, I don't think any friend of Pigg's would," said the man, gaining courage; so saying he wheeled about, and beckoning Jorrocks to follow him, led the way, across the sharp sandy heath, towards a precipitous range of rocks, whose heights commanded an extensive view over the forest and surrounding country. It was towards their rugged base that they now directed their steps.

Passing some large upright stones, that guarded the entrance to
a sort of outer court, they came all at once upon the smuggler's
cave.

"Bow your head and bow your body," said the man, turning
and suiting the action to the word as he reached the frowning
portcullis-like rock that guarded the entrance.

"Come on! come on! you've nothin' to fear," cried he, seeing
Jorrocks stood irresolute, "there's no honester man in the world
than your humble servant."

"Self-praise is no commendation," muttered our master, going
down on all-fours preparatory to creeping under the beetling rock.
This let him into the smuggler's ante-room, a cold, damp, dropping den, formed from a natural cavity in the rock. Beyond was
a larger, loftier cave, and over a bright wood fire, illuminating
the hard walls, was a fine Venetian-shaped girl, in a tight blue
bodice and red flannel petticoat, chucking the savoury contents of
a frying-pan up in the air.

Her back being turned, she was not aware of the enterers,
until her temporary lord and master exclaimed, "Sally! Here's
old keep-the-tambourine-a-roulin's master."

"Lawk, Jim! 'ow could you bring a gent when I 'aven't got
my stockin's on?" exclaimed the lady, whisking around and showing the beautiful symmetry of her delicate white legs. She then
turned her lustrous eyes upon our friend and basilisked him with
a smile. Mr. Jorrocks stood transfixed. He thought he had never
seen a greater beauty. Sir Archey Depecarde's housekeeper was
nothing to her.

"Take a seat, sir, take a seat," said the smuggler, sweeping a
bundle of nets and snares off a stool—for of course he combined
the trade of a poacher with that of smuggler—and placing it behind our master. Mr. Jorrocks did as he was bid, and sat lost
in the novelty of the scene, the beauty of the lady, and the savouri-
ness of the pig's-fry she was cooking.

"You'll take your dinner with us, sir, I hope," said the smuggler, possessing himself of our master's hat and whip. "You'll take
your dinner with us, sir, I hope," adding, as he chucked them
into a corner, "Any friend of Pigg's is welcome here."

"Much plissur," replied Mr. Jorrocks, who all of a sudden
waxed "uncommon hungry."

"Get the gent a plate and things, Ann," said the smuggler to the little girl who had reported J.'s vagaries on his back.

The implements of eating were quickly placed on the already set-out table, and our party were presently at work at the fry, which was followed by roast potatoes and a jugged hare, late a tough old denizen of the forest; oatcake, cheese, and bottled ale completed the repast. Mr. Jorrocks played a most satisfactory knife and fork, declaring, as he topped up with a heavy cannonade of whisky, that he couldn't have dined better with the Grocers' Company.

"Good stuff that," said the smuggler, with a knowing wink at the bright sparkling whisky.

"Capital," replied Mr. Jorrocks, replenishing his glass.

"I toast you, sir," said the smuggler, bowing, glass in hand, to our master.

"You do me proud," said Mr. Jorrocks, returning the salute.

"Not at all, sir," replied the condescending host. "I believe you to be a most respectable man."

Mr. Jorrocks next looked towards the lady, who acknowledged the compliment with a sweet glance.

The smuggler then, as in duty bound, gave the health of his royal partner, the Queen, after which other loyal and patriotic toasts followed, and Mr. Jorrocks gave the ladies generally, adding, as he leered at his hostess, that he "liked a fine, well-flavoured ooman." He then began to get noisy. It was the old story.

"You must (hiccup) with my 'ounds (hiccup), best 'ounds goin' (hiccup), best 'ounds in (hiccup) England. Best 'ounds in (hiccup) Europe—best 'ounds in (hiccup) Europe, Hasia, Haf-rica, 'Merica— (hiccup) ." Then, as he rolled about on his stool, forgetting there was no back to it, he lost his balance, and kicking up the ricketty table with his toes, came heavily down on his back. What happened after is matter of uncertainty, for the next thing our master remembers was finding himself getting trans-ferred from a light-tilted cart on a bright frosty night into a Handley Cross fly, at Rosemary Lane gate; but when he came to pay the man his fare he found his purse was gone, which he might have thought had dropped out of his pocket into the car, were it not that his watch was wanting too. However, being at home, he just told Betsey to pay the fare, and clambered upstairs to bed as if nothing " 'ticlar" had happened. And next day Pigg gave such a wonderful account of the run, and how he would have killed the fox half-a-dozen times if he had only had Jorrocks to help him, that our master, forgetting all his promises to Diana, very soon had another turn at the forest.

Mr. Jorrocks's next adventure in the hunting line originated in a very furious letter from a gentleman, signing himself "John Gollarfield, farmer, Hardpye Hill," complaining bitterly of the devastation of his hen-roost, and calling loudly for vengeance against the foxes. Accordingly our master made a meet for Hardpye Hill, instead of Langton Pound, as he intended.

The road to the hill lying through some roomy enclosures, and Christmas having let loose its enterprise upon the country, great was the spurting and racing that marked the line there. Mr. Jorrocks, arrayed in his best pink, jogged pompously on with his cavalcade, receiving the marked attention of the country. Arrived at the hill, he turned into a grass field to give his hounds a roll and hear the news of the day—how Miss Glancey was after Captain Small—how Mrs. Buss had captivated old Frill. Then, when the cantering, smoking cover hack swells came up, they resolved themselves into a committee of taste, scrutinising this hound and that, passing their opinions on the pack generally, and on the Bugginson hounds in particular. Some thought they were coarse, some thought they were common; but when they heard they were drafts from the Quorn, they were unanimous in thinking they must be good—especially when Mr. Jorrocks broadly hinted he had given Day ten guineas a couple for them. The noise the party made prevented their hearing sundry ominous moans and lows in the neighbourhood, which gradually rose to a roar, until a simultaneous crash, and cry of "Mind the bull!" drew all eyes to the bank of the adjoining fence, where, with head down and tail up, a great roan bull was seen poising himself preparatory to making a descent upon the field. Down he came, with a roar that shook the earth to the very centre, and sent the field flying in all directions. Mr. Jorrocks, who was on foot among his hounds, immediately rushed to his horse, which Ben had let loose, but making a bad shot at the stirrup, he became a *point d'appui* for the bull, who after him with a vigour and determination that looked very like a finisher. Our master was carried, clinging to the neck, half across the field in a "now on, now off" sort of way that would have made any one feel very uncomfortable who had an annuity depending on his life. At last he got fairly into his saddle, and setting himself down to ride, he threw his heart boldly over a stiff "on and off," and shoved Xerxes at it in a way that proved too many for the bull. Ploughing up the pasture with his feet, in his effort to stop himself as he neared it, he tossed his great wide-horned head in the air, and uttering a frightful bellow that thundered through the valley and reverberated on Hardpye Hill, he turned, tail erect, to take a run at some one else. And having succeeded by the aid of gates in placing a couple more enclosures between them, Mr. Jorrocks sought a rising ground, from which he thought over the magnitude of his adventure, and how he would like to have Leech to draw him taking the leap. And having gained breath as he magnified it, and having duly congratulated himself upon his escape, he out with his horn and blew his hounds together, leaving Hardpye Hill as he came, and entering among the anathemas in his Journal the following:

"Con-found all farmers says I, wot don't tie up their bulls!"

A bad beginning in this case did not make a good ending, for though our master drew on till dark, which it was at half-past two, he never had a touch of a fox, and he sent word to Gollarfield, by the mole-catcher, that he was a "rug'lar 'umbog," and Pigg desired the man to add that he would fight him for what he pleased.

The smuggler was right in his estimate of Pigg's abilities, for, in addition to his great talents for hunting, he had a turn for low gambling, which the uninitiated sometimes confuse with legitimate sporting. Among other things, he was in the habit of betting on the weight of people's pigs, backing his own opinion as to what they were, or would feed up to, against the opinions of others; quite as useful and praiseworthy a pursuit, by the way, as people backing horses they have never seen, and over whose running they can exercise no control: be that as it may, however, Pigg was in the habit of exercising his judgment in that way, and had been highly successful at Handley Cross. He had come nearer the weight of Giles Jollyjowle's pig than eleven others, and had completely distanced all competitors in his estimate of Blash, the barber's, Hampshire hogs. He had also carried off the sweepstakes at two goose clubs, and received the second prize in a race for a hat. In addition to all this, his "cousin" Deavilboger, who, notwithstanding their little difference about hunting, had still a sort of sneaking regard for "wor James," had marked his appreciation of the festive season of the year, by sending him a large grey hen of whisky, so that, what with his winnings and it, James was generally in a state of half fuddle. He would take as much as he could manage if kept quiet, and more than he could manage if put into motion. Now, as bad luck would have it, our uneasy, insatiable master, wishing to retrieve his blank day before the usual stoppage of the season, thought to get something out of the fire by a quiet "bye" at Newtimber Forest, the scene of his former misfortunes. Pigg, who had just paid his second morning visit to the hen, did not make any decided objection to the proposal, backed as it was by Mr. Jorrock's plausible observation, that at that critical season of the year it "be'oved them to get every day they possibly could," and it was not until they reached the Copperchink Gate, and Pigg pressed a sovereign on the woman's acceptance for the toll, desiring her, when told to wait for his change, to "keept it," adding, that their " 'ard Maister had plenty o' brass," that Jorrocks was aware how matters stood. Recollecting, however, the "Cat and Custard-pot" scene, Mr. Jorrocks did not make any observation, but quietly getting his silver, trotted on as if it was "all right," hoping Pigg would sober as he went. When they got to Foggythorpe Green, where the road diverges through the fields, another scene occurred. Pigg wanted to pay the field-gates, and holloaed at a woman who happened to be passing, to "tak' her money," tendering a shilling, as if he had been kept waiting at a turnpike-gate for an hour. Next, as he was making, as he thought, a most sagacious steer through a gate, his eye deceived him as to the number of posts, and, catching by his toe, he was swept head foremost off into a complete hip-bath of mud. He was too wise, however, to let go his hold of the bridle, and as the horse kept smelling at him as he lay under his nose, Pigg kept vociferating, "Sink, they dinna mak' their yets hafe wide enough! They dinna mak' their yets hafe wide enough, ar say!" At length Mr. Jorrocks got him raised and scraped, and stuck straight on his horse, and they proceeded on their course together. Arrived at the wood, Mr. Jorrocks, thinking the best plan would

be to humour him, said if Pigg would go one way, he would go
the other, which James assenting to, the hounds dashed into cover,
and master and man proceeded to "yoicks" and crack their whips,
having the hounds in a widening space between them. The wood
was thick and rough, and as Jorrocks proceeded, Pigg's unearthly
notes gradually died out, and our master had all the noise to
himself. Being fond of the sound of his own voice, he proceeded,
yoicking and cracking his whip, exhorting the hounds to "find
'im," and keeping a good lookout ahead, when, to his surprise,
at a cross ride, Pigg's horse came snorting and cantering towards
him. Pigg, feeling uncomfortable, had laid down to sleep, and
left his horse to his own devices. "W-o-a-y, my man! W-o-a-y!"
cried Jorrocks, fishing at him with his whip as he approached,
which only caused the horse to start and rush past him at a gallop.
"W-H-O-A-Y, my man," roared Jorrocks, as the horse went scut-
tling down the ride without rhyme or reason. "Con-found the
hanimal," continued Mr. Jorrocks, as he eyed him staring about
from side to side with the reins all dangling about his feet. "Con-
found the hanimal," repeated he, "was there ever sich a daft divil
as that?—was there ever sich a misfortunit individual as John
Jorrocks? Cuss that Pigg, I wish I'd never seen 'im—worst varmint
I ever knew. Yoicks, Lavender, good betch! Bet a guinea 'at we
find a fox, and the 'ounds run clean away from me. Lose either
them or my dinner, or both. Well," continued Mr. Jorrocks,
spurring on to where Lavender was feathering,—"well, needs must
when a certain old gen'l'man drives, but if I 'ad my own way,
it would be ' 'ome, sweet 'ome,' for me. Dublin Bay 'addocks, with
appropriate sauce, goose, and happle pye. Oh dear! A fox! for
a 'underd; a fox! for anything that anybody likes to say," continued our master, staring his eyes out as he gets his horse short
by the head. "Now for ten miles as the crow flies, with ten bottom-
less brucks, and Berwickshire doubles without end. Ah! thank
'eavens it's not!" continued he, as a great banging hare bounced
out of the wood, and took down the ride with Lavender full cry
after her, and Jorrocks cracking his whip full cry after Lavender.
At length he stopped her, and taking advantage of the partial
scoring to cry off the hounds, he out with his horn and blew a
shrill reverberating blast that drew out the rest, and away he
rode with the hounds all clustering about his horse's heels as if

he was going to lay them on to a scent, but in reality to get them
out of cover. The horn operated doubly, for a smock-frocked coun-
tryman, having caught Pigg's horse, came cantering up to its
sound, and Jorrocks and he were presently on the Woodford and
Handley Cross Road. Promising the man half a crown and his
dinner for seeing him safely home, Mr. Jorrocks started away at
a brisk trot, hoping he was getting rid of Pigg for good. And when
"wor James" awoke, and learnt from a tape-selling tramp what had
happened, he was very wroth, and vowed "he wouldn't stand
such work—he wadn't be robbed in that sort of way—no, he wadn't.
He'd hev redress. He'd hev justice—yis, he'd hev justice—he wasn't
to be treated in that sort of way;" and he talked and fretted himself into believing that he had been most infamously used. Finding
there was a magistrate in the neighbouring village of Yelverton,
thither he directed his steps, and gaining an audience, boldly
accused his master of stealing his horse, and applied for a warrant
for his apprehension. The justice, seeing the maudlin state he
was in, humoured the application, but pretending it would be
necessary, in consequence of a recent decision that a man may
help himself to a horse to forward him on a journey, to see that
Mr. Jorrocks had not taken it for that purpose, he got Pigg into
his dog-cart and had him driven over to Handley Cross.

And when Mr. Jorrocks reproved him for his improprieties,
he replied that he (Jorrocks) "had no business out a hontin' on a
drinkin' day."

We will again have recourse to our worthy friend's journal
for an outline of such proceedings as are not of sufficient importance to demand separate chapters to themselves. The following
seems an original idea.

"Notice from the churchwardens and overseers, that in consequence of several mad dogs havin' made their appearance, all
dogs were to be muzzl'd, and requirin' me to see that the 'ounds
were properly muzzl'd before they went out to hunt. Wrote and
told them I didn't believe there were such a set of jackasses in
Her Majesty's dominions as to suppose an M.F.H. would go out
with a pack of muzzl'd hounds.—Absurd! This is Mello's doing.
Will pay him off.

"New Year's Day.—Sich a crowd! Sich compliments of the
season, and sich screws. Old Doleful grinnin' about on Fair Rosa-

mond like Death on the Pale 'Oss. Found in the Cloud Quarries,
but might as well have been in the clouds, the field surrounded it
so, and drove the fox into the mouth of the 'ounds. A young
gentleman in nankeens and patent leather boots, rode over old
Barbara. 'That's right!' exclaimed Pigg, 'ride amang 'em!—ride
amang 'em! Kill a hund or two; we've plenty mair at Hyem! It
mun be a poor concern that won't stand a hund a-day.' Differ
from Pigg there though. Howsomever, old Barbara ain't worth
much. Declared she was the best in the pack notwithstandin'.

"Staunton Snivey.—Batsay brought up shavin' water, saying
Binjimin wished to be excused 'unting, havin' got the gout. All
moonshine, I dare say! Boy has no passion for the chase. Have a
good mind to stuff him full of Hunter's pills, and see if they will
have any effect upon him. Wot business has a boy like him with
the gout! Only for rear-admirals, town counsellors, and such like
cocks. Caught Charley pinchin' Belinda under the table. Mounted
him on Xerxes, as Ben couldn't go. Largish field, Captain Thompson (who never pays his three pounds) observed he never saw a
pack of fox-hounds without a whip before, and muttered somethin' about Master livin' out of the hounds. Shall set Fleecy at him.

"Drew Longford Plantations; then on to Fawsley Wood.
Found immediately, but Reynard inclined to hang in cover. No
great scent either, but cover surrounded with foot-people and
little holiday boys. Bin useful in coaxin' them into crowds, to
listen to his 'hallegations,' as he calls his lies. At length Reynard
broke from the West end, and made straight for Iver Heath,
runnin' a wide circuit by Staunton Snivey, and over the hill, up
to Bybury Wood. Scent poor and pace bad. All the holiday hobble-
dehoy boys treadin' on the 'ounds' tails. A short check at Farmer
Hayband's, and thought all was over, when Priestess hit it off in
a grass field behind the barn, and away they went with the scent
improvin' at every yard. Pace changed from an 'unting run to a
reg'lar bust, and quite straight over the cream of the country.

"How the trail lengthened! A quarter of a mile, increasin' as
they went. Young gen'lemen, charged to bring home the brush,
found their grass ponies beginnin' to gape. Captain Shortflat made
Duncan Nevin's mare cry Capevi on Hutton Bank top, and many
bein' anxious to give in, great was the assistance he received.
Major Spanker would bleed her in the jugular, Mr. Wells thought

the thigh vein, and another thought the toe, so that the mare stood a good chance of being bled to death, if Duncan's man who was cruising about hadn't fortinately cast up and saved her from her friends.

"On the hounds went for Crew, passing Limbury, leaving Argod Dingle to the right, over the Lily-white Sand Railway near the station at Stope, pointing for Gore Cross, the fox finally taking refuge in a pig-sty behind the lodge of Button Park. Piggy at home and unfortunately killed, but who would grudge a pig after such a werry fine run?

"Pigg rode like a trump!—seven falls—knocked a rood of brickwall down with his 'ead. What a nob that must be! Charley left one of his Yorkshire coat-laps in a hedge—Barnington lost his hat—Hudson his whip—Mr. Ramshay a stirrup, and Captain Martyn his cigar-case. Only seven out of a field of sixty—day fine and bright—atmosphere clear, as if inclining for frost—hope not.

"January 7th.—Reg'lar decided black frost—country iron-bound—landscape contracted—roads dry as bones—mud scrapin's like granite—never saw so sudden a change; thought yesterday it looked like somethin'; the day changed, and hounds ran so hard in the afternoon; Pigg thinks it won't last, but I think it will; 'opes he'll be right.

"8th.—Frost semper eadem, 'arder and 'arder as Ego would say; windows frost fretted—laurels nipped—water-jugs frozen—shavin'-brush stiff—sponge stuck to water-bottle, and towel 'ard. Pigg still says it won't last—wish he may be right—little hail toward night.

"9th.—Alternate sun and clouds—slight powderin' of snow on cold and exposed places—largish flakes began to fall toward afternoon, and wind got up—purplish sun-set—walked hounds before Sulphur Wells Hall, after feedin', but they had a cold, dingy look, and I hadn't heart to blow my 'orn. Gabriel Junks doesn't seem to care about the cold, and gives no indication of a change.—Oh for one of his screams!

"10th.—Awoke, and found the country under two feet of snow. Well, it's always somethin' to know the worst, and be put out of suspense. Wind high, and drifted a large snow-wreath before the garden-gate—tempestersome day.—Can't stir out without gettin' up to the hocks in snow. Desired Binjimin to sweep the way to the stable and kennel. Boy got a broom, and began 'issing as if he were cleanin' an 'oss. Letter from Giles Shortland, requestin' the M.F.H. to subscribe to a ploughin' match at Tew. Answered that I should be werry 'appy to subscribe, and wish I could see them at work. Old Dame Tussac came with eight turkey-heads in a bag—fox had killed them last night, and she wanted pay. The bodies were at home—told her to bring the bodies—will make werry good stock for soup: one doesn't know but she may have sold the bodies. Wrote Bowker to go self and wife to sleep in my bed in Great Coram Street, to get it well haired. Shall run up to town and see the pantomime, and how things go on at the shop.

"Old Doleful called with a requisition for me to give a sportin' lector—axed wot I should lector upon—said he thought 'scent' would be a very good subject. Told him, all that could be said about scent was that it was a werry queer thing. Nothin' so queer as scent 'cept a woman. Told him to compose an oration upon it himself if he could. He then said summering the 'unter would be a good subject. Told him that corn and a run in the carriage was the true way of summering the 'unter. Riding to 'ounds he then thought would do. Told him I wasn't a 'g-u-r-r along! there are three couple of 'ounds on the scent' man at all, and ridin' arter 'ounds wouldn't draw. Didn't seem to take the difference but took his departure, which was just as well.

"LETTER FROM BOWKER.

" 'Honoured Sir,—Yours is received, and Mrs. B. and I will be proud to act the part of warming-pans. I suppose we may expect you in a day or two. You will be sorry to hear the poor Billy was hung this morning. *He died game.* As it was strongly suspected he had accomplices, a mitigation of punishment was offered if he would disclose his confederates. Billy listened sullenly to the offer, and passing his fingers through his thick curly hair, he said, "Look here, masters, if every hair on this head was a life, I wouldn't peach to save a single one." At length he confessed—*"I did boil the exciseman!"* said he. Poor Billy! All the little beggarly boys, and hoarse-throated scoundrels in the town are screaming his dying *speech* and confession about, when *"I did boil the exciseman,"* was all that he said. I am greatly distressed at poor Billy's fate.

> *'Take him for all and all,*
> *We ne'er shall look upon his like again.'*

" 'London is suicidically gloomy to-day—I feel as if I could cut my throat—would that I could leave it!—But

> *'The lottery of my destiny*
> *Bars me the right of voluntary choosing.'*

" 'I'm about tired of Old Twist. Our business is fast falling off, and an old man's trade never rallies. Might I take the liberty of asking if you think a snuff and cigar shop would answer at Handley Cross? I have a splendid new nigger, five feet six, with a coronet full of party-coloured feathers on his head, a sky-blue jacket with gold lace, and a pair of broad red-striped trousers, leaving half his black thighs bare, that I thought of setting at the door in Eagle Street, but would reserve him for the Cross, if you thought it would do. Of course, I would carry on business in Eagle Street as well—at least for the present; but I have plenty of canisters, wooden rolls of tobacco to stock a branch establishment, and Mrs. Bowker fancies a change of air would do her asthma good. Pray excuse the freedom, and believe me to remain,

" 'Dear Sir,

" 'Yours most respectfully,

" 'WM. BOWKER.

" 'To J. Jorrocks, Esq.' "

The Old Apple Tree Gang

By H. B. MARTIN

THE ST. ANDREWS clubhouse, an imposing and artistically modern edifice, stands majestically on a prominent eminence at Mt. Hope in Westchester County, New York, a fitting monument to American golf. The imperishable fame of the mother club—the first to be organized in this country and to preserve its continuity—will last forever in the history of golf in the United States.

We shall trace the nomadic wanderings of these original pathfinders from that inauspicious beginning in Reid's cowpasture to their present home where they have been comfortably located for forty years and where they are destined to remain unless something unforeseen changes their plans. It was not without many trials and tribulations that the little club carried on before moving up the valley to settle permanently.

It will be necessary to turn back a few years to a clear crisp winter's day in February, 1888, to ascertain what prompted the organization of that first golf club. It was on February twenty-second, Washington's Birthday to be exact, that John Reid invited some of his cronies to his cowpasture across the street from his home in Yonkers for the purpose of playing a game of golf. The "sticks" brought over by Lockhart had already been satisfactorily tested and approved, so the principals who were to play such an important part in that first game were all set and ready to go. Washington's Birthday being a holiday, the men were hanging around the house with not much to do. As the weather was favorable there was a keen interest exhibited by the participants in the foray and by the gallery that had come to look on.

From "Fifty Years of American Golf," Dodd, Mead.

That morning bright and early three improved holes were laid out, not much in the way of a test, but something that would serve the purpose. There was only one set of clubs, enough for two players by passing them back and forth, so it was decided that John Reid and John B. Upham should play and the others look on.

This preliminary exhibition was impressed very much upon the minds of all concerned. In a controversy about the first golf played at Yonkers, Alexander P. W. Kinnan, one of the onlookers, volunteered the information that it was on February 22, 1888; and this date was corroborated by Kingman N. Putnam who was also there and recalled with regret that he was not able to play on account of a shortage of golfing material. Other spectators were Henry O. Tallmadge, who lived next door to the pasture and who was much younger than the other members of the original players, Harry Holbrook and John C. Ten Eyck.

Had the start been delayed three weeks, the weather would not have been so propitious, as it would have encountered the greatest blizzard in the history of New York—the famous snow-storm of March 12, which tied up traffic for several days. Later, with the coming of the first crocuses of spring and the opportunity to get out on the cowpasture again at hand, enthusiasm was revived and the miniature playground was becoming cramped and inadequate. Some more clubs and balls had been secured, so all who were interested could play. The three short holes did not allow enough room to give vent to the player's feelings, especially when he elected to let out at the ball. The decision was quickly made to move to a larger field around the corner, where they planned to build a real course with both length and breadth. There were thirty acres in the parcel of land that they selected on the northeast corner of Broadway and Shonnard Avenue. It was owned by John C. Shotts, the local butcher, a thrifty German who thought it wise to buy land in the vicinity of New York City and hold on to it. Shotts' thirty acres were preempted, but the wise old German made no complaint, as he considered it poor business to exact the meager rent the land would bring him from a class of men who were his best customers.

The little band of pioneers was off to a new start and they went about playing the game with a determination and perseverance that must be admired. They withstood the gibes of the populace and turned a deaf ear to criticism. They went on about their recreation, tending strictly to their own affairs. This little group must be given credit for American golf, because they were the first to start the little ball rolling and to keep it rolling through all these years. There were other attempts to play golf in this country, as we shall see later, but none of these other venturesome pioneers had the temerity to follow through.

The new layout on the butcher's meadow offered possibilities. It was rolling terrain and, as it was good pasture land, the turf was highly satisfactory. The main hazard was a road, or footpath, which wound its way through the property. It had not occurred to any of the original players that an old tomato can was about the right size and shape for a golf hole so the holes were merely scooped out with the blade of a cleek. The greens, once worthy of the name since they had originally a grass surface, were soon worn bare from constant tramping.

Golfers will be interested in the photograph of this old course, the first picture of a golf game in the United States. It was made by S. Hedding Fitch, a brother of Judge Theodore Fitch whose nearly completed home is shown in the background. It will be noticed that there were no caddie bags in those days and the original caddies, Warren and Fred Holbrook, sons of Harry Holbrook, one of the principals, carried the clubs over their shoulders. Bob Davis extracted an interesting interview from Frederick Holbrook shortly before he died. It is substantially as follows:

"The first clubhouse was a table in Mr. Fitch's backyard. The only club furnishings consisted of a couple of boards supported on two empty barrels. Tubs of ice, pails of water and other paraphernalia were arranged underneath. I suppose this architectural monstrosity should have been called a bar. At all events it was presided over by a colored employee of Mr. Reid's. That was the first 'nineteenth hole' in the United States. Later a tent was placed directly north of the stable where the club took up its quarters during the summer months. Reid's servant was a handy man and helped to keep the grass on the fairways in playable condition. Mr. Tallmadge had a gardener who was also willing to lend a hand in cutting grass and doing odd jobs."

Outside those mentioned the original pioneers included Dr.

Henry Moffat, Perit C. Meyers, George Hunter and W. D. Baldwin. As they established their first nine-hole course, all these players were self-taught. The first golf medal to be offered for competition in the United States was the club championship medal which was won in 1889 by Perit C. Meyers. Later another medal was offered, for play in the handicap singles, which was won by John C. Ten Eyck. This medal can be seen on display at the St. Andrews Club and is now among its treasured possessions. The original championship medal is in possession of Harold A. Sands, whose father, W. H. Sands, by virtue of having won the club championship three times, became the owner of the prize. St. Andrews' many appeals to Harold Sands to return it to the original source where it can be placed on display have gone for naught. The owner cherishes it more than the club and is reluctant to let it pass out of his hands.

The original golf sticks included three wooden clubs, a driver, a brassie and a spoon; and three irons, a cleek, a sand iron and a putter. Henry O. Tallmadge, the only one of the original pioneers alive, has supplied the author with much information about those early days. He recalls that six clubs constituted a set and that each player had a special mark, usually a band of paint around the shaft, to distinguish his property. Only two guttie balls were carried, as few balls were lost. The ball generally favored was the Eclipse which cost 35 cents. Clubs cost from $2 to $2.50 each. Repairs were something to worry about, as clubs were forever being broken. John Reid was president of the J. L. Mott Iron Works at Mott Haven and he saved the men some trouble by turning over the repair jobs to one of his carpenters.

That original course on Broadway was all that was needed to secure peace and happiness, filling the cup of joy to overflowing for those early golfers. Discussions came up from time to time about acquiring more land and building a better course, but it was always decided negatively by John Reid, who was first, last and always a conservative. So the old stamping ground remained the home of St. Andrews until encroaching civilization drove them out. They had stuck like leeches for four years and might have remained longer had the city fathers of Yonkers not seen fit to extend Palisade Avenue farther north, right through the heart of the old golf course. There were no chattels except the few sets of clubs, a tent and a wicker demijohn. So like the ancient Arabs they silently folded their tent and stole away although it may not have been in the middle of the night; the following day, however, found them pleasantly located and ready to carry on. The trail had led northward up the newly planned Palisade Avenue about a quarter of a mile. The little band of wanderers found refuge in an apple orchard on the Weston estate.

It required the greater part of one day to lay out the new course, as there was more or less difficulty experienced in adapting the links to the ground available. The holes had to be woven in and out among the apple trees without sacrificing so much as a limb. There were thirty-four acres, so the course could be stretched a little. This land too was preempted but the golfers were not unwelcome as they had by this time become necessary evils in the community. It was still thought unnecessary to adopt the tomato can standardization which other early courses had popularized. The original way of making holes was plenty good enough for the apple orchard, so the holes were again scooped out with the cleek. St. Andrews may have been more or less instrumental in selling golf to the rest of the United States, but it could never persuade the new clubs to follow its rather primitive method of making a hole in the green. Some of the other courses had tomato cans, pea cans and flower pots, and one club had imported steel cups from the other side of the Atlantic.

It was on this new course on Palisade Avenue that the players became known as the "Old Apple Tree Gang," a name that seemed to be decidedly appropriate, as apple trees made the principal hazards; one in particular which stood near the first tee became an integral part of the club itself since it served as a locker room and a nineteenth hole. In the crotch of the friendly tree the men in the hot days of summer laid their coats. From one of the branches hung a basket of sandwiches and from another the old wicker demijohn of Scotland's favorite thirst-quencher.

Just thirteen players had come up from the old cowpasture course, not altogether an unlucky number as things turned out. Once settled in the new quarters the club instituted an active membership drive, and in the next two years seven members were added. The newcomers who were induced to try out the game and joined in the summer of '92 to make up the famous "gang" were

Walter E. Hodgeman, William R. Innis and Rev. W. M. Bottome. John F. Thompson, David Henderson, Rev. William S. Rainsford and Irving K. Taylor were in the class of '93. These men completed the list of twenty immortals who have enjoyed the privilege of St. Andrews since the old apple orchard days.

The famous old apple tree has been preserved as a fitting symbol of early American golf. Those interested in antiquity and curious enough to want to see this old heirloom will find it enshrined in the garden of the Daniels residence at 625 Palisade Avenue, Yonkers. Some time ago Bob Davis, St. Andrews' able historian—who, like most newspaper men, was interested in anything that possessed historical possibilities—was permitted to extract a piece of wood from the tree, which he mounted and sent to the Prince of Wales, now King Edward VIII, who in turn presented it to the St. Andrews Golf Club in Scotland when he was captain of the Royal and Ancient Club.

The new membership didn't exactly blend with the original thirteen, and the spirit of supreme contentedness began to diminish. There developed dissatisfaction in the ranks, due to certain growing factions. In most clubs there are conservatives and progressives, and this was true of the first club. Reid was a conservative and his closest friends strung along with him. He insisted that it was not the intention of the St. Andrews Club to teach the rest of the United States the game of golf or to establish any precedents or set any standards in golf course construction. He pointed out that the little organization had plenty of honest recreation and no heartaches and that it might be folly to expand. Harry Tallmadge was a decided liberal and was heartily supported by W. D. Baldwin and Walter E. Hodgeman. These men argued that all the other courses of importance had nine holes and Chicago had put in eighteen holes at Wheaton. All of these clubs had at least twice as many members as St. Andrews. Shinnecock Hills had a membership of 75 and they too were talking about eighteen holes; they had a fine clubhouse too. It was this latter club that awakened the old apple tree gang from its lethargy.

The conservatives might stand the gibes that were hurled their way in connection with "cowpasture pool," but they were nothing compared to what they had to take from the liberals. One wit suggested that they became dormie six that first summer back in

'88 and remained that way (this was a slap at the old six-hole layout). They were also charged with never getting away from the shade of the old apple tree, a bit of irony that was not exactly appreciated. With these indictments against the members, the club arose *en masse* and decided to do something about it.

A committee on selecting a new site was organized for action and without much hesitation decided upon the Odell farm at Grey Oaks. Again we pick up the trail of the nomads, which was east by north, about three miles up the Sawmill River Road. The old farm lay between a long stretch of abruptly rising ground called Snake Hill, and the Road. Nine holes were laid out and by May eleventh the club was on the move. It was a happy little group that filed out of the old apple orchard with their cherished possessions under their arms to follow the trail northward. At last they were going some place and the twenty members, born of a new spirit, were united and determined to wage war against Colonel Bogey as a single unit. For six years they had never had a clubhouse, but now they were to have a real home, a locker room to shelter them from the Hudson's breezes and a place to store their golfing kits.

There was romance and mystery connected with the new quarters and some apprehension on the part of some of the gang. In taking over the Odell Mansion the club did so with the full knowledge that the place was supposed to be haunted. A tragedy had been enacted there some time after the War of 1812, and ghosts had made it so uncomfortable for tenants that it was impossible to keep the property rented. It was one of the oldest farmhouses in Westchester County, originally built by Jacob Odell about 1790. Odell was an American patriot and later fought in the War of 1812.

When the story was sprung that the farmhouse was haunted some of the timid members of the club possessed with more or less of an imagination were not so keen about sharing the new clubhouse with spooks or apparitions. They had looked forward to this important occasion for six long years and when at last the day and hour had arrived for them to occupy their own home they wanted it free and clear of spectral visitors.

It was pointed out that the little band was composed of just thirteen members when they made the trek up Palisade Avenue to the apple orchard and no hard luck had ever pursued them. Those who entered the premises with any apprehension found their fears allayed, for just as soon as the old apple tree gang walked in the ghosts walked out. A crowd of golfers, especially when they came as an organized gang, was too much for an honest and intelligent ghost to countenance. This was flattering to the St. Andrews stalwarts who feared no mortal in the flesh and blood, let alone an unseen foe.

Arthur L. Livermore, now a prominent New York attorney, was looking after the Odell property and had leased the grounds to the club. He was persuaded to join the group and, since he had been a tennis player of no mean ability, he was willing to try golf. This settled lawn tennis so far as he was concerned. Livermore was so sure of himself that he listened to no advice the first time he tried to play. After missing the little ball and falling down completely on his haunches, he had some wholesome respect for the game. He enlisted the services of the new professional, Samuel Tucker, and got a foundation of the swing that stood him well in hand. Before the year was over he was one of the leading players in the club. Livermore took an unflagging interest in the game and also in the affairs of the club.

Harry Tallmadge recalls that it took at least a couple of days to lay out the new course, but it was worth the time spent on it. It was not long before Willie Tucker joined his brother Samuel, and being a lad possessed with some ideas of golf architecture he helped rearrange some of the holes. Willie was later to lay out some important golf courses in the United States and Canada. Once St. Andrews were settled in their new home no one could accuse them of being laggards. Instead, they were almost immediately recognized as leaders in everything that was for the betterment of the game. One of the most enthusiastic was John Reid himself, who played the game at every opportunity and took it upon himself to see that no guest ever came to the club without being accorded a welcome. The sentiment that clustered around the old apple tree gang was soon forgotten in the rush of newcomers to join the club.

The course was attractive because it was accessible by train rather than by horse and buggy. It was just a little beyond Yonkers on the N. Y. & Putnam R. R. Today the old site is almost within

the shadow of New York's skyscrapers, but times and conditions
have changed in transportation facilities.

The list of new members who joined the first summer were
Henry W. Taft, Andrew Carnegie, William H. Sands, John Ken-
drick Bangs, who often brought Sir Arthur Conan Doyle around,
Peter Fletcher, one of the first golfers to come to this country
from Carnoustie, Francis V. Hoppin, Harold Sanderson, J. Q. A.
Johnston, Rev. Roderick Terry, Oliver Harriman, John G. Peene,
mayor of Yonkers, Gerrett Smith, C. T. Barney, H. Mortimer
Brooks, Daniel Chauncey, Judge Horace Russell, J. F. Thompson,
C. C. Worthington, who made the Worthington mowers and
founded Shawnee-on-Delaware, George E. Armstrong, R. Bage
Kerr who later became secretary of the U.S.G.A., succeeding Tall-
madge, S. D. Bowers, Thomas W. Stiles, Harry Beecher and
Francis B. Allen.

St. Andrews soon acquired the reputation of having the best
golf team in the entire country. "Those crack St. Andrews golfers"
cleaned up every team they played, as a rule. Some of the stars
were Arthur L. Livermore, W. H. Sands, Larry Stoddard, David
Henderson, Johnnie Upham, Rev. W. S. Rainsford and H. Holbrook Curtis.

The old apple tree gang had never found any incentive to
dress for golf affairs because red coats didn't seem to go in the
cowpastures and the apple orchard. But when the Shinnecock
Hills boys and the Newport swells came out in their scarlet melton
coats, fancy knickers or flannels, and gaiters resembling elongated
spats, it made the Grey Oaks golfers sit up and take notice.

St. Andrews then adopted a uniform. The club, to a man,
appeared in full golfing regalia after they had taken the most
meticulous care in choosing their colors. There was first of all
the red coat with the brass buttons; but the St. Andrews dandies
in addition wore blue checked waistcoats, pearl gray hats with
blue and white bands, gray knickers, Scotch plaid hose, and gray
gaiters. A blue checked cap was for the links. To make the St.
Andrews coat distinctive, the collar was a blue field with the silver
cross of St. Andrew on it. One might choose his own tie but there
was always the uniform winged collar, the badge of a gentleman
of those days.

It was decided to run up the club colors on the flagpole on

the clubhouse ground, so Reid ordered a flag made. When it was unfurled to the Hudson breezes the members were prouder than ever of their new home; but this was only for a few brief and fleeting moments. Dave Henderson alighted from a train, gave one look at the flag and then broke into laughter. He rushed into the clubhouse where the boys were arrayed in their scarlet coats. "Take 'em off!" said Henderson with a tone of authority. "Get out your green coats and your shillalahs, begorra! It's St. Patrick's Day in the mornin'!"

The astonished members looked askance, as much as to say, "What in the devil is the matter with you? Have you gone off your nut?"

"Go out on the lawn and take a squint at the St. Patrick's flag," continued Henderson. "I thought this was supposed to be St. Andrews Golf Club."

The men rushed out on the lawn, but as none of them knew the difference between the two flags that they were supposed to pass judgment upon, it was explained that the flag displayed bore a red cross on a white field (St. Patrick's cross) while St. Andrew should be represented by a blue field with a silver or white cross. In both cases the cross is in the shape of an X, the only similarity. When Reid's attention was called to the mistake he admitted the error and St. Patrick's flag came down immediately. Later on the proper standard was hoisted in its place; all of this at Reid's expense since he admitted that the joke was on him. It turned out that the flagmaker knew the difference in the two flags and remonstrated with Tallmadge when he placed the order, but the honorable secretary insisted that Reid, being a Scotchman, knew what he was talking about.

Everyone took a pride in wearing those red coats. It was an ancient Scottish custom and time-honored. And there was an old country tradition that went with it. Any golfer appearing without his red coat was fined two shillings, some clubs fining the offender two quarters of Scotch. David Henderson paid dearly for playing in a match one day without taking time to change. He arrived at the club very late and, being pressed for time, went out on the links in his shirt sleeves. His zeal was costly in the extreme because some outsider stole a valuable watch and over a hundred dollars in bills from his coat and waistcoat which he had flung on the grass, not dreaming that it would be disturbed. He was so elated at winning his match that afternoon that he was welling to forget his financial loss; provided he was sure that the boys downtown in shipping circles, where he was well known, would not chaff him about it.

It was Harry Tallmadge who was instrumental in bringing Willie Park, Jr., the famous British professional, to this country. Willie was quite as capable a golfer as his famous father and had won the British open in 1887 and again in 1889. His fame as a player had not diminished any when he came over here in '95 to lay out courses and play exhibitions, and in other ways promote the game. Willie wore a red coat with a blue collar from his home course at Musselburgh. On the lapel of Willie's coat were the words "Far and Sure." Mr. Tallmadge, taking one look at the motto, remarked, "I guess we had better not get our coats mixed, as your coat would not look so well on some of us duffers."

Park played an exhibition match at St. Andrews shortly after he arrived. It was probably one of the most unusual matches ever played, and golfers who are always ready with an alibi will please take notice. He was matched against Willie Campbell of Brookline, who showed up with one hand swollen to twice the size of the other, due to an infection, and carefully wrapped in bandages. But he was showing no part of the quitter. Park came out holding his head on one side because of a huge boil on the back of his neck, covered with sticking plaster. This bothered him no little, but he too was willing to play for the edification of the large gallery, since there was much money wagered on the outcome. Park broke the course record that afternoon by two strokes, scoring an 81 and winning 6 and 5. However, Campbell was giving an exhibition of putting with that bad hand that made the gallery gasp in astonishment.

Golf in the nineties ran headlong into some of the old blue laws that were lying dormant on the statute books. Sunday baseball was taboo in New York State, although the law was not always enforced. In Yonkers the authorities were compelled to put a stop to Sunday games on account of the disturbance created in some peaceful neighborhoods. The ball players retaliated by taking their vengeance out of the Saegkill Golf Club whose members were peacefully pursuing the little white pill over hill and dale without arousing the displeasure of anyone. However, if baseball must stop on the Sabbath golf should cease also.

One Sunday afternoon Officer Tiernan arrived at the club to put a stop to the nonsense. He had come only to warn the offenders, but what was his surprise when H. O. Tallmadge and Benjamin Adams insisted upon being arrested, intending to make a test case out of it. The officer engaged a seagoing hack and took them to the police station where they furnished bail. The next day an unsympathetic judge was all for sending them to jail and imposing as large a fine as possible. However, he thought twice about the matter, and his final decision was to dismiss the case, much to the satisfaction of the intrepid officer of the law who meant no harm.

St. Andrews from the moment it left the old orchard at Yonkers began to make golf history. The members climbed on a pedestal of fame that might have been theirs in the very beginning if they had only seized the opportunity. The first thing the club did was to stage the initial amateur championship at match play. Later they became a factor in interclub play, and in the early winter Tallmadge gave a dinner that resulted in the organization of the U.S.G.A.

The first thing the club did of importance in '95 was to become incorporated; this happened on April 14. There seemed to be a surprise among clubs, then securely organized, that St. Andrews had not taken this step toward permanency earlier. John Reid in '96 sponsored a tournament at Van Cortlandt Park to awaken interest in public links. In the spring of '97, just before the club left Grey Oaks, or St. Andrews as the station was called then, the club took the initiative again and called the clubs in the district together to organize the Metropolitan Golf Association.

In the middle of August, '97, the St. Andrews Golf Club was on the move again. There was a rush to join the famous old club and a desire on the part of the golfers to establish an eighteen-hole links with a modern clubhouse where they could take their place under the sun and hold their head as high as other organizations who were boasting about their championship courses.

The club moved straight up the valley this time to Mt. Hope, again following the old Sawmill River Road. In October St. Andrews opened the new course officially with an inaugural tournament that brought the best amateurs in the country together.

Golf was at a somewhat lower ebb in '98, with the sinking of the Maine and the call to arms. The Johnnies went marching off to war and came marching home again. It was all over quickly but it lasted long enough to spoil a summer's golf for some of the lads who enlisted. There were other things happening to attract attention. Gold was discovered in large quantities in Alaska and many sought their fortune in the Klondike. The rush to Dawson City was even greater than the mad rush of the "Forty-niners" to San Francisco. Going to the Klondike was a hazardous undertaking and many who started to make the journey never got there.

After controlling the destinies of the club for nine years John Reid requested that his successor be named. The honor of leading the pilgrims was invested in John C. Ten Eyck, whose administration was anything but a pleasant one. Bob Davis commented upon the incident as follows:

"About this time an economic upheaval overtook the zealots. The upkeep of the Mt. Hope course, the development of new holes, an increase in the cost of everything, brought about a condition that required drastic measures to overcome. As a matter of fact, St. Andrews was on the point of sinking. Captain Ten Eyck threw up his periscope, scanned the seas, and spotted Joseph P. Thomas on the horizon. Mr. Thomas was chairman of the executive committee and displayed qualities of such proportions and diplomacy of such fine caliber that President Ten Eyck urged him to take the helm. Having retired from his New England connections with the Havemeyers and seeking recreation and relaxation outdoors, he turned his entire attention to club matters.

"Mr. Thomas was a free-spoken man and often used language that was anything but eloquent, but it was expressive and usually to the point. Once, in playing a game, he sliced his drive, which upset him considerably. Turning to his opponent he remarked: 'Right there is where we will build a trap. We'll show these short-driving, slicing so-and-so's that they can't get away with anything like that up here.'

"He was the St. Andrews Club and all the officers and officials rolled into one, an indefatigable worker who produced results and had the confidence and support of the members. He remained in office ten years and, as John Reid once said of him, 'he was the mainstay of the club.' "

Thomas was succeeded by Austin G. Fox, who remained in office ten years. His administration was also prosperous and progressive. In the midst of his term the World War broke out and eighty-three of the members enlisted for service. When Jock Hutchinson came to this country from St. Andrews, Scotland, it was here that he secured his first position as pro. For several years before the War the late Dan Healy was steward and manager, and no club was better handled. Dan always claimed that a club restaurant should be self-supporting, and he managed to show a profit each year.

To be a member of St. Andrews is an honor and distinction, as there is a feeling of permanency there that is not merely tradition. The conservatism of John Reid in the beginning has had something to do with a policy that has been followed through these fifty years. Today St. Andrews is as solid as the Rock of Gibraltar and could well serve as a model for all clubs who wish to balance their budgets. The club has a splendid curling rink which is well patronized by the members throughout the winter months. The club is proud of its golf course and has kept up with the march of progress. It has the finest watering system of any club in America, which is an insurance against summer droughts and parched fairways.

The castle on the hill which St. Andrews is proud to call its home is a paradise of security. A visitor is impressed with the cordial hospitality of the members and the efficiency of the employees who have been schooled to receive the guest with wholesome honor and respect.

There are many treasured trophies in the clubhouse at St. Andrews. Among the most important in age is the singles handicap medal which was played for in 1890 and '91. This was won first in August, '90, by H. O. Tallmadge. A month later W. D. Baldwin won and in November of that year it was won for the first time by J. C. Ten Eyck. In 1891 Dr. Henry Moffat won, in February; then Ten Eyck gained possession of the medal by winning it in June and later on in October of that year. Each name is inscribed on a gold bar. The medal is about the size of a half dollar, with the figure of a golfer engraved thereon. Ten Eyck returned the medal to the club.

St. Andrews would like to have among its mementos what is known as the first golf medal to be offered as a prize in America. This is the club championship medal played for first in '89 and won that year by P. C. Meyers.

It was won in 1890 by J. B. Upham, in 1891 by Dr. Henry Moffat, who also successfully defended his title in 1892. George Hunter came along the following year to claim recognition, and won the club championship in 1893. William H. Sands, who was fast improving as a golfer, having played abroad, won the medal three straight years in succession, '95, '96 and '97.

The most valuable trophy at St. Andrews is the George H. Hazen Cup which is played for once a year, the winner having his name engraved thereon. It reposes in a case set into the wall of the main lounge, a black velvet background bringing it out in all its splendor. It is a piece of antique Irish silver very handsomely engraved and bearing the Dublin hallmarks of 1834.

Horseshoes

By RING LARDNER

THE SERIES ended Tuesday, but I had stayed in Philadelphia an extra day on the chance of there being some follow-up stuff worth sending. Nothing had broken loose; so I filed some stuff about what the Athletics and Giants were going to do with their dough, and then caught the eight o'clock train for Chicago.

Having passed up supper in order to get my story away and grab the train, I went to the buffet car right after I'd planted my grips. I sat down at one of the tables and ordered a sandwich. Four salesmen were playing rum at the other table and all the chairs in the car were occupied; so it didn't surprise me when somebody flopped down in the seat opposite me.

I looked up from my paper and with a little thrill recognized my companion. Now I've been experting round the country with ball players so much that it doesn't usually excite me to meet one face to face, even if he's a star. I can talk with Tyrus without getting all fussed up. But this particular player had jumped from obscurity to fame so suddenly and had played such an important though brief part in the recent argument between the Macks and McGraws that I couldn't help being a little awed by his proximity.

It was none other than Grimes, the utility outfielder Connie had been forced to use in the last game because of the injury to

From "The Collected Short Stories of Ring Lardner," Charles Scribner's Sons.

Joyce—Grimes, whose miraculous catch in the eleventh inning had robbed Parker of a home run and the Giants of victory, and whose own homer—a fluky one—had given the Athletics another World's Championship.

I had met Grimes one day during the spring he was with the Cubs, but I knew he wouldn't remember me. A ball player never recalls a reporter's face on less than six introductions or his name on less than twenty. However, I resolved to speak to him, and had just mustered sufficient courage to open a conversation when he saved me the trouble.

"Whose picture have they got there?" he asked, pointing to my paper.

"Speed Parker's," I replied.

"What do they say about him?" asked Grimes.

"I'll read it to you," I said:

" 'Speed Parker, McGraw's great third baseman, is ill in a local hospital with nervous prostration, the result of the strain of the World Series, in which he played such a stellar role. Parker is in such a dangerous condition that no one is allowed to see him. Members of the New York team and fans from Gotham called at the hospital today, but were unable to gain admittance to his ward. Philadelphians hope he will recover speedily and will suffer no permanent ill effects from his sickness, for he won their admiration by his work in the series, though he was on a rival team. A lucky catch by Grimes, the Athletics' substitute outfielder, was all that prevented Parker from winning the title for New York. According to Manager Mack, of the champions, the series would have been over in four games but for Parker's wonderful exhibition of nerve and—' "

"That'll be plenty," Grimes interrupted. "And that's just what you might expect from one o' them doughheaded reporters. If all the baseball writers was where they belonged they'd have to build an annex to Mattewan."

I kept my temper with very little effort—it takes more than a peevish ball player's remarks to insult one of our fraternity; but I didn't exactly understand his peeve.

"Doesn't Parker deserve the bouquet?" I asked.

"Oh, they can boost him all they want to," said Grimes; "but when they call that catch lucky and don't mention the fact that

Parker is the luckiest guy in the world, somethin' must be wrong
with 'em. Did you see the serious?"

"No," I lied glibly, hoping to draw from him the cause of his
wrath.

"Well," he said, "you sure missed somethin'. They never was
a serious like it before and they won't never be one again. It went
the full seven games and every game was a bear. They was one
big innin' every day and Parker was the big cheese in it. Just as
Connie says, the Ath-a-letics would of cleaned 'em in four games
but for Parker; but it wasn't because he's a great ball player—it
was because he was born with a knife, fork and spoon in his
mouth, and a rabbit's foot hung round his neck.

"You may not know it, but I'm Grimes, the guy that made the
lucky catch. I'm the guy that won the serious with a hit—a home-
run hit; and I'm here to tell you that if I'd had one-tenth o'
Parker's luck they'd of heard about me long before yesterday.
They say my homer was lucky. Maybe it was; but, believe me, it
was time things broke for me. They been breakin' for him all
his life."

"Well," I said, "his luck must have gone back on him if he's
in a hospital with nervous prostration."

"Nervous prostration nothin'," said Grimes. "He's in a hospital because his face is all out o' shape and he's ashamed to appear
on the street. I don't usually do so much talkin' and I'm ravin'
a little to-night because I've had a couple of drinks; but—"

"Have another," said I, ringing for the waiter, "and talk some
more."

"I made two hits yesterday," Grimes went on, "but the crowd
only seen one. I busted up the game and the serious with the one
they seen. The one they didn't see was the one I busted up a
guy's map with—and Speed Parker was the guy. That's why he's
in a hospital. He may be able to play ball next year; but I'll bet
my share o' the dough that McGraw won't reco'nize him when
he shows up at Marlin in the spring."

"When did this come off?" I asked. "And why?"

"It come off outside the clubhouse after yesterday's battle,"
he said; "and I hit him because he called me a name—a name I
won't stand for from him."

"What did he call you?" I queried, expecting to hear one of the delicate epithets usually applied by conquered to conqueror on the diamond.

" 'Horseshoes!' " was Grimes' amazing reply.

"But, good Lord!" I remonstrated, "I've heard of ball players calling each other that, and Lucky Stiff, and Fourleaf Clover, ever since I was a foot high, and I never knew them to start fights about it."

"Well," said Grimes, "I might as well give you all the dope; and then if you don't think I was justified I'll pay your fare from here to wherever you're goin'. I don't want you to think I'm kickin' about trifles—or that I'm kickin' at all, for that matter. I just want to prove to you that he didn't have no license to pull that Horseshoes stuff on me and that I only give him what was comin' to him."

"Go ahead and shoot," said I.

"Give us some more o' the same," said Grimes to the passing waiter. And then he told me about it.

Maybe you've heard that me and Speed Parker was raised in the same town—Ishpeming, Michigan. We was kids together, and though he done all the devilment I got all the lickin's. When we was about twelve years old Speed throwed a rotten egg at the teacher and I got expelled. That made me sick o' schools and I wouldn't never go to one again, though my ol' man beat me up and the truant officers threatened to have me hung.

Well, while Speed was learnin' what was the principal products o' New Hampshire and Texas I was workin' round the freight-house and drivin' a dray.

We'd both been playin' ball all our lives; and when the town organized a semi-pro club we got jobs with it. We was to draw two bucks apiece for each game and they played every Sunday. We played four games before we got our first dough. They was a hole in my pants pocket as big as the home plate, but I forgot about it and put the dough in there. It wasn't there when I got home. Speed didn't have no hole in his pocket—you can bet on that! Afterward the club hired a good outfielder and I was canned. They was huntin' for another third baseman too; but, o' course, they didn't find none and Speed held his job.

The next year they started the Northern Peninsula League.

We landed with the home team. The league opened in May and blowed up the third week in June. They paid off all the outsiders first and then had just money enough left to settle with one of us two Ishpeming guys. The night they done the payin' I was out to my uncle's farm, so they settled with Speed and told me I'd have to wait for mine. I'm still waitin'!

Gene Higgins, who was manager o' the Battle Creek Club, lived in Houghton, and that winter we goes over and strikes him for a job. He give it to us and we busted in together two years ago last spring.

I had a good year down there. I hit over .300 and stole all the bases in sight. Speed got along good too, and they was several big-league scouts lookin' us over. The Chicago Cubs bought Speed outright and four clubs put in a draft for me. Three of 'em—Cleveland and the New York Giants and the Boston Nationals—needed outfielders bad, and it would of been a pipe for me to of made good with any of 'em. But who do you think got me? The same Chicago Cubs; and the only outfielders they had at that time was Schulte and Leach and Good and Williams and Stewart, and one or two others.

Well, I didn't figure I was any worse off than Speed. The Cubs had Zimmerman at third base and it didn't look like they was any danger of a busher beatin' him out; but Zimmerman goes and breaks his leg the second day o' the season—that's a year ago last April—and Speed jumps right in as a regular. Do you think anything like that could happen to Schulte or Leach, or any o' them outfielders? No, sir! I wore out my uniform slidin' up and down the bench and wonderin' whether they'd ship me to Fort Worth or Siberia.

Now I want to tell you about the miserable luck Speed had right off the reel. We was playin' at St. Louis. They had a one-run lead in the eighth, when their pitcher walked Speed with one out. Saier hits a high fly to center and Parker starts with the crack o' the bat. Both coachers was yellin' to him to go back, but he thought they was two out and he was clear round to third base when the ball come down. And Oakes muffs it! O' course he scored and the game was tied up.

Parker come in to the bench like he'd did something wonderful.

"Did you think they was two out?" ast Hank.

"No," says Speed, blushin'.

"Then what did you run for?" says Hank.

"I had a hunch he was goin' to drop the ball," says Speed; and Hank pretty near falls off the bench.

The next day he comes up with one out and the sacks full, and the score tied in the eighth. He smashes one on the ground straight at Houser and it looked like a cinch double play; but just as Hauser was goin' to grab it the ball hit a rough spot and hopped a mile over his head. It got between Oakes and Magee and went clear to the fence. Three guys scored and Speed pulled up at third. The papers come out and said the game was won by a three-bagger from the bat o' Parker, the Cubs' sensational kid third baseman. Gosh!

We go home to Chi and are havin' a hot battle with Pittsburgh. This time Speed's turn come when they was two on and two out, and Pittsburgh a run to the good—I think it was the eighth innin'. Cooper gives him a fast one and he hits it straight up in the air. O' course the runners start goin', but it looked hopeless because they wasn't no wind or high sky to bother anybody. Mowrey and Gibson both goes after the ball; and just as Mowrey was set for the catch Gibson bumps into him and they both fall down. Two runs scored and Speed got to second. Then what does he do but try to steal third—with two out too! And Gibson's peg pretty near hits the left field seats on the fly.

When Speed comes to the bench Hank says:

"If I was you I'd quit playin' ball and go to Monte Carlo."

"What for?" says Speed.

"You're so dam' lucky!" says Hank.

"So is Ty Cobb," says Speed. That's how he hated himself!

First trip to Cincy we run into a couple of old Ishpeming boys. They took us out one night, and about twelve o'clock I said we'd have to go back to the hotel or we'd get fined. Speed said I had cold feet and he stuck with the boys. I went back alone and Hank caught me comin' in and put a fifty-dollar plaster on me. Speed stayed out all night long and Hank never knowed it. I says to myself: "Wait till he gets out there and tries to play ball without no sleep!" But the game that day was called off on account o' rain. Can you beat it?

I remember what he got away with the next afternoon the same as though it happened yesterday. In the second innin' they walked him with nobody down, and he took a big lead off first base like he always does. Benton throwed over there three or four times to scare him back, and the last time he throwed, Hobby hid the ball. The coacher seen it and told Speed to hold the bag; but he didn't pay no attention. He started leadin' right off again and Hobby tried to tag him, but the ball slipped out of his hand and rolled about a yard away. Parker had plenty o' time to get back; but, instead o' that, he starts for second. Hobby picked up the ball and shot it down to Groh—and Groh made a square muff.

Parker slides into the bag safe and then gets up and throws out his chest like he'd made the greatest play ever. When the ball's throwed back to Benton, Speed leads off about thirty foot and stands there in a trance. Clarke signs for a pitch-out and pegs down to second to nip him. He was caught flat-footed—that is, he would of been with a decent throw; but Clarke's peg went pretty near to Latonia. Speed scored and strutted over to receive our hearty congratulations. Some o' the boys was laughin' and he thought they was laughin' with him instead of at him.

It was in the ninth, though, that he got by with one o' the worst I ever seen. The Reds was a run behind and Marsans was on third base with two out. Hobby, I think it was, hit one on the ground right at Speed and he picked it up clean. The crowd all got up and started for the exits. Marsans run toward the plate in the faint hope that the peg to first would be wild. All of a sudden the boys on the Cincy bench begun yellin' at him to slide, and he done so. He was way past the plate when Speed's throw got to Archer. The bonehead had shot the ball home instead o' to first base, thinkin' they was only one down. We was all crazy, believin' his nut play had let 'em tie it up; but he comes tearin' in, tellin' Archer to tag Marsans. So Jim walks over and tags the Cuban, who was brushin' off his uniform.

"You're out!" says Klem. "You never touched the plate."

I guess Marsans knowed the umps was right because he didn't make much of a holler. But Speed sure got a pannin' in the clubhouse.

"I suppose you knowed he was goin' to miss the plate!" says Hank sarcastic as he could.

Everybody on the club roasted him, but it didn't do no good.

Well, you know what happened to me. I only got into one game with the Cubs—one afternoon when Leach was sick. We was playin' the Boston bunch and Tyler was workin' against us. I always had trouble with lefthanders and this was one of his good days. I couldn't see what he throwed up there. I got one foul durin' the afternoon's entertainment; and the wind was blowin' a hundred-mile gale, so that the best outfielder in the world couldn't judge a fly ball. That Boston bunch must of hit fifty of 'em and they all come to my field.

If I caught any I've forgot about it. Couple o' days after that I got notice o' my release to Indianapolis.

Parker kept right on all season doin' the blamedest things you ever heard of and gettin' by with 'em. One o' the boys told me about it later. If they was playin' a double-header in St. Louis, with the thermometer at 130 degrees, he'd get put out by the umps in the first innin' o' the first game. If he started to steal the catcher'd drop the pitch or somebody'd muff the throw. If he hit a pop fly the sun'd get in somebody's eyes. If he took a swell third strike with the bases full the umps would call it a ball. If he cut first base by twenty feet the umps would be readin' the mornin' paper.

Zimmerman's leg mended, so that he was all right by June; and then Saier got sick and they tried Speed at first base. He'd never saw the bag before; but things kept on breakin' for him and he played it like a house afire. The Cubs copped the pennant and Speed got in on the big dough, besides playin' a whale of a game through the whole serious.

Speed and me both went back to Ishpeming to spend the winter—though the Lord knows it ain't no winter resort. Our homes was there; and besides, in my case, they was a certain girl livin' in the old burg.

Parker, o' course, was the hero and the swell guy when we got home. He'd been in the World's Serious and had plenty o' dough in his kick. I come home with nothin' but my suitcase and a hardluck story, which I kept to myself. I hadn't even went good enough in Indianapolis to be sure of a job there again.

That fall—last fall—an uncle o' Speed's died over in the Soo and left him ten thousand bucks. I had an uncle down in the

Lower Peninsula who was worth five times that much—but he had good health!

This girl I spoke about was the prettiest thing I ever see. I'd went with her in the old days, and when I blew back I found she was still strong for me. They wasn't a great deal o' variety in Ishpeming for a girl to pick from. Her and I went to the dance every Saturday night and to church Sunday nights. I called on her Wednesday evenin's, besides takin' her to all the shows that come along—rotten as the most o' them was.

I never knowed Speed was makin' a play for this doll till along last Feb'uary. The minute I seen what was up I got busy. I took her out sleigh-ridin' and kept her out in the cold till she'd promised to marry me. We set the date for this fall—I figured I'd know better where I was by that time.

Well, we didn't make no secret o' bein' engaged; down in the poolroom one night Speed come up and congratulated me. He says:

"You got a swell girl, Dick! I wouldn't mind bein' in your place. You're mighty lucky to cop her out—you old Horseshoes, you!"

"Horseshoes!" I says. "You got a fine license to call anybody Horseshoes! I suppose you ain't never had no luck?"

"Not like you," he says.

I was feelin' too good about grabbin' the girl to get sore at the time; but when I got to thinkin' about it few minutes afterward it made me mad clear through. What right did that bird have to talk about me bein' lucky?

Speed was playin' freeze-out at a table near the door, and when I started home some o' the boys with him says:

"Good night, Dick."

I said good night and then Speed looked up.

"Good night, Horseshoes!" he says.

That got my nanny this time.

"Shut up, you lucky stiff!" I says. "If you wasn't so dam' lucky you'd be sweepin' the streets." Then I walks on out.

I was too busy with the girl to see much o' Speed after that. He left home about the middle o' the month to go to Tampa with the Cubs. I got notice from Indianapolis that I was sold to Baltimore. I didn't care much about goin' there and I wasn't anxious to leave home under the circumstances. So I didn't report till late.

When I read in the papers along in April that Speed had been traded to Boston for a couple o' pitchers I thought: "Gee! He must of lost his rabbit's foot!" Because, even if the Cubs didn't cop again, they'd have a city serious with the White Sox and get a bunch o' dough that way. And they wasn't no chance in the world for the Boston Club to get nothin' but their salaries.

It wasn't another month, though, till Shafer, o' the Giants, quit baseball and McGraw was up against it for a third baseman. Next thing I knowed Speed was traded to New York and was with another winner—for they never was out o' first place all season.

I was gettin' along all right at Baltimore and Dunnie liked me; so I felt like I had somethin' more than just a one-year job— somethin' I could get married on. It was all framed that the weddin' was comin' off as soon as this season was over; so you can believe I was pullin' for October to hurry up and come.

One day in August, two months ago, Dunnie come in the clubhouse and handed me the news.

"Rube Oldring's busted his leg," he says, "and he's out for the rest o' the season. Connie's got a youngster named Joyce that he can stick in there, but he's got to have an extra outfielder. He's made me a good proposition for you and I'm goin' to let you go. It'll be pretty soft for you, because they got the pennant cinched and they'll cut you in on the big money."

"Yes," I says; "and when they're through with me they'll ship me to Hellangone, and I'll be draggin' down about seventy-five bucks a month next year."

"Nothin' like that," says Dunnie. "If he don't want you next season he's got to ask for waivers; and if you get out o' the big league you come right back here. That's all framed."

So that's how I come to get with the Ath-a-letics. Connie give me a nice, comf'table seat in one corner o' the bench and I had the pleasure o' watchin' a real ball club perform every afternoon and sometimes twice.

Connie told me that as soon as they had the flag cinched he was goin' to lay off some o' his regulars and I'd get a chance to play.

Well, they cinched it the fourth day o' September and our next engagement was with Washin'ton on Labor Day. We had two games and I was in both of 'em. And I broke in with my usual lovely luck, because the pitchers I was ast to face was Boehling, a nasty lefthander, and this guy Johnson.

The mornin' game was Boehling's and he wasn't no worse than some o' the rest of his kind. I only whiffed once and would of had a triple if Milan hadn't run from here to New Orleans and stole one off me.

I'm not boastin' about my first experience with Johnson though. They can't never tell me he throws them balls with his arm. He's got a gun concealed about his person and he shoots 'em up there. I was leadin' off in Murphy's place and the game was a little delayed in startin', because I'd watched the big guy warm up and wasn't in no hurry to get to that plate. Before I left the bench Connie says:

"Don't try to take no healthy swing. Just meet 'em and you'll get along better."

So I tried to just meet the first one he throwed; but when I stuck out my bat Henry was throwin' the pill back to Johnson. Then I thought: Maybe if I start swingin' now at the second one I'll hit the third one. So I let the second one come over and the umps guessed it was another strike, though I'll bet a thousand bucks he couldn't see it no more'n I could.

While Johnson was still windin' up to pitch again I started to swing and the big cuss crosses me with a slow one. I lunged at it twice and missed it both times, and the force o' my wallop throwed me clean back to the bench. The Ath-a-letics was all laughin' at me and I laughed too, because I was glad that much of it was over.

McInnes gets a base hit off him in the second innin' and I ast him how he done it.

"He's a friend o' mine," says Jack, "and he lets up when he pitches to me."

I made up my mind right there that if I was goin' to be in the league next year, I'd go out and visit Johnson this winter and get acquainted.

I wished before the day was over that I was hittin' in the catcher's place, because the fellers down near the tail-end of the battin' order only had to face him three times. He fanned me on three pitched balls again in the third, and when I come up in the sixth he scared me to death by pretty near beanin' me with the first one.

"Be careful!" says Henry. "He's gettin' pretty wild and he's liable to knock you away from your uniform."

"Don't he never curve one?" I ast.

"Sure!" says Henry. "Do you want to see his curve?"

"Yes," I says, knowin' the hook couldn't be no worse'n the fast one.

So he give me three hooks in succession and I missed 'em all; but I felt more comf'table than when I was duckin' his fast ball. In the ninth he hit my bat with a curve and the ball went on the ground to McBride. He booted it, but throwed me out easy— because I was so surprised at not havin' whiffed that I forgot to run!

Well, I went along like that for the rest o' the season, runnin' up against the best pitchers in the league and not exactly murderin' 'em. Everything I tried went wrong, and I was smart enough to know that if anything had depended on the games I wouldn't of been in there for two minutes. Joyce and Strunk and Murphy wasn't jealous o' me a bit; but they was glad to take turns restin', and I didn't care much how I went so long as I was sure of a job next year.

I'd wrote to the girl a couple o' times askin' her to set the exact date for our weddin'; but she hadn't paid no attention. She said she was glad I was with the Ath-a-letics, but she thought the Giants was goin' to beat us. I might of suspected from that that somethin' was wrong, because not even a girl would pick the Giants to trim that bunch of ourn. Finally, the day before the serious started, I sent her a kind o' sassy letter sayin' I guessed it was up to me to name the day, and askin' whether October twentieth was all right. I told her to wire me yes or no.

I'd been readin' the dope about Speed all season, and I knowed he'd had a whale of a year and that his luck was right with him; but I never dreamed a man could have the Lord on his side as strong as Speed did in that World's Serious! I might as well tell you all the dope, so long as you wasn't there.

The first game was on our grounds and Connie give us a talkin' to in the clubhouse beforehand.

"The shorter this serious is," he says, "the better for us. If it's

a long serious we're goin' to have trouble, because McGraw's
got five pitchers he can work and we've got about three; so I
want you boys to go at 'em from the jump and play 'em off their
feet. Don't take things easy, because it ain't goin' to be no snap.
Just because we've licked 'em before ain't no sign we'll do it
this time."

Then he calls me to one side and ast me what I knowed about
Parker.

"You was with the Cubs when he was, wasn't you?" he says.

"Yes," I says; "and he's the luckiest stiff you ever seen! If he
got stewed and fell in the gutter he'd catch a fish."

"I don't like to hear a good ball player called lucky," says
Connie. "He must have a lot of ability or McGraw wouldn't use
him regular. And he's been hittin' about .340 and played a
bangup game at third base. That can't be all luck."

"Wait till you see him," I says; "and if you don't say he's the
luckiest guy in the world you can sell me to the Boston Bloomer
Girls. He's so lucky," I says, "that if they traded him to the St.
Louis Browns they'd have the pennant cinched by the Fourth o'
July."

And I'll bet Connie was willin' to agree with me before it was
over.

Well, the Chief worked against the Big Rube in that game.
We beat 'em, but they give us a battle and it was Parker that
made it close. We'd gone along nothin' and nothin' till the
seventh, and then Rube walks Collins and Baker lifts one over
that little old wall. You'd think by this time them New York
pitchers would know better than to give that guy anything he
can hit.

In their part o' the ninth the Chief still had 'em shut out and
two down, and the crowd was goin' home; but Doyle gets hit in
the sleeve with a pitched ball and it's Speed's turn. He hits a foul
pretty near straight up, but Schang misjudges it. Then he lifts
another one and this time McInnes drops it. He'd ought to of
been out twice. The Chief tries to make him bite at a bad one
then, because he'd got him two strikes and nothin'. He hit at it
all right—kissed it for three bases between Strunk and Joyce!
And it was a wild pitch that he hit. Doyle scores, o' course, and
the bugs suddenly decide not to go home just yet. I fully ex-

pected to see him steal home and get away with it, but Murray cut into the first ball and lined out to Barry.

Plank beat Matty two to one the next day in New York, and again Speed and his rabbit's foot give us an awful argument. Matty wasn't so good as usual and we really ought to of beat him bad. Two different times Strunk was on second waitin' for any kind o' wallop, and both times Barry cracked 'em down the third-base line like a shot. Speed stopped the first one with his stomach and extricated the pill just in time to nail Barry at first base and retire the side. The next time he throwed his glove in front of his face in self-defense and the ball stuck in it.

In the sixth innin' Schang was on third base and Plank on first, and two down, and Murphy combed an awful one to Speed's left. He didn't have time to stoop over and he just stuck out his foot. The ball hit it and caromed in two hops right into Doyle's hands on second base before Plank got there. Then in the seventh Speed bunts one and Baker trips and falls goin' after it or he'd of threw him out a mile. They was two gone; so Speed steals second, and, o' course, Schang has to make a bad peg right at that time and lets him go to third. Then Collins boots one on Murray and they've got a run. But it didn't do 'em no good, because Collins and Baker and McInnes come up in the ninth and walloped 'em where Parker couldn't reach 'em.

Comin' back to Philly on the train that night, I says to Connie: "What do you think o' that Parker bird now?"

"He's lucky, all right," says Connie smilin'; "but we won't hold it against him if he don't beat us with it."

"It ain't too late," I says. "He ain't pulled his real stuff yet."

The whole bunch was talkin' about him and his luck, and sayin' it was about time for things to break against him. I warned 'em that they wasn't no chance—that it was permanent with him.

Bush and Tesreau hooked up next day and neither o' them had much stuff. Everybody was hittin' and it looked like anybody's game right up to the ninth. Speed had got on every time he come up—the wind blowin' his fly balls away from the outfielders and the infielders bootin' when he hit 'em on the ground.

When the ninth started the score was seven apiece. Connie and McGraw both had their whole pitchin' staffs warmin' up. The crowd was wild, because they'd been all kinds of action. They wasn't no danger of anybody's leavin' their seats before this game was over.

Well, Bescher is walked to start with and Connie's about ready to give Bush the hook; but Doyle pops out tryin' to bunt. Then Speed gets two strikes and two balls, and it looked to me like the next one was right over the heart; but Connolly calls it a ball and gives him another chance. He whales the groove ball to the fence in left center and gets round to third on it, while Bescher scores. Right then Bush comes out and the Chief goes in. He whiffs Murray and has two strikes on Merkle when Speed makes a break for home—and, o' course, that was the one ball Schang dropped in the whole serious!

They had a two-run lead on us then and it looked like a cinch for them to hold it, because the minute Tesreau showed a sign o' weakenin' McGraw was sure to holler for Matty or the Rube. But you know how quick that bunch of ourn can make a two-run lead look sick. Before McGraw could get Jeff out o' there we had two on the bases.

Then Rube comes in and fills 'em up by walkin' Joyce. It was Eddie's turn to wallop and if he didn't do nothin' we had Baker comin' up next. This time Collins saved Baker the trouble and whanged one clear to the woods. Everybody scored but him—and he could of, too, if it'd been necessary.

In the clubhouse the boys naturally felt pretty good. We'd copped three in a row and it looked like we'd make it four straight, because we had the Chief to send back at 'em the followin' day.

"Your friend Parker is lucky," the boys says to me, "but it don't look like he could stop us now."

I felt the same way and was consultin' the time-tables to see whether I could get a train out o' New York for the West next evenin'. But do you think Speed's luck was ready to quit? Not yet! And it's a wonder we didn't all go nuts durin' the next few days. If words could kill, Speed would of died a thousand times. And I wish he had!

They wasn't no record-breakin' crowd out when we got to the Polo Grounds. I guess the New York bugs was pretty well discouraged and the bettin' was eight to five that we'd cop that battle and finish it. The Chief was the only guy that warmed up for us and McGraw didn't have no choice but to use Matty, with the whole thing dependin' on this game.

They went along like the two swell pitchers they was till Speed's innin', which in this battle was the eighth. Nobody scored, and it didn't look like they was ever goin' to till Murphy starts off that round with a perfect bunt and Joyce sacrifices him to second. All Matty had to do then was to get rid o' Collins and Baker—and that's about as easy as sellin' silk socks to an Eskimo.

He didn't give Eddie nothin' he wanted to hit, though; and finally he slaps one on the ground to Doyle. Larry made the play to first base and Murphy moved to third. We all figured Matty'd walk Baker then, and he done it. Connie sends Baker down to second on the first pitch to McInnes, but Meyers don't pay no attention to him—they was playin' for McInnes and wasn't takin' no chances o' throwin' the ball away.

Well, the count goes to three and two on McInnes and Matty comes with a curve—he's got some curve too; but Jack happened to meet it and—Blooie! Down the left foul line where he always hits! I never seen a ball hit so hard in my life. No infielder in the world could of stopped it. But I'll give you a thousand bucks if that ball didn't go kerplunk right into the third bag and stop as dead as George Washington! It was child's play for Speed to pick it up and heave it over to Merkle before Jack got there. If anybody else had been playin' third base the bag would of ducked out o' the way o' that wallop; but even the bases themselves was helpin' him out.

The two runs we ought to of had on Jack's smash would of been just enough to beat 'em, because they got the only run o' the game in their half—or, I should say, the Lord give it to 'em.

Doyle'd been throwed out and up come Parker, smilin'. The minute I seen him smile I felt like somethin' was comin' off and I made the remark on the bench.

Well, the Chief pitched one right at him and he tried to duck. The ball hit his bat and went on a line between Jack and Eddie. Speed didn't know he'd hit it till the guys on the bench wised him up. Then he just had time to get to first base. They tried the hit-and-run on the second ball and Murray lifts a high fly that Murphy didn't have to move for. Collins pulled the old bluff about the ball bein' on the ground and Barry yells, "Go on!

Go on!" like he was the coacher. Speed fell for it and didn't know where the ball was no more'n a rabbit; he just run his fool head off and we was gettin' all ready to laugh when the ball come down and Murphy dropped it!

If Parker had stuck near first base, like he ought to of done, he couldn't of got no farther'n second; but with the start he got he was pretty near third when Murphy made the muff, and it was a cinch for him to score. The next two guys was easy outs; so they wouldn't of had a run except for Speed's boner. We couldn't do nothin' in the ninth and we was licked.

Well, that was a tough one to lose; but we figured that Matty was through and we'd wind it up the next day, as we had Plank ready to send back at 'em. We wasn't afraid o' the Rube, because he hadn't never bothered Collins and Baker much.

The two lefthanders come together just like everybody'd doped it and it was about even up to the eighth. Plank had been goin' great and, though the score was two and two, they'd got their two on boots and we'd hit ourn in. We went after Rube in our part o' the eighth and knocked him out. Demaree stopped us after we'd scored two more.

"It's all over but the shoutin'!" says Davis on the bench.

"Yes," I says, "unless that seventh son of a seventh son gets up there again."

He did, and he come up after they'd filled the bases with a boot, a base hit and a walk with two out. I says to Davis:

"If I was Plank I'd pass him and give 'em one run."

"That wouldn't be no baseball," says Davis—"not with Murray comin' up."

Well, it mayn't of been no baseball, but it couldn't of turned out worse if they'd did it that way. Speed took a healthy at the first ball; but it was a hook and he caught it on the handle, right up near his hands. It started outside the first-base line like a foul and then changed its mind and rolled in. Schang run away from the plate, because it looked like it was up to him to make the play. He picked the ball up and had to make the peg in a hurry.

His throw hit Speed right on top o' the head and bounded off like it had struck a cement sidewalk. It went clear over to the seats and before McInnes could get it three guys had scored and Speed was on third base. He was left there, but that didn't make no difference. We was licked again and for the first time the gang really begun to get scared.

We went over to New York Sunday afternoon and we didn't do no singin' on the way. Some o' the fellers tried to laugh, but it hurt 'em. Connie sent us to bed early, but I don't believe none o' the bunch got much sleep—I know I didn't; I was worryin' too much about the serious and also about the girl, who hadn't sent me no telegram like I'd ast her to. Monday mornin' I wired her askin' what was the matter and tellin' her I was gettin' tired of her foolishness. O' course I didn't make it so strong as that— but the telegram cost me a dollar and forty cents.

Connie had the choice o' two pitchers for the sixth game. He could use Bush, who'd been slammed round pretty hard last time out, or the Chief, who'd only had two days' rest. The rest of 'em —outside o' Plank—had a epidemic o' sore arms. Connie finally picked Bush, so's he could have the Chief in reserve in case we had to play a seventh game. McGraw started Big Jeff and we went at it.

It wasn't like the last time those two guys had hooked up. This time they both had somethin', and for eight innin's runs was as scarce as Chinese policemen. They'd been chances to score on both sides, but the big guy and Bush was both tight in the pinches. The crowd was plumb nuts and yelled like Indians every time a fly ball was caught or a strike called. They'd of got their money's worth if they hadn't been no ninth; but, believe me, that was some round!

They was one out when Barry hit one through the box for a base. Schang walked, and it was Bush's turn. Connie told him to bunt, but he whiffed in the attempt. Then Murphy comes up and walks—and the bases are choked. Young Joyce had been pie for Tesreau all day or else McGraw might of changed pitchers right there. Anyway he left Big Jeff in and he beaned Joyce with a fast one. It sounded like a tire blowin' out. Joyce falls over in a heap and we chase out there, thinkin' he's dead; but he ain't, and pretty soon he gets up and walks down to first base. Tesreau had forced in a run and again we begun to count the winner's end. Matty comes in to prevent further damage and Collins flies the side out.

"Hold 'em now! Work hard!" we says to young Bush, and he

walks out there just as cool as though he was goin' to hit fungoes.

McGraw sends up a pinch hitter for Matty and Bush whiffed him. Then Besher flied out. I was prayin' that Doyle would end it, because Speed's turn come after his'n; so I pretty near fell dead when Larry hit safe.

Speed had his old smile and even more chest than usual when he come up there, swingin' five or six bats. He didn't wait for Doyle to try and steal, or nothin'. He lit into the first ball, though Bush was tryin' to waste it. I seen the ball go high in the air toward left field, and then I picked up my gloves and got ready to beat it for the gate. But when I looked out to see if Joyce was set, what do you think I seen? He was lyin' flat on the ground! That blow on the head had got him just as Bush was pitchin' to Speed. He'd flopped over and didn't no more know what was goin' on than if he'd croaked.

Well, everybody else seen it at the same time; but it was too late. Strunk made a run for the ball, but they wasn't no chance for him to get near it. It hit the ground about ten feet back o' where Joyce was lyin' and bounded way over to the end o' the foul line. You don't have to be told that Doyle and Parker both scored and the serious was tied up.

We carried Joyce to the clubhouse and after a while he come to. He cried when he found out what had happened. We cheered him up all we could, but he was a pretty sick guy. The trainer said he'd be all right, though, for the final game.

They tossed up a coin to see where they'd play the seventh battle and our club won the toss; so we went back to Philly that night and cussed Parker clear across New Jersey. I was so sore I kicked the stuffin' out o' my seat.

You probably heard about the excitement in the burg yesterday mornin'. The demand for tickets was somethin' fierce and some of 'em sold for as high as twenty-five bucks apiece. Our club hadn't been lookin' for no seventh game and they was some tall hustlin' done round that old ball park.

I started out to the grounds early and bought some New York papers to read on the car. They was a big story that Speed Parker, the Giants' hero, was goin' to be married a week after the end o' the serious. It didn't give the name o' the girl, sayin' Speed had refused to tell it. I figured she must be some dame he'd met round the circuit somewheres.

They was another story by one o' them smart baseball reporters sayin' that Parker, on his way up to the plate, had saw that Joyce was about ready to faint and had hit the fly ball to left field on purpose. Can you beat it?

I was goin' to show that to the boys in the clubhouse, but the minute I blowed in there I got some news that made me forget about everything else. Joyce was very sick and they'd took him to a hospital. It was up to me to play!

Connie come over and ast me whether I'd ever hit against Matty. I told him I hadn't, but I'd saw enough of him to know he wasn't no worse'n Johnson. He told me he was goin' to let me hit second—in Joyce's place—because he didn't want to bust up the rest of his combination. He also told me to take my orders from Strunk about where to play for the batters.

"Where shall I play for Parker?" I says, tryin' to joke and pretend I wasn't scared to death.

"I wisht I could tell you," says Connie. "I guess the only thing to do when he comes up is to get down on your knees and pray."

The rest o' the bunch slapped me on the back and give me all the encouragement they could. The place was jammed when we went out on the field. They may of been bigger crowds before, but they never was packed together so tight. I doubt whether they was even room left for Falkenberg to sit down.

The afternoon papers had printed the stuff about Joyce bein' out of it, so the bugs was wise that I was goin' to play. They watched me pretty close in battin' practice and give me a hand whenever I managed to hit one hard. When I was out catchin' fungoes the guys in the bleachers cheered me and told me they was with me; but I don't mind tellin' you that I was as nervous as a bride.

They wasn't no need for the announcers to tip the crowd off to the pitchers. Everybody in the United States and Cuba knowed that the Chief'd work for us and Matty for them. The Chief didn't have no trouble with 'em in the first innin'. Even from where I stood I could see that he had a lot o' stuff. Bescher and Doyle popped out and Speed whiffed.

Well, I started out makin' good, with reverse English, in our

part. Fletcher booted Murphy's ground ball and I was sent up
to sacrifice. I done a complete job of it—sacrificin' not only myself
but Murphy with a pop fly that Matty didn't have to move for.
That spoiled whatever chance we had o' gettin' the jump on 'em;
but the boys didn't bawl me out for it.

"That's all right, old boy. You're all right!" they said on the
bench—if they'd had a gun they'd of shot me.

I didn't drop no fly balls in the first six innin's—because none
was hit out my way. The Chief was so good that they wasn't hittin'
nothin' out o' the infield. And we wasn't doin' nothin' with
Matty, either. I led off in the fourth and fouled the first one. I
didn't molest the other two. But if Connie and the gang talked
about me they done it internally. I come up again—with Murphy
on third base and two gone in the sixth, and done my little
whiffin' specialty. And still the only people that panned me was
the thirty thousand that had paid for the privilege!

My first fieldin' chance come in the seventh. You'd of thought
that I'd of had my nerve back by that time; but I was just as scared
as though I'd never saw a crowd before. It was just as well that
they was two out when Merkle hit one to me. I staggered under it
and finally it hit me on the shoulder. Merkle got to second, but
the Chief whiffed the next guy. I was gave some cross looks on
the bench and I shouldn't of blamed the fellers if they'd cut loose
with some language; but they didn't.

They's no use in me tellin' you about none o' the rest of it—
except what happened just before the start o' the eleventh and
durin' that innin', which was sure the big one o' yesterday's pas-
time—both for Speed and yours sincerely.

The scoreboard was still a row o' ciphers and Speed'd had
only a fair amount o' luck. He'd made a scratch base hit and
robbed our bunch of a couple o' real ones with impossible stops.

When Schang flied out and wound up our tenth I was leanin'
against the end of our bench. I heard my name spoke, and I turned
round and seen a boy at the door.

"Right here!" I says; and he give me a telegram.

"Better not open it till after the game," says Connie.

"Oh, no; it ain't no bad news," I said, for I figured it was an
answer from the girl. So I opened it up and read it on the way
to my position. It said:

"Forgive me, Dick—and forgive Speed too. Letter follows."

Well, sir, I ain't no baby, but for a minute I just wanted to sit down and bawl. And then, all of a sudden, I got so mad I couldn't see. I run right into Baker as he was pickin' up his glove. Then I give him a shove and called him some name, and him and Barry both looked at me like I was crazy—and I was. When I got out in left field I stepped on my own foot and spiked it. I just had to hurt somebody.

As I remember it the Chief fanned the first two of 'em. Then Doyle catches one just right and lams it up against the fence back o' Murphy. The ball caromed round some and Doyle got all the way to third base. Next thing I seen was Speed struttin' up to the plate. I run clean in from my position.

"Kill him!" I says to the Chief. "Hit him in the head and kill him, and I'll go to jail for it!"

"Are you off your nut?" says the Chief. "Go out there and play ball—and quit ravin'."

Barry and Baker led me away and give me a shove out toward left. Then I heard the crack o' the bat and I seen the ball comin' a mile a minute. It was headed between Strunk and I and looked like it would go out o' the park. I don't remember runnin' or nothin' about it till I run into the concrete wall head first. They told me afterward and all the papers said that it was the greatest catch ever seen. And I never knowed I'd caught the ball!

Some o' the managers have said my head was pretty hard, but it wasn't as hard as that concrete. I was pretty near out, but they tell me I walked to the bench like I wasn't hurt at all. They also tell me that the crowd was a bunch o' ravin' maniacs and was throwin' money at me. I guess the ground-keeper'll get it.

The boys on the bench was all talkin' at once and slappin' me on the back but I didn't know what it was about. Somebody told me pretty soon that it was my turn to hit and I picked up the first bat I come to and starts for the plate. McInnes come runnin' after me and ast me whether I didn't want my own bat. I cussed him and told him to mind his own business.

I didn't know it at the time, but I found out afterward that they was two out. The bases was empty. I'll tell you just what I had in my mind: I wasn't thinkin' about the ball game; I was determined that I was goin' to get to third base and give that

guy my spikes. If I didn't hit one worth three bases, or if I didn't
hit one at all, I was goin' to run till I got round to where Speed
was, and then slide into him and cut him to pieces!

Right now I can't tell you whether I hit a fast ball, or a slow
ball, or a hook, or a fader—but I hit somethin'. It went over
Bescher's head like a shot and then took a crazy bound. It must
of struck a rock or a pop bottle, because it hopped clear over the
fence and landed in the bleachers.

Mind you, I learned this afterward. At the time I just knowed
I'd hit one somewheres and I starts round the bases. I speeded up
when I got near third and took a runnin' jump at a guy I thought
was Parker. I missed him and sprawled all over the bag. Then,
all of a sudden, I come to my senses. All the Ath-a-letics was out
there to run home with me and it was one o' them I'd tried to
cut. Speed had left the field. The boys picked me up and seen to
it that I went on and touched the plate. Then I was carried into
the clubhouse by the crazy bugs.

Well, they had a celebration in there and it was a long time
before I got a chance to change my clothes. The boys made a big
fuss over me. They told me they'd intended to give me five hundred bucks for my divvy, but now I was goin' to get a full
share.

"Parker ain't the only lucky guy!" says one of 'em. "But even
if that ball hadn't of took that crazy hop you'd of had a triple."

A triple! That's just what I'd wanted; and he called me lucky
for not gettin' it!

The Giants was dressin' in the other part o' the clubhouse;
and when I finally come out there was Speed, standin' waitin'
for some o' the others. He seen me comin' and he smiled. "Hello,
Horseshoes!" he says.

He won't smile no more for a while—it'll hurt too much. And
if any girl wants him with his ear, and his jaw a couple o' feet
foul—she's welcome to him. They won't be no contest!

Grimes leaned over to ring for the waiter.

"Well," he said, "what about it?"

"You won't have to pay my fare," I told him.

"I'll buy a drink anyway," said he. "You've been a good listener
—and I had to get it off my chest."

"Maybe they'll have to postpone the wedding," I said.

"No," said Grimes. "The weddin' will take place the day after tomorrow—and I'll bat for Mr. Parker. Did you think I was goin' to let him get away with it?"

"What about next year?" I asked.

"I'm goin' back to the Ath-a-letics," he said. "And I'm goin' to hire somebody to call me 'Horseshoes!' before every game—because I can sure play that old baseball when I'm mad."

Excerpts from a Chapter on Chile

By S. KIP FARRINGTON JR.

NO WORDS of mine could ever do justice to the broadbill swordfish as the greatest sporting game fish of them all; nor would I attempt to describe his idiosyncrasies, let alone instruct the angler in the fine art of hooking and catching him. I bow to the superior knowledge of Michael Lerner and W. E. S. Tuker, who know more about swordfish and swordfishing than any other two men in the world; there are several men who fish out of Catalina, too, like George Pillsbury and Joe Peeler, who also know a thing or two about the fish and the game. I will say, though, that no matter how many years a man has spent fishing for broadbill, his knowledge will be relatively meager until he has tried the waters of Chile.

In nine years of swordfishing—going out as often as I could afford to and whenever I could spare time from business—I had baited thirty-six, had four strikes, hooked two, and caught one. Six years I labored and twenty-eight swordfish I baited before I got my first one. My intended victims were mostly seen off Montauk, but they include four or five baited off Fire Island, Block Island, Martha's Vineyard, and Nova Scotia. The rest were baited off Bimini and Catalina. The one I did succeed in luring to his doom was caught off Montauk.

In contrast, I present an outline of the first Farrington Chilean venture, in 1939, when my wife and I were fishing off Tocopilla with Mr. Tuker and George Garey. During just fifteen days of actual fishing, usually alone in Mr. Garey's boat, I presented baits to twenty fish, had twelve strikes, hooked seven, and caught three

From "Pacific Game Fishing," Coward McCann, Inc.

—and was then informed by my host that I had had the poorest luck of any man who had fished off there! Mrs. Farrington, who went out in Mr. Tuker's boat—alone, when Mr. Tuker could not take time off from business—presented baits to seventeen fish, had fourteen strikes, hooked twelve, and caught one. Between the two of us and while we were fighting our own fish, we sighted no less than seventy-three albacora, this number including breachers and other finning fish. One day we counted twenty-one and another day eighteen.

It may interest the reader to know what happened in 1939 when Mrs. Farrington was able to catch only one out of the twelve broadbill she hooked. In the first place, the pressure was on her from the start, for no woman had ever caught a broadbill, or for that matter, a marlin, off the entire South American coast. Everyone down there, including her head fishing guide, said that the albacora wasn't a woman's fish; and they all believed it, too, though if Mr. Tuker and Mr. Garey shared this opinion, they were too polite to say so. I think this was enough to tie the jinx on her.

I am, by the way, very superstitious about fishing. For me, the first fish of any trip is always the hardest to catch, particularly after I have traveled thousands of miles to the grounds and have a limited time. Even on the finest grounds in the world I am a notoriously poor starter, and with but one exception, and that was off Panama, my jinx has harried me. Then again, Mrs. Farrington and I, as well as the Lerners and several other of our fishing friends, always have two strikes on us before we go to bat, because everyone expects us to catch fish every time we go after them and never can understand it when we don't. I would never think of making a trip to a far away place for less than two weeks of fishing, at the very least. Trying to get results in a shorter time isn't fair to the place or to the guides, any more than it is to yourself or the fish.

I doubt whether my wife gave the subject of jinxes much thought, for the first morning off Tocopilla in 1939 she baited and hooked the first broadbill she sighted, after having been in the proper water for less than half an hour. She had had the fish on hardly twenty minutes when he cut the leader wire with his sword. Two trips later a second fish threw the hook after an hour and ten minutes.

At eleven-thirty the following Sunday morning, in a very rough sea—one of the few bad days I have ever seen off Tocopilla —my wife hooked her third broadbill, a very large one. She did not know it then, naturally, but that was the only time the fish was to be seen during the fight—which was still going furiously at four o'clock that afternoon when I jumped off the bow of my boat, Mr. Garey's Quinchihuie, on to Mr. Tuker's boat. The seas were by this time as high as any I have ever fished on in the Pacific off South America, and the wind was blowing stronger all the time. The fish was sulking about 150 feet down, directly behind the boat, and every time line could be recovered, it would be immediately lost again in the high swells. Meanwhile Mrs. Farrington had wrenched her back—which hardly improved the situation.

At five o'clock Mr. Tuker suggested that she let me take over the rod, but she refused. Another hour went by, and I could see that she was really suffering. When her host again urged her to turn over the rod to me I echoed his suggestion—even though the fish would then be disqualified, we wanted to satisfy our curiosity about where he was hooked, for it was evident the hook wasn't hurting him. But Mrs. Farrington still refused. Sea after sea broke over her.

The rough weather was greatly hampering the crew, and their efforts to circle against the fish and try to get him on another course were unavailing. He was swimming slowly to the northward, and we were now about twenty-five miles from where he had been hooked. At about six-forty-five, after we had attempted to plane him three or four times, he came up just beneath the surface and, with a terrific drag on the reel, made a run of more than 1,500 feet. It was one of the fastest I have ever seen a swordfish make, and this after he had been hooked for seven hours and fifteen minutes! Then he went down again, this time to a depth of about one hundred feet.

After that performance I urged my wife once more to let me take the fish. Besides my concern for her, I knew Mr. Tuker had to go to his office in the morning and couldn't stay out there all night; also that his boat crews, when he doesn't have them fishing, worked on the harbor tugs that haul nitrate barges to the various ships. It wasn't until an hour later, however, at seven forty-five, after she had fought the fish for eight hours and fifteen minutes, that she would consent to quit. She had taken a far worse licking than she had in that skiff off Liverpool, Nova Scotia, in 1936, when she fought a 493-pound tuna for ten hours and thirty-five minutes—the longest battle with a fish a woman has ever fought and won. In addition to the injury to her back—which bothers her to this day—she had black and blue welts on her thighs and sides from being thrown against the iron arm holders of the chair. She had worn out three pairs of fishing gloves, and her right hand was covered with blisters. To make matters worse, she hadn't had anything to eat since six o'clock that morning. So I stepped into the chair to relieve an angler for the first and only time I have ever done so—and I hope for the last time.

I was confident, as I took the rod in my hand, that I could put this fellow in his place without much further delay. I didn't give a damn whether or not I lost him; he was disqualified anyway, so here was my chance to go all out on a broadbill. I got my first surprise when I started to put more tension on the pilot wheel, or star drag, and found I could increase it only about a quarter of a turn beyond Mrs. Farrington's limit. In the hour and a quarter that followed, though I put to use every trick I had learned in my whole fishing career, I couldn't regain more than fifty feet of line, and promptly that would be lost again. My opponent was surging harder than any other fish I had ever handled, and the rod and reel were subjected to a strain few others have undergone.

It grew dark, and in the rays of the flashlight being played on the line we could see the giant squid plainly as they came up to the surface and gobbled down the pieces of Chilean bread that were thrown over to them. Redoubling my efforts at nine-thirty made no change in the situation. Then a few minutes past ten o'clock, the only time it has ever happened to me, the rod broke, split between the second and third guides. I jumped up and grabbed the line, and we tried to get the stubborn devil in that way; but under the boat, about ten minutes later, he put an end to the battle with his sword. I could only agree with my wife, as the line was hauled back into the boat, that that albacora deserved his freedom if ever a fish did, and Mr. Tuker joined us in a salute to the gladiator for the game fight he waged for ten hours and a half.

Sure enough, I hooked a small fish around two o'clock and had him alongside in about four minutes. Juan, my expert guide, didn't hesitate a second about taking the leader. Up to that point, the fish hadn't been acting very green; and, believe me, I wanted him in a bad way, particularly as my wife was two fish ahead of me. I jumped out of the chair, picked up the Tycoon small-bail hook gaff, leaned over the stern, and stuck the gaff into his back. Then the fireworks began! He really put on a show as he thrashed about, wetting us all down and tearing the small hook right out of my hand. Then a terrific kick from his tail splashed the water into my face and took the lenses right out of my sun glasses, which I had foolishly forgotten to take off; when I straightened up I found one of the temples gone, and as I took them off they broke in two in my hand. At first I couldn't believe that it was only the force of the water that had done this to the glasses; I thought sure his tail must have hit me. Luckily for me, it hadn't, and the moving picture film showed that his tail hadn't even touched me. The fish weighed only 390 pounds and was the smallest we caught on the trip. He was boated in six minutes.

The following day I lost two, each a trifle larger than the 390-pounder. My experience with these three fish led me to believe that if they can be fought hard enough at the beginning of the battle it will sometimes be possible to catch them before they realize what has happened; while otherwise you might pull the hook out of them anyway. It also seems logical that a fast first round should prevent their getting really warmed up to the battle. Of course, if they are hooked in the heart, stomach, or eye, you will catch them very quickly anyway—just as you will any other species of large fish. But it is certainly fun to catch one in fast time after all we lose in the long battles. Tuker's 860-pound world-record fish was hooked in the eye and caught in fifteen minutes.

When we went out the following Monday, June 9, Juan had us work the grounds to the north of Tocopilla instead of to the south. About eleven o'clock we sighted a good-sized fish and baited him; he struck, but I had him on for just two or three minutes when he threw the hook. I always take the precaution to leave the bait out a while after a swordfish has got off and then reel it in very quickly. This was one of the times it worked. Just as the leader was coming out of the water right under the stern of the boat, Senor Albacora appeared on the surface, chasing the bait just like a big marlin. I can't begin to describe a sword-fisherman's mixed feelings of surprise and delight when it is his good fortune to have a fish act like this. It was my second experience. What a sight to watch him slam that bait within twenty-five feet of me and go through all the acrobatics a swordfish performs when striking a bait! Needless to say, I hooked him, and he was in the boat thirty-eight minutes later.

Just as we were about to lift him out we sighted another fish finning within 200 feet of us. In our haste to start on the new-comer we forgot to tie up the first one's mouth, and he lost about forty or fifty pounds of squid that had been in his stomach. Even so, a glance had shown me that he was the largest swordfish I had ever caught, and, as I threw the second bait over, I had the colossal cheek to say to myself: "Now if I can only hook this one and catch him in fast time, I may have the big chance to be the first man to catch three in a day."

I hooked him all right, but little did I guess what I had let myself in for. Five hours later, in a fairly rough sea, he had just as much strength as he'd had in the first hour. Believe me, I wanted that fish more than any I had ever hooked, for taking two broadbill swordfish in one day had long been the ambition of my angling career; only five men had done it thus far.

Well, everything went wrong for me that afternoon. To start with, I came mighty close to being cut off from the fish when Harry Smith, the great Pathé photographer, jumped aboard from Mrs. Farrington's boat. It was the first time the two boats had been close together the whole day, and, fearing that it would jinx me if the others learned of it, I cautioned the crew not to tell any of them—and this included Mrs. Farrington, Ellis, Bob Donahue, the other cameraman, and the crew—that I already had one in the boat. It makes me smile when I recall Smith's exclamation of surprise when he saw the fish; his comment may have been slightly profane, but it sounded pretty good to me.

The other boat went off to bait another fish and then, to my dismay, returned to put Arthur Swain aboard, Mrs. Farrington

having felt that possibly I could use an extra man to relieve one
of my crew. This time we locked outriggers and came very near
to breaking them off. You can imagine the humor this put me in.
I expressed my emotional attitude by making certain genealogical
references and ended, as I recall, with the injunction to get the
hell away from me and stay away. They must have wondered at
my bad humor; for, of course, they didn't know that the one I
had on was the second of the day. I remember how I hurt poor
Juan's feelings by throwing a glass overboard when he didn't take
it out of my hand as quickly as I expected him to. I was more
worked up than I had ever been while fighting a fish, and of
course I had no time to eat anything. However, I did have an
orange quartered for me, and I sucked on that, as hockey players
do between periods. It's a great pick-up—as I had found many
times, along with my teammates on the St. Nicholas Hockey Club
in New York.

Every moment I was fighting that fish as hard as I had ever
fought one, putting into the scrap every bit of knowledge I had
acquired from the day I started to fish; and time after time I tried
to plane him up. The crew was marvelous and on the alert every
minute. Victor never left the wheel, and how he did handle that
boat! He would circle with the fish twenty-five or thirty times
in one direction, then reverse the boat and circle against him as
many times in the opposite direction. From quarter-past five to
six o'clock we didn't stop circling. My worthy adversary stayed
down about 250 feet, swimming in the northerly course they all
seem to prefer when hooked off Tocopilla.

Winter had begun in Chile, and about six-thirty (though
Chileans have an hour of daylight saving time the year round)
the skies grew dark. I was determined I wasn't going to stay out
for another all-night session; I knew from past experiences how
tough these fights get after dark.

Suddenly I began to recover some line and lift the fish. Then
Juan, leaning over the side, announced that the albacora seemed
to be about done in. What a feeling! My second broadbill of the
day, and it looked as if I had him coming. Believe me, I never
worked harder as we backed into the waves, up and down on
every swell, with the water flying over me. Eight minutes later,
at five minutes to seven, Juan grabbed the leader for the first

time it had been out of the water after six hours and eight minutes, Meinie, Juan's assistant, gaffed my prize in his usual faultless fashion, and we had him alongside. Instantly I was out of the chair and imploring them to get him into the boat. Arthur Swain had rigged the searchlight; and, though it was a grand sight to see my second broadbill in one day under its rays, I have known searchlights to bring sharks around. Two years before, I had seen a little mako weighing not more than fifty pounds make a rush at my tiny broadbill in the same position. That time, one of Mr. Garey's crew grabbed a lance that they had on board and, with an aim that was simply amazing, had lanced the little shark loose in the water. Even though no fish had ever been mutilated by a shark in those waters, I was taking nothing for granted, and we turned our attention to getting him aboard without a second's delay.

Juan was just putting the tail rope around the albacora when suddenly, out of the dark, as if shot from a gun, a little blue shark that couldn't have been more than three feet long charged the swordfish. I will let you imagine my feelings. My two swordfish in one day and a six-hour-and-eight-minute fight looked as if they were going out the window, just because of a damned little shark! Juan slashed at the toyo with the tail rope. It turned and came back. I threw a persuader at him, and again he came back for what I thought would end up in a bite from the body of my fish and disqualification. But, quick as he turned and came back, Juan was quicker, God bless him! Like a flash he grabbed my detachable gaff handle from the cockpit floor and, with the most perfect punch ever seen outside the prize ring, hit the little scavenger squarely on the head. That was the last we saw of him, and for the second time in forty-five seconds Juan had saved my fish. Thirty seconds later the tail rope was on Senor Albacora and we were heaving and hauling on the block and tackle and lifting him out of the water.

The quick examination by flashlight and the longer one on shore that night disclosed that my long-awaited fishing victory had been won and that the fish had not been touched. I might add that the gaff used here had been presented to me three years before by Phil Swaffield, a great California sportsman, who has been president of the Catalina Tuna Club. Mr. Swaffield had the gaff engraved "From Phil to Kip" on the copper head where the hook fits into it, and it is the only engraved gaff I have ever seen. It has gaffed a lot of important fish for me in the four years I have owned it, but no task it was ever called upon to do meant more to me than the job the handle did in Juan's hands that night.

After we had the fish in the boat, the Santa Teresita came alongside and my wife heard about my great good fortune. As with Ellis and Donahue, she had had no inkling, but I don't think we fooled the Chilean crew for a minute; they were much too experienced not to have known something unusual was going on. Then I heard for the first time about the terrible luck Mrs. Farrington had run into that morning. While I was fighting my first fish she had baited and hooked an albacora, which, according to her crew, was the largest they had ever seen hooked on rod and reel. She had the fish on 24-thread and her old 16-ounce rod and brought him alongside after a fifty-minute fight. The guide had hold of the leader for a couple of minutes, so everyone on board got a look and agreed, when they saw the 853-pounder I caught the last afternoon, that my wife's fish was two feet longer than mine. He broke loose from the guide and went under the boat, and Mrs. Farrington jumped up, unbuckled her harness, and, dipping her rod up to the reel over the side, released the drag and cleared the fish from under the stern. Fifteen minutes later she had him back again; then for the second time he broke loose, and seventeen minutes later Mrs. Farrington called out the old familiar words, "Se fue!"—the "grande albacora" had cut the cable leader with his sword. There was no question in the minds of those who saw the fish that it weighed well over a thousand pounds and would easily have been the largest fish ever caught on rod and reel by anyone, man or woman. So once again the big one got away.

My trip back to port that night was by far the most enjoyable I have ever had on a homeward-bound fishing boat. So jubilant did I feel that I steered the boat in myself for the entire three hours, giving Victor a well-deserved rest. There was one bottle of Coca-Cola left on board, and I never drank one that tasted any better.

The Delight Makers

By VAN CAMPEN HEILNER

THE TITLE of this chapter was borrowed from one of the most delightful books on fishing that has ever been written, Charles Frederick Holder's *Log of a Sea Angler.* Coupled with Walton's *Complete Angler* and Van Dyke's *Little Rivers,* they form a classic trilogy that belongs to the immortals.

There are so many "delight makers" which I can remember. They have been of every size and shape and under every conceivable surroundings. From the gray-green seas of the Aleutians to the chilling waters of the Humboldt Current off the South American coasts, from the headlands of Nova Scotia to the blue of the Caribbean they have furnished down the years a succession of marvelous memories that time can never erase.

One of the earliest was the barracuda. Dr. E. W. Gudger, the eminent authority on the barracuda, in his delightful book on this subject mentions some of the earlier historians' accounts of this voracious fish. According to the Sieur de Rochefort in his *Natural History of the Antilles,* written in 1665:

"Among the monsters greedy and desirous of human flesh, which are found on the coasts of the islands, the Becune is one of the most formidable. It is a fish which has the figure of a pike, and which grows to six or eight feet in length and has a girth in proportion. When it has perceived its prey, it launches itself in fury, like a bloodthirsty dog, at the men whom it has perceived in the water. Furthermore it is able to carry away a part of that which it has been able to catch, and its teeth have so much venom that its smallest bite becomes mortal if one does not have recourse at that very instant to some powerful remedy in order to abate and turn aside the force of the poison."

Pere Labat had some interesting observations to make in 1742:

"As it is not obliged to turn on its side like the shark when it wishes to bite, it is infinitely more dangerous. Our savages, who attack and kill Requins (sharks) and Pantoufliers (hammerhead sharks) with knives, do not dare to run that risk with Becunes, because, moving with such extraordinary speed, they carry away an arm, a leg, or a head as if they had been cut off with the blow of a sabre. It has happened several times that horses and other animals crossing (the river Gallion) by swimming have had their legs cut off or half their bellies carried away."

Dr. Gudger goes on to state that "Bullen (1904) quotes the apocryphal stories current throughout the West Indies as to the diabolical ferocity of the barracuda and ends by giving an eye-witness account of the fear of this fish which is universal throughout these islands. A pair of can hooks had been lost overboard in 40 feet of water, and for a small reward a band of eight negroes, swimming about the vessel and paying no attention to some sharks in the near vicinity, endeavored to recover these. All went well until the cry of 'couter!', 'couter!' was raised, whereupon bedlam broke loose. Crazed with fear, the negroes fairly climbed over each other to come aboard by the help of ropes flung out to them. Even when safe on the ship their demoralized panic-stricken condition was painful to witness."

My earliest recollections date from the Ragged Keys, a small group of islands southeasterly from Miami where over twenty years ago I first came in contact with this great sea pike. The tide ran swiftly through the cuts and channels there and there was a rock off the northernmost key where on the incoming tide there were always barracuda. We trolled for them with spoons and strips of cut-fish bait with very light rods and when they struck they went right into the air and put on as pretty a jumping exhibition as you would want.

They were most always solitary. If you poled slowly across the flats you could see them drifting along, more like ghosts than fish, their big staring eyes ever alert for prey, the black blotches on their flanks showing distorted through the water. When we were down in the diving helmet in the Bahamas the barracuda always made us nervous. They seemed to be always watching, always drifting closer, always ready to strike at the first sign of helplessness.

Many's the time I've had barracuda rush up to a hooked fish I've had on the line and literally tear him to pieces before my eyes. Some years ago a man who entered a live fish well at Key West was terribly cut by a barracuda and when I was in Puerto Rico a girl bather was severely bitten by one. I consider them more dangerous than the shark.

I caught a huge one once on Sombrero Reef down the keys. There is a lighthouse there, a great affair on stilts that stands up on the reef, and the water all about is shallow. There are plenty of big amberjacks there too, but there was one barracuda that was a honey. When I hooked him he went into the air, shaking his head like a dog, and he never stopped jumping 'til I had him to the boat. He weighed fifty pounds.

Did you ever have a guide who was adept at the grains? I did. His name was Eddie Pent and he won the grains championship on the west coast by tossing a pair of grains into a six-inch pipe at a hundred paces. Or so he told me. But he certainly could grain barracuda because I saw him. He rarely missed. The pole would whistle through the air in a graceful arc and zing! there was a becune speared squarely through the side. Graining is an art. The whole trick is in allowing for the refraction of the water because the fish is never actually where he appears to be. Always throw this side of him if you expect to score.

I never knew you could catch barracuda still-fishing on the bottom until one day in the Bahamas when I was fishing for bonefish I made a long cast for what in the ruffled water I took to be the world's record bonefish. It instantly seized my conch bait and was off in a wild dash while I nearly passed out from excitement. Then it jumped and I saw it was a picuda. It weighed twenty-two pounds but I was disappointed because when I had first seen it I thought I was headed for stardom. Baby barracudas make great bait for marlin, but they have a disgusting slime and smell perfectly horrible.

There's a big deep hole right out from the garbage dump at Catalina that's a grand place for yellowtail. They're the California cousin of the amberjack and they look like them and act like them. We used to go down there from Avalon with a big tankful of live baby mackerel for bait. The guide would anchor the boat and start dipping out the bait with a goldfish net and scattering them about the surface. There wouldn't be a thing in sight and then suddenly you'd see them coming, way down deep in the crystal blue. But they wouldn't be yellowtail; they'd be barracuda. Not the barracuda of the Atlantic but a cousin. An edible one, served in all the restaurants on the Pacific Coast. There'd be a hundred of them, maybe, all milling about and grabbing the mackerel but not touching the one on the hooks.

And then suddenly you'd see the yellowtail. Maybe only a pair at first or three. They wouldn't come close and they'd flash past and take the live bait on the run. Then the guide would pinch a couple of the mackerel and hurt them so they'd swim around in circles on the surface. And that would do the trick. If there's one thing a fish can't resist, it's another fish that's crippled or wounded. They'd go wild then and in between the free mackerel you'd slip one with a hook through its lips. If you don't think yellowtail can burn up the line take your three-six tackle and try them. They're one of the grandest sporting fish that swims.

And that goes for amberjack too. If you run into some of those and you haven't got live bait to hold the school, don't bring your fish aboard until you have another one hooked. Fish like to chase another fish that's hooked, the same as chickens like to chase one with a worm, and as long as you keep one in the water the school won't leave. If you want some of the finest and biggest amberjack in the sea, go to the Dry Tortugas not far from Key West, Fla. Here is probably some of the grandest all-round reef fishing in the country. The sea is literally boiling with fish and if you have friends that you want to "break in" to the game of salt water fishing for big game take them there and they'll catch fish to their hearts' content. Later they can graduate to tuna and marlin.

Groupers aren't much fun to catch but they certainly eat well. If you've never eaten grouper chowder prepared by a Bahama native with tomatoes, potatoes and a few other things for good measure you have missed an epicure's dream. It's worth going grouper fishing for the chowder alone. Every time I hook a grouper, my jaws begin to ache thinking about the chowder. And it's better the second day than the first. Make a great big potful. It will keep, that is if there's any left to keep.

The only unpleasant thing is that when you hook a grouper he'll make for the rocks instanter. Keep him out of them if you can, and for that you'll need at least an 18 thread line, for if once he reaches them the chances are he's lost and you might as well cut the line. The only thing I have ever found at all successful after once a grouper had reached the rocks on me and I couldn't dislodge him, was to give him a great deal of slack line. After about five or ten minutes, when he has gotten over his fright and believes that whatever was after him has gone, he may come out and then you have to horse him to the surface. Some of the groupers are really very beautiful in color and some are very large, a hundred pounds or more. They're heavy and strong but not fast or spectacular.

The great jewfish and his relative the giant black sea bass of California are very spectacular to be photographed with but that is about all you can say about them. There are some monster jewfish lying on the bottom under the trestles of the old Overseas Extension of the F.E.C. and if you want to go down there and get one you're welcome to him. I had an old sockdolager on for over an hour once at Trestle No. 5 and as I couldn't do much with him and didn't want to stay out all night fighting the monster, I finally got in as much line as I could and cut it. The greatest pleasure I ever got out of a giant black sea bass was from one whose picture was on a postal card sold in Avalon. Standing beside him was a very cute person in a one-piece bathing suit and fishermen friends to whom I mailed it could never quite make up their minds which they preferred to catch.

My greatest pleasure in life has come from fighting fish on light tackle. I've caught a lot on heavy tackle but it seems to me like a lot of unnecessary hard work. Hours of clinging to a straining rod, strapped in a harness, feet braced against the gunwale, sweat pouring into your eyes, may be some people's idea of relaxation and enjoyment, but it's not the writer's. I have had so much fun with light tackle that I am perfectly willing to let my past experience with giant tuna, marlin and sharks suffice and leave the further capture of these great gladiators to my host of friends who are pursuing them relentlessly from one end of the earth to the other. There are so many other fish which I can take on light tackle which give me greater pleasure. One of them is the snapper.

The snapper is something to catch and something to eat. He is the "pan fish" supreme of the Florida Keys and the Bahamas and the pargo of Cuba. As a rule you will find that he only bites at night or appears to. But it's because he's too wise and in the daytime he sees you or the line or the boat and it's something else again. There are some monster snappers in the harbor mouth at Bimini. Some of them must weigh twelve pounds or more. Go down there some slack water and start to chum with conch and see what comes up from the bottom. We finally found that by using a small hook and a very long "mist" leader baited with a piece of marlin that we could get them. But you have to chum. It's the same with all kinds of chumming. Once you get the fish coming, slip a piece of chum with a hook in it overboard and you should get results. It doesn't always work as the tuna fishermen off Seabright will tell you but it will often enough to satisfy you.

I was trolling among the Ragged Keys once and had a terrific strike. I did not know what I had hooked and as the fish rushed off and continued to put up a hard and fast fight my bewilderment increased. When I got him in it turned out to be a fourteen-pound mutton fish, a fish similar to a red snapper in appearance, but what a fighter! I've caught a lot since and my hat is off to them every time.

I owe a great many pleasant memories to members of the caranx family. Anyone who has caught a jack crevalle will know what I mean. In the Hawaiian Islands they grow to very large size and they call them ulua. They get them in New Zealand too, in fact in warm seas all over the world. No matter where you go you're liable to run into a member of the caranx family and you may be sure you will be royally entertained. A more dogged, fierce and gamy fighter for its size I do not know.

My memories of him go back to certain moonlit nights among the passes down the keys when we were trolling for tarpon. There would come a hard strike and a fast tattoo on the end of the line and in due course into the boat, spanking the bottom with vigor, would come a crevalle. I've caught them on hand lines with the Cuban market fishermen and even then they put up a good fight but if you want them at their best try them on a bait casting rod or a salt water fly rod.

There have been so many delight makers in my memories. The snook or robalo, sometimes called sergeant fish. We were away at the head of Harney's River once on the West Coast, fishing for black bass. We were catching them and throwing them back in the water as fast as we could cast. We'd caught over fifty and then some snook showed up and took all our plugs and we had to quit. And I know a place in Cuba where the robalo are as thick as mullet and must weigh up to forty pounds.

I was sitting in the club in New York talking fish as usual with a friend who had just returned from his first southern fishing trip. He was enthusiastic. His eyes sparkled and he gesticulated as he told me of all the wonderful denizens of the deep that had fallen to his rod. "And then," he said, "there was that terrific fish, I can't think of the name just now, but you must know it, that . . . that 'bat out of hell fish'!" "Ah!" I said, "you must mean the wahoo." "That's it!" he almost shouted. "What a fish!"

What a fish indeed! The first wahoo I ever saw I thought at first was a kingfish. Some of the best kingfishing I've ever had has come just about sunset. We would be coming back to port from a day's fishing when suddenly a great form would shoot into the air behind the boat. Maybe he had the bait in his mouth as he came up, maybe he got it on the way down, but he seldom missed it either way. One of those sights you never forget happened off Long Key one winter. A kingfish of about fifteen pounds had taken my partner's bait and he had him almost to the boat when suddenly a big barracuda shot into the air with the kingfish crosswise in his jaws. As he came down the form of an enormous shark appeared on the surface and snatched kingfish, barracuda and all. It happened so quickly we hardly had time to realize what had occurred but the whole scene was photographed in our minds in the same manner that a flash of lightning brings into relief certain scenes at night. The shark ran out all my friend's line and broke it.

Just outside the harbor at Miami is excellent ground for kingfish and where you find the commercial boats you will generally find the kingfish. They are delicious eating and afford excellent sport on light tackle.

But to get back to that first wahoo. It was off Long Key around

1917. We were heading back for the trestle from the reef when
I saw something off to one side coming through the water at tremendous speed. It was going so fast that it left a long white streak
in the water like the wake of a torpedo. Before I had time to decide just what it was I received a tremendous strike. It was such
a hard strike that the rod was almost snatched from my hand. The
line flew off the reel at a frightful speed and then a great fish
jumped way back. It looked like a huge kingfish and yet there was
something unfamiliar about it. Then the line came all slack and
I thought he was gone. At that moment another similar fish
jumped abreast of the boat and at the same time I saw there was
a great belly in my line and that whatever I had hooked had
rushed toward us, past us in fact, and was now ahead of the boat!
It was inconceivable to me that it was my fish which had just
leaped abreast of us.

Then something jumped way off the bow and by then my line
had come taut again and there was no doubt that it was all one
and the same fish. Why he hadn't gotten off was a mystery. And
what manner of fish this was that was putting on such an amazing
display of speed and pyrotechnics was beyond comprehension.

I was nearly an hour getting him in and when we boated him
I was surprised to find he weighed only forty-three pounds. It was
an evil-looking fish with a long pointed head, a great mackerel-like
tail and a long dorsal that looked almost like a sail. I have seen
a great many wahoo since and they have always performed according to reputation. My friend Harry Stelwagon caught an 86-
pounder off Bimini while I was with him and of all the goings-on
you ever saw that one took the prize. He seemed to be on all sides
of the boat at once and once almost leaped over it. He was a
magnificent fish and I have a movie of him to prove it. The world's
record at present is a fish of 124¾ pounds taken by J. B. Stickney
in 1935 in Hawaiian waters where it is known as the ono. In
Cuba and most Spanish-speaking countries it is called peto. There
are some very large wahoo in the Bahamas where it is sometimes
called queen fish, but no matter under what name you find him
he will give you a marvelous run for your money.

Speaking of fish nearly jumping over boats, my friend Jack
Drake, of Chicago, and I were nearly killed by a wahoo doing this
very thing. We were approaching the Bocas or Dragon's Mouths

off the island of Trinidad in a small cruiser. The mighty Orinoco empties out through these islands into the Caribbean and with the prevailing trade winds against the current creates a very nasty sea. There was a heavy following sea, a dirty discolored sea, for the great South American river stains the blue of the ocean for many miles from its mouth. We were standing on the top of the after cabin with our arms leaning on the roof of the pilothouse in front of us and watching the kingfish which were leaping all about in the white-capped sea. I don't suppose a space of two feet separated us. Suddenly, what we took to be a kingfish of about thirty pounds leaped high directly in front of the bow and, whistling over the top of the pilothouse, passed directly between us, hit the edge of the back cockpit and bounced into the sea. I saw it clearly enough to see it was a wahoo. With the following sea we were making about eighteen knots, and this coupled with the speed of the fish would have been sufficient, had it hit either of us, to have either killed us or thrown us into the sea. We were too surprised to realize our danger until afterwards.

Memories, memories, of all that numberless band of delight makers. Days off Catalina with the calm blue Pacific all churned to foam with the leaping albacora and we trolling feathers through the schools to be instantly fast to these fighting little demons. The big white sea bass that I had on off Seal Rocks and he finally ran in the kelp on me and cut the line. The big cobia or crab-eater that I hooked on the American Shoals reef and that gave me one of the best fights of my life. The great permit or giant pompano that I had on off Tavernier, that cut through the water so fast it sounded like someone ripping a piece of sailcloth. Days on the "Mud" off the west coast of Andros Island with the bonefish tails working in with the flooding tide. Other days on the miles of flats off Cape Sable where we got three sawfish in one day and caught the dainty ladyfish than which there isn't a prettier leaper. Fishing in the "Aquarium" at Caesar's Creek for parrot fish and angel fish and then going to call on Israel Lafayette Jones, proprietor of the Coral Isle apiaries and taking the thick mangrove blossom honey and pouring it on big slices of bread. Wandering through the desolate ruins of the fort on the Dry Tortugas and thinking of the unfortunate Dr. Mudd and then fishing for grunts and snappers in the channel by the reef and catching a great green moray and having to cut the line because your guide wouldn't stay in the boat unless you did. Going down to Cay Sal bank with the sponge fleet and eating tern's eggs. Catching loggerhead turtles in the moonlight as they hurried back to the ocean and "turning" them and then following their trail back until you found their eggs all buried in the sand, and eating them too. Standing on the wild oat slopes of San Clemente with the wind from the Pacific blowing clean and sweet in your face and then see far below you the great sickle-shaped fin and tail of a broadbill on the surface. The day we caught so many papagallo off the coast of Ecuador, and then when we got to shore found that one of our Indians had taken a big drink of formaldehyde we had left in a whisky bottle, thinking it was whisky. His throat was paralyzed for a week and it was a wonder it didn't kill him. There were hundreds more; I can close my eyes and see them pass in endless review. But the most beautiful of all, to me, has been the dolphin.

Nature, with all her masterpieces, outdid herself in the creation of this lovely creature. The blue of every sea in the world, the purple of distant mountain peaks, the gold of every sunrise and sunset since Time began, the lush green of tropical mountains rising from a cobalt sea; these and a thousand other colors all were blended to make the dolphin.

As if his color was not enough he is endowed with speed, leaping abilities and a good flavor. Dolphin like flying fish and wherever you find the latter you'll find the former. Many's the time I've watched a dolphin chasing flying fish. Just behind and just beneath the surface the dolphin with incredible speed would keep pace with his prospective prey and the moment the hapless winged quarry hit the water, the dolphin had him. I timed over a hundred flying fish in the South Atlantic with a stop watch and their average time in the air was between four and five seconds. Some stayed up as long as seven. With the speed at which a flying fish travels, seven seconds is a long time, and for a dolphin, handicapped as he is by the resistance of the water, to keep pace with one of these bird-like creatures and to capture it is an amazing thing.

Off the Diamond Shoals in North Carolina, where the Gulf Stream comes within ten miles of the land, the closest point of approach north of Palm Beach is, according to Breder, the greatest concentration point for flying fish in the North Atlantic. I have observed great numbers of dolphin around the lightship there and it follows there must be, at certain seasons of the year, great numbers of marlin and other tropical fishes. With new big game angling grounds opening up every year, this particular locality, I feel certain, is eventually destined to be one of the greatest.

It was way down the keys in the early days right after the railroad had first come to Key West. The sun was just setting on its "pedestal" across the Bay of Florida and the trestle was a dim line of arches on the horizon as we turned homeward. Then I had the last strike of the day and into the air shot a dorado which in the lovely language of Castile means "golden." Leaping, twisting, shaking his head like a bull terrier I brought him closer until, lifting him over the side, he lay quivering in the cockpit.

Then occurred that unforgettable sight, the death of a dolphin. Like fields of wheat rippling in the summer wind, the waves of color washed across his body. First gold, then blue, then gold and blue, amethyst, cerulean and jade kept beat with his dying heart. And then the last gasp, and like the quick descent of a tropic night the colors were gone and with it the sunset.

> *Parting day dies like the dolphin*
> *Whom each pang embues*
> *With a new color as it gasps away*
> *The last still loveliest*
> *'Til, 'tis gone, and all is gray.*
> *—Byron.*

The Warwick Woodlands

By FRANK FORESTER

DAY THE FIRST

IT WAS A fine October evening when I was sitting on the back stoop of his cheerful little bachelor's establishment in Mercer street, with my old friend and comrade, Henry Archer. Many a frown of fortune had we two weathered out together; in many of her brightest smiles had we two revelled—never was there a stauncher friend, a merrier companion, a keener sportsman, or a better fellow, than this said Harry; and here had we two met, three thousand miles from home, after almost ten years of separation, just the same careless, happy, dare-all do-no-goods that we were when we parted in St. James's Street,—he for the West, I for the Eastern World—he to fell trees, and build log huts in the backwoods of Canada,—I to shoot tigers and drink arrack punch in the Carnatic. The world had wagged with us as with most others: now up, now down, and laid us to, at last, far enough from the goal for which we started—so that, as I have said already, on landing in New York, having heard nothing of him for ten years, whom the deuce should I tumble on but that same worthy, snugly housed, with a neat bachelor's menage, and everything ship-shape about him?—So, in the natural course of things, we were at once inseparables.

Well—as I said before, it was a bright October evening, with the clear sky, rich sunshine, and brisk breezy freshness, which indicate that loveliest of American months,—dinner was over, and with a pitcher of the liquid ruby of Latour, a brace of half-pint beakers, and a score—my contribution—of those most exquisite of smokables, the true old Manilla cheroots, we were consoling the inward man in a way that would have opened the eyes, with

349

abhorrent admiration, of any advocate of that coldest of comforts
—cold water—who should have got a chance peep at our snuggery.

Suddenly, after a long pause, during which he had been stimulating his ideas by assiduous fumigation, blowing off his steam in
a long vapory cloud that curled a minute afterward about his
temples,—'What say you, Frank, to a start tomorrow?' exclaimed
Harry,—'and a week's right good shooting?'

'Why, as for that,' said I, 'I wish for nothing better—but where
the deuce would you go to get shooting?'

'Never fash your beard, man,' he replied, 'I'll find the ground
and the game too, so you'll find share of the shooting!—Holloa!
there—Tim, Tim Matlock.'

And in brief space that worthy minister of mine host's pleas-
ures made his appearance, smoothing down his short black hair,
clipped in the orthodox bowl fashion, over his bluff good-natured
visage with one hand, while he employed its fellow in hitching up
a pair of most voluminous unmentionables, of thick Yorkshire
cord.

A character was Tim—and now I think of it, worthy of brief
description. Born, I believe—bred, certainly, in a hunting stable,
far more of his life passed in the saddle than elsewhere, it was not
a little characteristic of my friend Harry to have selected this piece
of Yorkshire oddity as his especial body servant; but if the choice
were queer, it was at least successful, for an honester, more faithful, hard-working, and withal, better hearted, and more humorous
varlet never drew curry-comb over horsehide, or clothes-brush
over broadcloth.

His visage was, as I have said already, bluff and good-natured,
with a pair of hazel eyes, of the smallest—but, at the same time,
of the very merriest—twinkling from under the thick black eyebrows, which were the only hairs suffered to grace his clean-shaven
countenance. An indescribable pug nose, and a good clean-cut
mouth, with a continual dimple at the left corner, made up his
phiz. For the rest, four feet ten inches did Tim stand in his stockings, about two-ten of which were monopolized by his back, the
shoulders of which would have done honor to a six foot pugilist,—
his legs, though short and bowed a little outward, by continual
horse exercise, were right tough serviceable members, and I have
seen them bearing their owner on through mud and mire, when

straighter, longer, and more fair proportioned limbs were at an awful discount.

Depositing his hat then on the floor, smoothing his hair, and hitching up his smalls, and striving most laboriously not to grin till he should have cause, stood Tim, like 'Giafar awaiting his master's award!'

'Tim!' said Harry Archer—

'Sur!' said Tim.

'Tim! Mr. Forester and I are talking of going up to-morrow —what do you say to it?'

'Oop yonner?' queried Tim, in the most extraordinary West-Riding Yorkshire, indicating the direction, by pointing his right thumb over his left shoulder—'Weel, Ay'se nought to say aboot it —not Ay!'

'Soh! the cattle are all right, and the wagon in good trim, and the dogs in exercise, are they?'

'Ay'se warrant um!'

'Well, then, have all ready for a start at six to-morrow,—put Mr. Forester's Manton along with my Joe Spurling in the top tray of the case, my single gun and my double rifle in the lower, and see the magazine well filled—the Diamond gunpowder, you know, from Mr. Brough's. You'll put up what Mr. Forester will want, for a week, you know—he does not know the country yet, Tim; —and, hark you, what wine have I at Tom Draw's?'

'No but a case of claret.'

'I thought so, then away with you! down to the Baron's and get two baskets of the Star, and stop at Fulton Market, and get the best half hundred round of spiced beef you can—and then go up to Starke's at the Octagon, and get a gallon of his old Ferintosh—that's all, Tim—off with you! —No! stop a minute!' and he filled up a beaker and handed it to the original, who, shutting both his eyes, suffered the fragrant claret to roll down his gullet in the most scientific fashion, and then, with what he called a bow, turned right about, and exit.

The sun rose bright on the next morning, and half an hour before the appointed time, Tim entered my bedchamber, with a cup of mocha, and the intelligence that 'Measter had been oop this hour and better, and did na like to be kept waiting!'—so up I jumped, and scarcely had got through the business of rigging myself, before the rattle of wheels announced the arrival of the wagon.

And a model was that shooting wagon—a long, lightbodied box, with a low rail—a high seat and dash in front, and a low servant's seat behind, with lots of room for four men and as many dogs, with guns and luggage, and all appliances to boot, enough to last a month, stowed away out of sight, and out of reach of weather. The nags, both nearly thorough-bred, fifteen two inches high, stout, clean-limbed, active animals—the off-side horse a gray, almost snow-white—the near, a dark chestnut, nearly black—with square docks setting admirably off their beautiful round quarters, high crests, small blood-like heads, and long thin manes—spoke volumes for Tim's stable science; for though their ribs were slightly visible, their muscles were well filled, and hard as granite. Their coats glanced in the sunshine—the white's like statuary marble; the chestnut's like high polished copper—in short the whole turn-out was perfect.

The neat black harness, relieved merely by a crest, with every strap that could be needed, in its place, and not one buckle or one thong superfluous; the bright steel curbs, with the chains jingling as the horses tossed and pawed impatient for a start; the tapering holly whip; the bear-skins covering the seats; the topcoats spread above them—everything, in a word, without bordering on the slang, was perfectly correct and gnostic.

Four dogs—a brace of setters of the light active breed, one of which will out-work a brace of the large, lumpy, heavyheaded dogs,—one red, the other white and liver, both with black noses, their legs and sterns beautifully feathered, and their hair, glossy and smooth as silk, showing their excellent condition—and a brace of short-legged, bony, liver-colored spaniels—with their noses thrust one above the other, over or through the railings, and their tails waving with impatient joy—occupied the after portion of the wagon.

Tim, rigged in plain gray frock, with leathers and white tops stood, in true tiger fashion, at the horses' heads, with the forefinger of his right hand resting upon the curb of the gray horse, as with his left he rubbed the nose of the chestnut; viewing with a steady and experienced eye the gear, which seemed to give him perfect satisfaction. That moment I appeared on the steps

'In with you, Frank—in with you,' he exclaimed, disengaging the hand-reins from the terrets into which they had been thrust, 'I have been waiting here these five minutes. Jump up, Tim!'

And, gathering the reins up firmly, he mounted by the wheel, tucked the top-coat about his legs, shook out the long lash of his tandem whip, and lapped it up in good style.

'I always drive with one of these'—he said, half apologetically, as I thought—'they are so handy on the road for the cur dogs, when you have setters with you—they plague your life out else. Have you the pistol-case in, Tim, for I don't see it?'

'All raight, sur,' answered he, not over well pleased, as it seemed, that it should even be suspected that he could have forgotten anything—'All raight!'

'Go long, then,' cried Harry, and at the word the high bred nags went off; and though my friend was too good and too old a hand to worry his cattle at the beginning of a long day's journey —many minutes had not passed before we found ourselves on board the ferry-boat, steaming it merrily towards the Jersey shore.

'A quarter past six to the minute,' said Harry, as we landed at Hoboken.

'Let Shot and Chase run, Tim, but keep the spaniels in till we pass Hackensack.'

'Awa wi ye, ye rascals,' exclaimed Tim, and out went the high blooded dogs upon the instant, yelling and jumping in delight about the horses—and off we went, through the long sandy street of Hoboken, leaving the private race-course of that stanch sportsman, Mr. Stevenson on the left, with several powerful horses taking their walking exercise in their neat body clothes.

'That puts me in mind, Frank,' said Harry, as he called my attention to the thorough-breds, 'we must be back next Tuesday for the Beacon Races—the new course up there on the hill; you can see the steps that lead to it—and now is not this lovely?' he continued, as we mounted the first ridge of Weehawken, and looked back over the beautiful broad Hudson, gemmed with a thousand snowy sails of craft or shipping—'Is not this lovely, Frank? and, by the by, you will say, when we get to our journey's end, you never drove through prettier scenery in your life. Get away, Bob, you villain—nibbling, nibbling at your curb! get away, lads!'

And away we went at a right rattling pace over the hills, and through the cedar swamp; and, passing through a tollgate, stopped with a sudden jerk at a long low tavern on the left-hand side.

'We must stop here, Frank. My old friend, Ingliss, a brother trigger, too, would think the world was coming to an end if I drove by—twenty-nine minutes these six miles,' he added, looking at his watch, 'that will do! Now, Tim, look sharp—just a sup of water! Good day—good day to you, Mr. Ingliss; now for a glass of your milk punch'—and mine host disappeared, and in a moment came forth with two rummers of the delicious compound, a big bright lump of ice bobbing about in each among the nutmug.

'What, off again for Orange county, Mr. Archer? I was telling the old woman yesterday that we should have you by before long; well, you'll find cock pretty plenty, I expect; there was a chap by here from Ulster—let me see, what day was it—Friday, I guess—with produce, and he was telling, they have had no cold snap yet up there! Thank you sir, good luck to you!'

And off we went again, along a level road, crossing the broad, slow river from whence it takes its name, into the town of Hackensack.

'We breakfast here, Frank'—as he pulled up beneath the low Dutch shed projecting over half the road in front of the neat tavern—'How are you, Mr. Vanderbeck—we want a beefsteak, and a cup of tea, as quick as you can give it us; we'll make the tea ourselves; bring in the black tea, Tim—the nags as usual.'

'Aye! aye! sir'—'tak them out—leave t'harness on, all but their bridles'—to an old gray-headed hostler. 'Whisp off their legs a bit; Ay will be oot enoo!'

After as good a breakfast as fresh eggs, good country bread—worth ten times the poor trash of city bakers—prime butter, cream, and a fat steak could furnish, at a cheap rate, and with a civil and obliging landlord, away we went again over the red hills—an infernal ugly road, sandy, and rough, and stony—for ten miles farther to New Prospect.

'Now you shall see some scenery worth looking at,' said Harry, as we started again, after watering the horses, and taking in a bag with a peck of oats—'to feed at three o'clock, Frank, when we stop to grub, which we must do al fresco'—my friend explained—'for the landlord, who kept the only tavern on the road, went West this summer, bit by the land mania, and there is now no stopping place 'twixt this and Warwick,' naming the village for which we were bound. 'You have that beef boiled, Tim?'

'Ay'd been a fouil else, and aye so often oop t'road too,' answered he with a grin, 'and t'moostard is mixed, and t'pilot biscuit in, and a good bit o' Cheshire cheese! wee's do, Ay reckon. Ha! ha! ha!'

And now my friend's boast was indeed fulfilled; for when we had driven a few miles farther, the country became undulating, with many and bright streams of water; the hillsides clothed with luxuriant woodlands, now in their many-colored garb of autumn beauty; the meadow-land rich in unchanged fresh greenery—for the summer had been mild and rainy—with here and there a buckwheat stubble showing its ruddy face, replete with promise of quail in the present, and of hot cakes in future; and the bold chain of mountains, which, under many names, but always beautiful and wild, sweeps from the Highlands of the Hudson, west and southwardly, quite through New Jersey, forming a link between the White and Green Mountains of New Hampshire and Vermont, and the famous Alleghanies of the South.

A few miles farther yet, the road wheeled round the base of the Tourne Mountain, a magnificent bold hill, with a bare craggy head, its sides and skirts thick set with cedars and hickory—entering a defile through which the Ramapo, one of the loveliest streams eye ever looked upon, comes rippling with its crystal waters over bright pebbles, on its way to join the two kindred rivulets which form the fair Passaic. Throughout the whole of the defile, nothing can possibly surpass the loveliness of nature; the road hard and smooth, and level, winding and wheeling parallel to the gurgling river, crossing it two or three times in each mile, now on one side, and now on the other—the valley now barely broad enough to permit the highway and the stream to pass between the abrupt masses of rock and forest, now expanding into rich basins of green meadow-land, the deepest and most fertile possible—the hills of every shape and size—here bold, and bare, and rocky—there swelling up in grand round masses, pile above pile of verdure, to the blue firmament of autumn. By and by we drove through a thriving little village, nestling in a hollow of the hills, beside a broad bright pond, whose waters keep a dozen manufactories of cotton and of iron—with which mineral these hills abound—in constant operation; and passing by the tavern, the departure of whose owner Harry had so pathetically mourned, we wheeled again round a projecting spur of hill into a narrower defile, and reached another hamlet, far different in its aspect from the busy bustling place we had left some five miles behind.

There were some twenty houses, with two large mills of solid masonry; but of these not one building was now tenanted; the roof-trees broken, the doors and shutters either torn from their hinges, or flapping wildly to and fro; the mill wheels cumbering the stream with masses of decaying timber, and the whole presenting a most desolate and mournful aspect.

'Its story is soon told,' said Harry, catching my inquiring glance—'a speculating, clever New York merchant—a water-power —a failure—and a consequent desertion of the project; but we must find a berth among the ruins!'

And as he spoke, turning a little off the road, he pulled up on the green sward; 'there's an old stable here that has a manger in it yet! Now, Tim, look sharp!'

And in a twinkling the horses were loosed from the wagon, the harness taken off and hanging on the corners of the ruined hovels, and Tim hissing and rubbing away at the gray horse, while Harry did like duty on the chestnut, in a style that would have done no shame to Melton Mowbray!

'Come, Frank, make yourself useful! Get out the round of beef, and all the rest of the provant—it's on the rack behind; you'll find all right there. Spread our table-cloth on that flat stone by the waterfall, under the willow; clap a couple of bottles of the Baron's champagne into the pool there underneath the fall; let's see whether your Indian campaigning has taught you anything worth knowing!'

To work I went at once, and by the time I had got through— 'Come, Tim,' I heard him say, 'I've got the rough dirt off this fellow, you must polish him, while I take a wash, and get a bit of dinner. Holloa! Frank, are you ready!'

And he came bounding down to the water's edge, with his Newmarket coat in hand, and sleeves rolled up to the elbows, plunged his face into the cool stream, and took a good wash of his soiled hands in the same natural basin. Five minutes afterward we were employed most pleasantly with the spiced beef, white biscuit, and good wine, which came out of the waterfall as cool as Gunter could have made it with all his icing. When we had pretty well got through, and were engaged with our cheroots, up came Tim Matlock.

'T' horses have got through wi' t' corn—they have fed rarely —so I harnessed them, sur, all to the bridles—we can start when you will.'

'Sit down, and get your dinner then, sir—there's a heeltap in that bottle we have left for you—and when you have done, put up the things, and we'll be off. I say, Frank, let us try a shot with the pistols—I'll get the case—stick up that fellow-commoner upon the fence there, and mark off a twenty paces.'

The marking irons were produced, and loaded—'Fire—one— two—three'—bang! and the shivering of the glass announced that never more would that shape hold the generous liquor; the ball had struck it plump in the centre, and broken off the whole above the shoulder, for it was fixed neck downward on the stake.

'It is my turn now,' said I; and more by luck, I fancy, than skill, I took the neck off, leaving nothing but the thick ring of the mouth still sticking on the summit of the fence.

'I'll hold you a dozen of my best Regalias against as many of Manillas, that I break the ring.'

'Done, Harry!'

'Done!'

Again the pistol cracked, and the unerring ball drove the small fragment into a thousand splinters.

'That fotched 'um!' exclaimed Tim, who had come up to announce all ready. 'Ecod, measter Frank, you munna wager i' that gate wi' master, or my name beant Tim, but thou'lt be clean bamboozled.'

Well, not to make a short story long, we got under way again and, with speed unabated, spanked along at full twelve miles an hour for five miles farther. There, down a wild looking glen, on the left hand, comes brawling, over stump and stone, a tributary streamlet, by the side of which a rough track, made by the char-coal burners and the iron miners, intersects the main road; and up this miserable looking path, for it was little more, Harry wheeled at full trot.

'Now for twelve miles of mountain, the roughest road and wildest country you ever saw crossed in a phaeton, good master Frank.'

And wild it was, indeed, and rough enough in all conscience; narrow, unfenced in many places, winding along the brow of precipices without rail or breastwork, encumbered with huge blocks of stone, and broken by the summer rains! An English stage coachman would have stared aghast at the steep zigzags up the hills, the awkward turns on the descents, the sudden pitches, with now an unsafe bridge, and now a stony ford at the bottom; but through all this, the delicate quick finger, keen eye, and cool head of Harry, assisted by the rare mouths of his exquisitely bitted cattle, piloted us at the rate of full ten miles an hour; the scenery, through which the wild track ran, being entirely of the most wild and savage character of woodland; the bottom filled with gigantic timber trees, cedar, and pine, and hemlock, with a dense undergrowth of rhododendron, calmia and azalea, which, as my friend informed me, made the whole mountains in the summer season one rich bed of bloom. About six miles from the point where we had entered them we scaled the highest ridge of the hills, by a stratum of broken shaley limestone; and, passing at once from the forest into well cultivated fields, came on a new and lovelier prospect—a narrow deep vale scarce a mile in breadth—scooped, as it were, out of the mighty mountains which embosomed it on every side—in the highest state of culture, with rich orchards, and deep meadows, and brown stubbles, whereon the shocks of maize stood fair and frequent; and westward of the road, which, diving down obliquely to the bottom, loses itself in the woods of the opposite hill-side, and only becomes visible again when it emerges to cross over the next summit—the loveliest sheet of water my eye has ever seen, varying from half a mile to a mile in breadth, and about five miles long, with shores indented deeply with the capes and promontories of the woodclothed hills, which sink abruptly to its margin.

'That is the Greenwood Lake, Frank, called by the monsters here Long Pond!—"the fiends receive their souls therefor," as Walter Scott says—in my mind prettier than Lake George by far, though known to few except chance sportsmen like myself! Full of fish, perch of a pound in weight, and yellow bass in the deep

waters, and a good sprinkling of trout, towards this end! Ellis
Ketchum killed a five-pounder there this spring! and heaps of
summer-duck, the loveliest in plumage of the genus, and the
best too, me judice, excepting only the inimitable canvas-back.
There are a few deer, too, in the hills, though they are getting
scarce of late years. There, from that headland, I killed one, three
summers since; I was placed at a stand by the lake's edge, and the
dogs drove him right down to me; but I got too eager, and he
heard or saw me, and so fetched a turn, but they were close upon
him, and the day was hot, and he was forced to soil. I never saw
him till he was in the act of leaping from a bluff of ten or twelve
feet into the deep lake, but I pitched up my rifle at him, a snap
shot! as I would my gun at a cock in a summer brake, and by
good luck sent my ball through his heart. There is a finer view
yet when we cross this hill, the Bellevale mountain; look out,
for we are just upon it; there! Now admire!'

And on the summit he pulled up, and never did I see a landscape more extensively magnificent. Ridge after ridge the mountain sloped down from our feet into a vast rich basin ten miles
at least in breadth, by thirty, if not more, in length, girdled on
every side by mountains—the whole diversified with wood and
water, meadow, and pasture-land, and cornfield—studded with
small white villages—with more than one bright lakelet glittering
like beaten gold in the declining sun, and several isolated hills
standing up boldly from the vale!

'Glorious indeed! Most glorious!' I exclaimed.

'Right, Frank,' he said; 'a man may travel many a day, and
not see anything to beat the vale of Sugar-loaf—so named from
that cone-like hill, over the pond there—that peak is eight hundred
feet above tide water. Those blue hills, to the far right, are the
Hudson Highlands; that bold bluff is the far-famed Anthony's
Nose; that ridge across the vale, the second ridge I mean, is the
Shawangunks; and those rounded summits, farther yet—those are
the Kaatskills! But now a truce with the romantic, for there lies
Warwick, and this keen mountain air has found me a fresh appetite!'

Away we went again, rattling down the hills, nothing daunted
at their steep pitches, with the nags just as fresh as when they
started, champing and snapping at their curbs, till on a table-land

above the brook, with the tin steeple of its church peering from out the massy foliage of sycamore and locust, the haven of our journey lay before us.

'Hilloa, hill-oa, ho! whoop! who-whoop!' and with a cheery shout, as we clattered across the wooden bridge, he roused out the population of the village.

'Ya ha ha!—ya yah!' yelled a great woolly-headed coal-black negro. 'Here 'm massa Archer back again—massa ben well, I spect—'

'Well—to be sure I have, Sam,' cried Harry. 'How's old Poll? Bid her come up to Draw's to-morrow night—I've got a red and yellow frock for her—a deuce of a concern!'

'Yah ha! yah ha ha haah!' and amid a most discordant chorus of African merriment, we passed by a neat farm-house shaded by two glorious locusts on the right, and a new red brick mansion, the pride of the village, with a flourishing store on the left—and wheeled up to the famous Tom Draw's tavern—a long white house with a piazza six feet wide, at the top of eight steep steps, and a one-story kitchen at the end of it; pump with a gilt pine-apple at the top of it, and horse trough, a wagon shed and stable sixty feet long; a sign-post with an indescribable female figure swinging upon it, and an ice house over the way!

Such was the house, before we pulled up just as the sun was setting, amid a gabbling of ducks, a barking of terriers, mixed with the deep bay of two or three large heavy fox-hounds which had been lounging about in the shade, and a peal of joyous welcome from all beings, quadruped or biped, within hearing.

'Hulloa! boys! Walk in! walk in! What the eternal h--l are you about there?'

Well, we did walk into a large neat barroom, with a bright hickory log crackling upon the hearth-stone, a large round table in one corner, covered with draught-boards, and old newspapers, among which showed pre-eminent the 'Spirit of the Times'; a range of pegs well stored with great-coats, fishing rods, whips, game-bags, spurs, and every other stray appurtenance of sporting, gracing one end; while the other was more gaily decorated by the well furnished bar, in the right-hand angle of which my eye detected in an instant a handsome nine-pound double barrel, an old six foot Queen Ann's tower-musket, and a long smooth-bored rifle; and last, not least, outstretched at easy length upon the counter of his bar, to the left-hand of the gang-way—the right side being more suitably decorated with tumblers, and decanters of strange compounds—supine, with fair round belly towering upward, and head voluptuously pillowed on a heap of wagon cushions—lay in his glory—but no! hold!—the end of a chapter is no place to introduce—Tom Draw!

DAY THE SECOND

Much as I had heard of Tom Draw, I was, I must confess, taken altogether aback when I, for the first time, set eyes upon him. I had heard Harry Archer talk of him fifty times as a crack shot; as a top sawyer at a long day's fag; as the man of all others he would choose as his mate, if he were to shoot a match, two against two—what then was my astonishment at beholding this worthy, as he reared himself slowly from his recumbent position? It is true, I had heard his sobriquet, 'Fat Tom,' but, Heaven and Earth! such a mass of beef and brandy as stood before me, I had never even dreamt of. About five feet six inches at the very utmost in the perpendicular, by six or 'by'r lady'—nearer seven in circumference, weighing, at the least computation, two hundred and fifty pounds, with a broad jolly face, its every feature—well-formed and handsome, rather than otherwise—mantling with an expression of the most perfect excellence of heart and temper, and overshadowed by a vast mass of brown hair, sprinkled pretty well with gray!—Down he plumped from the counter with a thud that made the whole floor shake, and with a hand outstretched, that might have done for a Goliath, out he strode to meet us.

'Why, hulloa! hulloa! Mr. Archer,' shaking his hand till I thought he would have dragged the arm clean out of the socket— 'How be you, boy? How be you?'

'Right well, Tom, can't you see? Why confound you, you've grown twenty pounds heavier since July!—but here, I'm losing all my manners!—this is Frank Forester, whom you have heard me talk about so often! He dropped down here out of the moon, Tom, I believe! at least I thought about as much of seeing the man in the moon, as of meeting him in this wooden country—but here he is, as you see, come all the way to take a look at the natives. And so, you see, as you're about the greatest curiosity I know of in these parts, I brought him straight up here to take a peep! Look at him, Frank—look at him well! Now, did you ever see, in all your life, so extraordinary an old devil?—and yet, Frank, which no man could possibly believe, the old fat animal has some good points about him—he can walk some! shoot, as he says, first best! and drink—good Lord, how he can drink!'

'And that reminds me,' exclaimed Tom, who with a ludicrous mixture of pleasure, bashfulness, and mock anger, had been listening to what he evidently deemed a high encomium; 'that we haven't drinked yet; have you quit drink, Archer, since I was to York? What'll you take, Mr. Forester? Gin? yes, I have got some prime gin! You never sent me up them groceries though, Archer; well, then, here's luck! What, Yorkshire, is that you? I should ha' thought now, Archer, you'd have cleared that lazy Injun out afore this time!'

'Whoy, measter Draa—what 'na loike's that kind o' talk?—coom coom now, where'll Ay tak t' things tull?'

'Put Mr. Forester's box in the bed-room off the parlor—mine upstairs, as usual,' cried Archer. 'Look sharp and get the traps out. Now, Tom, I suppose you have got no supper for us?'

'Cooper, Cooper! you snooping little devil,' yelled Tom, addressing his second hope, a fine dark-eyed bright-looking lad of ten or twelve years; 'Don't you see Mr. Archer's come? I'll cure you! Supper—you're always eat! eat! eat! or, drink! drink!—drunk! Yes! supper; we've got pork and chickens—'

'Oh d--n your chickens,' chimed in Harry, 'old superannuated cocks which must be caught now, and then beheaded, and then soused into hot water to fetch off the feathers; and save you lazy devils the trouble of picking them. No, no, Tom! get us some fresh meat for to-morrow; and for to-night let us have some hot potatoes, and some bread and butter, and we'll find beef; eh, Frank? and now look sharp, for we must be up in good time to-morrow, and, to be so we must to bed betimes. And now, Tom, are there any cock?'

'Cock! yes, I guess there be, and quail, too, pretty plenty! quite a smart chance of them, and not a shot fired among them this fall, any how!'

'Well, which way must we beat to-morrow? I calculate to shoot three days with you here; and, on Wednesday night when we get

in, to hitch up and drive into Sullivan, and see if we can't get a
deer or two! You'll go, Tom?'

'Well, well, we'll see any how; but for to-morrow, why I guess
we must beat the 'Squire's swamp-hole first; there's ten or twelve
cock there, I know; I see them there myself last Sunday; and
then acrost them buck-wheat stubbles, and the big bog meadow,
there's a drove of quail there; two or three bevys got in one, I
reckon; leastwise I counted thirty-three last Friday was a week;
and through Seer's big swamp, over to the great spring!'

'How is Seer's swamp? too wet, I fancy,' Archer interposed,
'at least I noticed, from the mountain, that all the leaves were
changed in it, and that the maples were quite bare.'

'Pretty fair, pretty fair, I guess,' replied stout Tom, 'I harnt
been there myself though, but Jem was down with the hounds
arter an old fox t'other day, and sure enough he said the cock
kept flopping up quite thick afore him; but then the critter will
lie, Harry; he will lie like thunder, you know; but somehow I
concaits there be cock there too; and then, as I was saying, we'll
stop at the great spring and get a bite of summat, and then beat
Hell-hole; you'll have sport there for sartin! What dogs have you
got with you Harry?'

'Your old friends, Spot and Chase, and a couple of spaniels
for thick covert!'

'Now, gentlemen, your suppers are all ready.'

'Come, Tom,' cried Archer; 'you must take a bite with us—
Tim, bring in three bottles of champagne, and lots of ice, do
you hear?'

And the next moment we found ourselves installed in a snug
parlor, decorated with a dozen sporting prints, a blazing hickory
fire snapping and sputtering and roaring in a huge Franklin
stove; our luggage safely stowed in various corners, and Archer's
double gun-case propped on two chairs below the window.

An old-fashioned round table, covered with clean white linen
of domestic manufacture, displayed the noble round of beef
which we had brought up with us, flanked by a platter of magnificent potatoes, pouring forth volumes of dense steam through
the cracks in their dusky skins; a lordly dish of butter, that might
have pleased the appetite of Sisera; while eggs and ham, and pies
of apple, mince-meat, cranberry, and custard, occupied every va-

cant space, save where two ponderous pitchers, mantling with ale and cider, and two respectable square bottles, labelled 'Old Rum' and 'Brandy—1817,' relieved the prospect. Before we had sat down, Timothy entered, bearing a horse bucket filled to the brim with ice, from whence protruded the long necks and split corks of three champagne bottles.

'Now, Tim,' said Archer, 'get your own supper, when you've finished with the cattle; feed the dogs well to-night; and then to bed. And hark you, call me at five in the morning; we shall want you to carry the game-bag and the drinkables; take care of yourself, Tim, and good night!'

'No need to tell him that,' cried Tom, 'he's something like yourself; I tell you, Archer, if Tim ever dies of thirst, it must be where there is nothing wet, but water.'

'Now hark to the old scoundrel, Frank,' said Archer, 'hark to him pray, and if he doesn't out-eat both of us, and out-drink anything you ever saw, may I miss my first bird tomorrow—that's all! Give me a slice of beef, Frank; that old Goth could cut it an inch thick, if I let him touch it; out with a cork, Tom! Here's to our sport to-morrow!'

'Uh; that goes good!' replied Tom, with an oath, which, by the apparent gusto of the speaker, seemed to betoken that the wine had tickled his palate—'that goes good! that's different from the darned red trash you left up here last time.'

'And of which you have left none, I'll be bound,' answered Archer, laughing; 'my best Latour, Frank, which the old infidel calls trash.'

'It's all below, every bottle of it,' answered Tom; 'I wouldn't use such rotgut stuff, no, not for vinegar. 'Tain't half so good as that red sherry you had up here oncet; that was poor weak stuff, too, but it did well to make milk punch of; it did well instead of milk.'

'Now, Frank,' said Archer, 'you won't believe me, that I know; but it's true, all the same. A year ago, this autumn, I brought up five gallons of exceedingly stout, rather fiery, young, brown sherry —draught wine, you know!—and what did Tom do here, but mix it half and half, with brandy, nutmeg, and sugar, and drink it for milk punch!'

'I did so, by the eternal,' replied Tom, bolting a huge lump of beef, in order to enable himself to answer—'I did so, and good milk punch it made, too, but it was too weak! Come, Mr. Forester, we harn't drinked yet, and I'm kind o' gittin' dry!'

And now the mirth waxed fast and furious—the champagne speedily was finished, the supper things cleared off, hot water and Starke's Ferintosh succeeded, cheroots were lighted, we drew closer in about the fire, and, during the circulation of two tumblers —for to this did Harry limit us, having the prospect of unsteady hands and aching heads before him for the morrow—never did I hear more genuine and real humor, than went round our merry trio.

Tom Draw, especially, though all his jokes were not such altogether as I can venture to insert in my chaste paragraphs, and though at times his oaths were too extravagantly rich to brook repetition, shone forth resplendent. No longer did I wonder at what I had before deemed Harry Archer's strange hallucination; Tom Draw is a decided genius—rough as a pine knot in his native woods—but full of mirth, of shrewdness, of keen mother wit, of hard horse sense, and last, not least, of the most genuine milk of human kindness. He is a rough block; but, as Harry says, there is solid timber under the uncouth bark enough to make five hundred men, as men go now-a-days in cities!

At ten o'clock, thanks to the excellent precautions of my friend Harry, we were all snugly berthed, before the whiskey, which had well justified the high praise I had heard lavished on it, had made any serious inroads on our understanding but not before we had laid in a quantum to ensure a good night's rest.

Bright and early was I on foot the next day, but before I had half dressed myself I was assured, by the clatter of the breakfast things, that Archer had again stolen a march upon me; and the next moment my bed-room door, driven open by the thick boot of that worthy, gave me a full view of his person—arrayed in a stout fustian jacket—with half a dozen pockets in full view, and Heaven only knows how many more lying perdu in the broad skirts. Knee-breeches of the same material, with laced half-boots and leather leggings, set off his stout calf and well turned ankle.

'Up! up! Frank,' he exclaimed, 'it is a morning of ten thousand; there has been quite a heavy dew, and by the time we are afoot it will be well evaporated; and then the scent will lie, I promise you! make haste, I tell you, breakfast is ready!'

Stimulated by his hurrying voice, I soon completed my toilet, and entering the parlor found Harry busily employed in stirring to and fro a pound of powder on one heated dinner plate, while a second was undergoing the process of preparation on the hearth-stone under a glowing pile of hickory ashes.

At the side-table, covered with guns, dog-whips, nipple-wrenches, and the like, Tim, rigged like his master, in half-boots and leggins, but with a short roundabout of velveteen, in place of the full-skirted jacket, was filling our shot-pouches by aid of a capacious funnel, more used, as its odor betokened, to facilitate the passage of gin or Jamaica spirits than of so sober a material as cold lead.

At the same moment entered mine host, togged for the field in a huge pair of cow-hide boots, reaching almost to the knee, into the tops of which were tucked the lower ends of a pair of trowsers, containing yards enough of buffalo-cloth to have eked out the main-sail of a North River sloop; a waistcoat and single-breasted jacket of the same material, with a fur cap, completed his attire; but in his hand he bore a large decanter filled with a pale yellowish liquor, embalming a dense mass of fine and worm-like threads, not very different in appearance from the best vermi-celli.

'Come, boys, come—here's your bitters,' he exclaimed; and, as if to set the example, filled a big tumbler to the brim, gulped it down as if it had been water, smacked his lips, and incontinently tendered it to Archer, who, to my great amazement, filled himself likewise a more moderate draught, and quaffed it without hesi-tation.

'That's good, Tom,' he said, pausing after the first sip; 'that's the best I ever tasted here; how old's that?'

'Five years!' Tom replied; 'five years last fall! Daddy Tom made it out of my own best apples—take a horn, Mr. Forester,' he added, turning to me—'it's first best cider sperrits—better a darned sight than that Scotch stuff you make such an eternal fuss about, toting it up here every time, as if we'd nothing fit to drink in the country!'

And so to my sorrow I did taste it—old apple whiskey, with

Lord knows how much snake-root soaked in it for five years!
They may talk about gall being bitter; but, by all that's wonderful, there was enough of the amari aliquid in this fonte, to me
by no means of leporum, to have given an extra touch of bitterness
to all the gall beneath the canopy; and with my mouth puckered
up, till it was like anything on earth but a mouth, I set the glass
down on the table; and for the next five minutes could do nothing
but shake my head to and fro like a Chinese mandarin, amidst
the loud and prolonged roars of laughter that burst like thunder
claps from the huge jaws of Thomas Draw, and the subdued and
half respectful cachinnations of Tim Matlock.

By the time I had got a little better, the black tea was ready,
and with thick cream, hot buckwheat cakes, beautiful honey, and
—as a stand by—the still venerable round, we made out a very
tolerable meal.

This done, with due deliberation Archer supplied his several
pockets with their accustomed load—the clean-punched wads in
this—in that the Westley Richards' caps—here a pound horn of
powder—there a shot-pouch on Syke's lever principle, with double
mouth-piece—in another, screw-driver, nipple-wrench, and the
spare cones; and, to make up the tale, dog-whip, dram-bottle, and
silk handkerchief in the sixth and last.

'Nothing like method in this world,' said Harry, slapping his
low-crowned broad-brimmed mohair cap upon his head; 'take
my word for it. Now, Tim, what have you got in the bag?'

'A bottle of champagne, sur,' answered Tim, who was now
employed slinging a huge fustian game-bag, with a network front,
over his right shoulder, to counterbalance two full shotbelts which
were already thrown across the other—'a bottle of champagne,
sur—a cold roast chicken—t' Cheshire cheese—and t' pilot biscuits.
Is your dram-bottle filled wi' t' whiskey, please sur?'

'Aye, aye, Tim. Now let loose the dogs—carry a pair of couples
and leash along with you; and mind you, gentlemen, Tim carries
shot for all hands; and luncheon—but each one finds his own
powder, caps, &c.; and any one who wants a dram, carried his own
—the devil a-one of you gets a sup out of my bottle, or a charge
out of my flask! That's right, old Trojan, isn't it?' with a good
slap on Tom's broad shoulder.

'Shot! Shot—why Shot! don't you know me, old dog?' cried

Tom, as the two setters bounded into the room, joyful at their release—'good dog! good Chase!' feeding them with great lumps of beef.

'Avast! there Tom—have done with that,' cried Harry; 'you'll have the dogs so full that they can't run.'

'Why, how'd you like to hunt all day without your breakfast —hey?'

'Here, lads! here, lads! wh-e-ew!' and followed by his setters, with gun under his arm, away went Harry; and catching up our pieces likewise, we followed, nothing loth, Tim bringing up the rear with the two spaniels fretting in their couples, and a huge black thorn cudgel, which he had brought, as he informed me, 'all t'way from bonny Cawoods.'

It was as beautiful a morning as ever lighted sportsmen to their labors. The dew, exhaled already from the long grass, still glittered here and there upon the shrubs and trees, though a soft fresh south-western breeze was shaking it thence momently in bright and rustling showers; the sun, but newly risen, and as yet partially enveloped in the thin gauze-like mists so frequent at that season, was casting shadows, seemingly endless, from every object that intercepted his low rays, and chequering the whole landscape with that play of light and shade, which is the loveliest accessory to a lovely scene; and lovely was the scene, indeed, as e'er was looked upon by painter's or by poet's eye—how then should humble prose do justice to it?

Seated upon the first slope of a gentle hill, midway of the great valley heretofore described, the village looked due south, toward the chains of mountains, which we had crossed the preceding evening, and which in that direction bounded the landscape. These ridges, cultivated half-way up their swelling sides, which lay mapped out before our eyes in all the various beauty of orchards, yellow stubbles, and rich pastures dotted with sleek and comely cattle, were rendered yet more lovely and romantic, by here and there a woody gorge, or rocky chasm, channelling their smooth flanks, and carrying down their tributary rills, to swell the main stream at their base. Toward these we took our way by the same road which we had followed in an opposite direction on the previous night—but for a short space only—for having crossed the stream, by the same bridge which we had passed on entering the village, Tom Draw pulled down a set of bars to the left, and strode out manfully into the stubble.

'Hold up, good lads!—whe-ew-whewt!' and away went the setters through the moist stubble, heads up and sterns down, like fox-hounds on a breast-high scent, yet under the most perfect discipline; for at the very first note of Harry's whistle, even when racing at the top of their pace, they would turn simultaneously, alter their course, cross each other at right angles, and quarter the whole field, leaving no foot of ground unbeaten.

No game, however, in this instance, rewarded their exertions; and on we went across a meadow, and two other stubbles, with the like result. But now we crossed a gentle hill, and, at its base, came on a level tract, containing at the most ten acres of marsh land, overgrown with high coarse grass and flags. Beyond this, on the right, was a steep rocky hillock, covered with tall and thrifty timber of some thirty years' grows, but wholly free of underwood. Along the left-hand fence ran a thick belt of underwood, sumach and birch, with a few young oak trees interspersed; but in the middle of the swampy level, covering at most five or six acres, was a dense circular thicket composed of every sort of thorny bush and shrub, matted with cat-briers and wild vines, and over-shadowed by a clump of tall leafy ashes, which had not as yet lost one atom of their foliage, although the underwood beneath them was quite sere and leafless.

'Now then,' cried Harry, 'this is the 'Squire's swamp-hole! Now for a dozen cock! hey, Tom? Here, couple up the setters, Tim; and let the spaniels loose. Now Flash! now Dan! down charge, you little villains!' and the well broke brutes dropped on the instant. 'How must we beat this cursed hole?'

'You must go through the very thick of it, consarn you!' exclaimed Tom; 'at your old work already, hey? trying to shirk at first!'

'Don't swear so! you old reprobate! I know my place, depend on it,' cried Archer; 'but what to do with the rest of you!—there's the rub!'

'Not a bit of it!' cried Tom—'here Yorkshire—Ducklegs—here, what's your name—get away you with those big dogs—atwixt the swamp-hole, and the brush there by the fence, and look out that you mark every bird to an inch! You, Mr. Forester, go in there, under that butter-nut; you'll find a blind track there, right through the brush—keep that 'twixt Tim and Mr. Archer; and keep your eyes skinned, do! there'll be a cock up before you're ten yards in. Archer, you'll go right through and I'll—'

'You'll keep well forward on the right—and mind that no bird crosses to the hill; we never get them, if they once get over. All right! In with you now! Steady, Flash; steady! hie up, Dan!' and in a moment Harry was out of sight among the brush-wood, though his progress might be traced by the continual crackling of the thick underwood.

Scarce had I passed the butter-nut, when, even as Tom had said, up flapped a woodcock scarcely ten yards before me, in the open path, and rising heavily to clear the branches of a tall thorn bush, showed me his full black eye, and tawny breast, as fair a shot as could be fancied.

'Mark!' halloaed Harry to my right, his quick ear having caught the flap of the bird's wing, as he rose. 'Mark cock—Frank!'

Well—steadily enough, as I thought, I pitched my gun up! covered my bird fairly! pulled!—the trigger gave not to my finger. I tried the other. Devil's in it, I had forgot to cock my gun! and ere I could retrieve my error, the bird had topped the bush, and dodged out of sight, and off—'Mark! mark!—Tim!' I shouted.

'Ey! ey! sur—Ay see's um!'

'Why, how's that, Frank?' cried Harry. 'Couldn't you get a shot?'

'Forgot to cock my gun!' I cried; but at the self-same moment the quick sharp yelping of the spaniels came on my ear. 'Steady, Flash! steady, sir! Mark!' But close upon the word came the full round report of Harry's gun. 'Mark! again!' shouted Harry, and again his own piece sent its loud ringing voice abroad. 'Mark! now a third! mark, Frank!'

And as he spoke I caught the quick rush of his wing, and saw him dart across a space, a few yards to my right. I felt my hand shake; I had not pulled a trigger in ten months, but in a second's space I rallied. There was an opening just before me between a stumpy thick thorn-bush which had saved the last bird, and a dwarf cedar; it was not two yards over; he glanced across it; he was gone, just as my barrel sent its charge into the splintered branches.

'Beautiful!' shouted Harry, who looking through a cross glade, saw the bird fall, which I could not. 'Beautiful shot, Frank! Do all your work like that, and we'll get twenty couple before night!'

'Have I killed him!' answered I, half doubting if he were not quizzing me.

'Killed him? of course you have; doubled him up completely! But look sharp! there are more birds before me! I can hardly keep the dogs down, now! There! there goes one—clean out of shot of me, though! Mark! mark, Tom! Gad, how the fat dog's running!' he continued. 'He sees him! Ten to one he gets him! There he goes—bang! A long shot, and killed clean!'

'Ready!' cried I. 'I'm ready, Archer!'

'Bag your bird, then. He lies under that dock leaf, at the foot of yon red maple! That's it; you've got him. Steady now, till Tom gets loaded!'

'What did you do?' asked I. 'You fired twice, I think!'

'Killed two!' he answered. 'Ready, now!' and on he went, smashing away the boughs before him, while ever and anon I heard his cheery voice, calling or whistling to his dogs, or rousing up the tenants of some thickets into which even he could not force his way; and I, creeping, as best I might, among the tangled brush, now plunging half thigh deep in holes full of tenacious mire, now blundering over the moss-covered stubs, pressed forward, fancying every instant that the rustling of the briers against my jacket was the flip-flap of a rising woodcock. Suddenly, after bursting through a mass of thorns and wild vine, which was in truth almost impassable, I came upon a little grassy spot quite clear of trees, and covered with the tenderest verdure, through which a narrow rill stole silently; and as I set my first foot on it, up jumped, with his beautiful variegated back all reddened by the sunbeams, a fine and full-fed woodcock, with the peculiar twitter which he utters when surprised. He had not gone ten yards, however, before my gun was at my shoulder and the trigger drawn; before I heard the crack I saw him cringe; and, as the white smoke drifted off to leeward, he fell heavily, completely riddled by the shot, into the brake before me; while at the same moment, whir-r-r! up sprung a bevy of twenty quail, at least, startling me for the moment by the thick whirring of their wings, and skirring over the underwood right toward Archer. 'Mark, quail!' I shouted, and, recovering instantly my nerves, fired my one remaining barrel after the last bird! It was a long shot, yet I struck him fairly, and he rose instantly right upward, towering high! high! into the clear blue sky, and soaring still, till his life left him in the air, and he fell like a stone, plump downward!

'Mark him! Tim!'

'Ey! ey! sur. He's a de-ad un, that's a sure thing!'

At my shot all the bevy rose a little, yet altered not their course the least, wheeling across the thicket directly round the front of Archer, whose whereabout I knew, though I could neither see nor hear him. So high did they fly that I could observe them clearly, every bird well defined against the sunny heavens. I watched them eagerly. Suddenly one turned over; a cloud of feathers streamed off down the wind; and then, before the sound of the first shot reached my ears, a second pitched a few yards upward, and, after a heavy flutter, followed its hapless comrade.

Turned by the fall of the leading birds, the bevy again wheeled, still rising higher, and now flying very fast; so that, as I saw by the direction which they took, they would probably give Draw a chance of getting in both barrels. And so indeed it was; for, as before, long ere I caught the booming echoes of his heavy gun, I saw two birds keeled over, and, almost at the same instant, the cheery shout of Tim announced to me that he had bagged my towered bird! After a little pause, again we started, and, hailing one another now and then, gradually forced our way through brake and brier toward the outward verge of the dense covert. Before we met again, however, I had the luck to pick up a third woodcock, and as I heard another double shot from Archer, and two single bangs from Draw, I judged that my companions had not been less successful than myself. At last, emerging from the thicket, we all converged, as to a common point, toward Tim; who, with his game-bag on the ground, with its capacious mouth wide open to receive our game, sat on a stump with the two setters at a charge beside him.

'What do we score?' cried I, as we drew near; 'what do we score?'

'I have four woodcocks, and a brace of quail,' said Harry.

'And I, two cock and a brace,' cried Tom, 'and missed another cock; but he's down in the meadow here, behind that 'ere stump alder!'

'And I, three woodcock and one quail!' I chimed in, naught abashed.

'And Ay'se marked doon three woodcock—two more beside yon big un, that measter Draa made siccan a bungle of—and all t' quail—every feather on um—doon i' t' bog meadow yonner—ooh! but we'se mak grand sport o't!' interposed Tim, now busily employed stringing bird after bird up by the head, with loops and buttons in the game-bag!

'Well done then, all,' said Harry. 'Nine timber-doodles and five quail, and only one shot missed! That's not bad shooting, considering what a hole it is to shoot in. Gentlemen, here's your health,' and filling himself out a fair-sized wineglass-full of Ferintosh, into the silver cup of his dram-bottle, he tossed it off; and then poured out a similar libation for Tim Matlock. Tom and myself, nothing loth, obeyed the hint, and sipped our modicums of distilled waters out of our private flasks.

'Now, then,' cried Archer, 'let us pick up these scattering birds. Tom Draw, you can get yours without a dog! And now, Tim, where are yours?'

'T' first lies oop in yon boonch of brachens, ahint t' big scarlet maple; and t'other—'

'Well! I'll go to the first. You take Mr. Forester to the other, and when we have bagged all three, we'll meet at the bog meadow fence, and then hie at the bevy!'

This job was soon done, for Draw and Harry bagged their birds cleverly at the first rise; and although mine got off at first without a shot, by dodging round a birch tree straight in Tim's face, and flew back slap toward the thicket, yet he pitched in its outer skirt, and as he jumped up wild I cut him down with a broken pinion and a shot through his bill at fifty yards, and Chase retrieved him well.

'Cleverly stopped, indeed!' Harry halloaed; 'and by no means an easy shot! and so our work's clean done for this place, at the least!'

'The boy can shoot some,' observed Tom Draw, who loved to bother Timothy; 'the boy can shoot some, though he does come from Yorkshire!'

'Gad! and Ay wush Ay'd no but gotten thee i' Yorkshire, measter Draa!' responded Tim.

'Why! what if you had got me there?'

'What? Whoy, Ay'd clap thee in a cage, and hug thee round t' feasts and fairs loike; and shew thee to t' folks at so mooch a head. Ay'se sure Ay'd mak a fortune o't!'

'He has you there, Tom! ha! ha! ha!' laughed Archer. 'Tim's down upon you there, by George! Now, Frank, do fancy Tom Draw in a cage at borough-bridge or Catterick fair! Lord! how the folks would pay to look at him! Fancy the sign board too! The Great American Man-Mammoth! Ha! ha! ha! But come, we must not stay here talking nonsense, or we shall do no good. Show me Tim, where are the quail?'

'Doon i' t' bog meadow yonner! joost i' t' slack, see thee, there!' pointing with the stout black-thorn; 'amang yon bits o' bushes!'

'Very well—that's it; now let go the setters; take Flash and Dan along with you, and cut across the country as straight as you can go to the spring head, where McTavish frightened the bull out of the meadow, under the pin-oak tree. Well! put the champagne into the spring to cool, and rest yourself there till we come; we shan't be long behind you.'

Away went Tim, stopping from time to time to mark our progress, and over the fence into the bog meadow we proceeded; a rascally piece of broken tussocky ground, with black mud knee-deep between the hags, all covered with long grass. The third step I took, over I went upon my nose, but luckily avoided shoving my gun-barrels into the filthy mire.

'Steady, Frank, steady! I'm ashamed of you!' said Harry; 'so hot and impetuous; and your gun too at the full cock; that's the reason, man, why you missed firing at your first bird, this morning. I never cock either barrel till I see my bird; and, if a bevy rises, only one at a time. The birds will lie like stones; and we cannot walk too slow. Steady, Shot, have a care, sir!'

Never, in all my life, did I see anything more perfect than the style in which the setters drew those bogs. There was no more of racing, no more of impetuous dash; it seemed as if they knew the birds were close before them. At a slow trot, their sterns whipping their flanks at every step, they threaded the high tussocks. See! the red dog straightens his neck, and snuffs the air.

'Look to! look to, Frank! they are close before old Chase!'

Now he draws on again, crouching close to the earth. 'Toho! Shot!' Now he stands! no! no! not yet—at least he is not certain! He turns his head to catch his master's eye! Now his stern moves a little; he draws on again.

There! he is sure now! what a picture—his black full eye intently glaring, though he cannot see anything in that thick mass of herbage; his nostril wide expanded, his lips slavering from intense excitement; his whole form motionless, and sharply drawn, and rigid, even to the straight stern and lifted foot, as a block wrought to mimic life by some skilful sculptor's chisel; and, scarce ten yards behind, his liver-colored comrade backs him—as firm, as stationary, as immovable, but in his attitude, how different! Chase feels the hot scent steaming up under his very nostril; feels it in every nerve, and quivers with anxiety to dash on his prey, even while perfectly restrained and steady. Shot, on the contrary, though a few minutes since he too was drawing, knows nothing of himself, perceives no indication of the game's near presence, although improved by discipline, his instinct tells him that his mate has found them. Hence the same rigid form, still tail, and constrained attitude, but in his face—for dogs have faces —there is none of that tense energy, that evident anxiety; there is no frown upon his brow, no glare in his mild open eye, no slaver on his lip!

'Come up, Tom; come up, Frank, they are all here; we must get in six barrels; they will not move; come up, I say!'

And on we came, deliberately prompt, and ready. Now we were all in line: Harry the centre man, I on the right, and Tom on the left hand. The attitude of Archer was superb; his legs, set a little apart, as firm as if they had rooted in the soil; his form drawn back a little, and his head erect, with his eye fixed upon the dogs; his gun held in both hands, across his person, the muzzle slightly elevated, his left grasping trigger guard; the thumb of the right resting upon the hammer, and the fore-finger on the trigger of the left-hand barrel; but, as he said, neither cocked. 'Fall back, Tom, if you please, five yards or so,' he said, as coolly as if he were unconcerned, 'and you come forward, Frank, as many; I want to drive them to the left, into those low red bushes;

that will do: now, then, I'll flush them; never mind me, boys,
I'll reserve my fire.'

And, as he spoke, he moved a yard or two in front of us, and
under his very feet, positively startling me by their noisy flutter,
up sprang the gallant bevy; fifteen or sixteen well grown birds,
crowding and jostling one against the other. Tom Draw's gun as
I well believe, was at his shoulder when they rose; at least his
first shot was discharged before they had flown half a rood, and
of course harmlessly: the charge must have been driven through
them like a single ball; his second barrel instantly succeeded, and
down came two birds, caught in the act of crossing. I am myself
a quick shot, too quick if anything, yet my first barrel was exploded a moment after Tom Draw's second; the other followed,
and I had the satisfaction of bringing both my birds down handsomely; then up went Harry's piece—the bevy being now twenty
or twenty-five yards distant—cocking it as it rose, he pulled the
trigger almost before it touched his shoulder, so rapid was the
movement; and, though scarcely passed between the two reports,
and almost on the instant two quail were fluttering out their lives
among the bog grass.

Dropping his butt, without a word, or even a glance to the
dogs, he quietly went on to load; nor indeed was it needed: at the
first shot they dropped into the grass, and there they lay as motionless as if they had been dead, with their heads crouched between their paws; nor did they stir thence till the tick of the
gunlocks announced that we again were ready. Then lifting up
their heads, and rising on their fore-feet, they sat half erect,
eagerly waiting for the signal.

'Hold up, good lads!' and on they drew, and in an instant
pointed on the several birds. 'Fetch!' and each brought his burthen
to our feet; six birds were bagged at the rise, and thus before
eleven o'clock we had picked up a dozen cock, and within one
of the same number of fine quail, with only two shots missed. The
poor remainder of the bevy had dropped, singly, and scattered,
in the red bushes, whither we instantly pursued them, and where
we got six more, making a total of seventeen birds bagged out
of a bevy twenty strong at first.

One towered bird of Harry's, certainly killed dead, we could
not with all our efforts bring to bag; one bird Tom Draw missed

clean, and the remaining one we could not find again; another dram of whiskey, and into Seer's great swamp we started; a large piece of woodland, with every kind of lying. At one end it was open, with soft black loamy soil, covered with docks and colt's-foot leaves under the shade of large but leafless willows, and here we picked up a good many scattered woodcock; afterward we got into the heavy thicket with much tangled grass, wherein we flushed a bevy, but they all took to tree, and we made very little of them; and here Tom Draw began to blow and labor; the covert was too thick, the bottom too deep and unsteady for him.

Archer perceiving this, sent him at once to the outside; and three times, as we went along, ourselves moving nothing, we heard the round reports of his large calibre. 'A bird at every shot, I'd stake my life,' said Harry; 'he never misses cross shots in the open;' at the same instant, a tremendous rush of wings burst from the thicket: 'Mark! partridge! partridge!' and as I caught a glimpse of a dozen large birds fluttering up, one close upon the other, and darting away as straight and nearly as fast as bullets, through the dense branches of a cedar brake, I saw the flashes of both Harry's barrels, almost simultaneously discharged, and at the same time over went the objects of his aim; but ere I could get up my gun the rest were out of sight. 'You must shoot, Frank, like lightning, to kill these beggars; they are ruffed grouse, though they call them partridges here: see! are they not fine fellows?'

Another hour's beating, in which we still kept picking up, from time to time, some scattering birds, brought us to the spring head, where we found Tim with luncheon ready, and our fat friend reposing at his side, with two more grouse, and a rabbit which he had bagged along the covert's edge. Cool was the Star champagne; and capital was the cold fowl and Cheshire cheese; and most delicious was the repose that followed, enlivened with gay wit and free good humor, soothed by the fragrance of the exquisite cheroots, moistened by the last drops of the Ferintosh qualified by the crystal waters of the spring. After an hour's rest, we counted up our spoil; four ruffed grouse, nineteen woodcocks, with ten brace and a half of quail beside the bunny, made up our score—done comfortably in four hours.

'Now we have finished for today with quail,' said Harry, 'but we'll get ten full couple more of woodcock; come, let us be stirring; hang up your game-bag in the tree, and tie the setters to the fence; I want you in with me to beat, Tim; you two chaps must both keep the outside—you all the time, Tom; you, Frank, till you get to that tall thunder-shivered ash tree; turn in there, and follow up the margin of a wide slank you will see; but be careful, the mud is very deep, and dangerous in places; now then, here goes!'

And in he went, jumping a narrow streamlet into a point of thicket, through which he drove by main force. Scarce had he got six yards into the brake, before both spaniels quested; and, to my no small wonder, the jungle seemed alive with woodcock; eight or nine, at the least, flapped up at once, and skimmed along the tongue of coppice toward the high wood, which ran along the valley, as I learned afterward, for full three miles in length— while four or five more wheeled off to the sides, giving myself and Draw fair shots, by which we did not fail to profit; but I confess it was with absolute astonishment that I saw two of those turned over, which flew inward, killed by the marvelously quick and un-erring aim of Archer, where a less thorough sportsman would have been quite unable to discharge a gun at all, so dense was the tangled jungle. Throughout the whole length of that skirt of coppice, a hundred and fifty yards, I should suppose at the utmost, the birds kept rising as it were incessantly—thirty-five, or, I think, nearly forty, being flushed in less than twenty minutes, although comparatively few were killed, partly from the difficulty of the ground, and partly from their getting up by fours and fives at once. Into the high wood, however, at the last we drove them: and there, till daylight failed us, we did our work like men. By the cold light of the full moon we wended homeward, rejoicing in the possession of twenty-six couple and a half of cock, twelve brace of quail—we found another bevy on our way home and bagged three birds almost by moonlight—five ruffed grouse, and a rabbit. Before our wet clothes were well changed, supper was ready, and a good blow-out was followed by sound slumbers and sweet dreams, fairly earned by nine hours of incessant walking.

A Red-Letter Day

By EDWYN SANDYS

THE SUN looms large above a sea of gauzy haze which piles like airy surf against the forest's rim. It is a windless, dreamy morning, rich with the magic of the Indian summer, the glory of painted leaves, the incense of ripe fruit. In the full fatness of autumn's latter days the world is songless, silent, fat. Those things which sleep—that drowse the long, white silence soon to be—are round well-nigh to bursting. Those things that durst not face the nip of steel-skied nights have fled to kindlier climes, while those other things which neither sleep nor flee are revelling in a rich abundance. They know what must come when Kee-way-din whines about their brushy eaves and the strange, cold white feathers fall. They know that the brushy and still leafy cover will be flattened and that the white wolf of the North will plunge and ramp and howl across far leagues of whiteness. They know the present business of their kind is to eat—eat till craws and skins are tight as drumheads, to wax fat because fat things do not freeze, while they can, if need be, doze for days when times are bad. All this eating and fat content is lazy business and sleep lasts long.

Up in the pleasant room, too, Sleep herself sits by a narrow cot upon which lies a silent figure. The kindly goddess knows that under her spell men do no wrong, and so, with light hand laid across his eyes, she sits and watches. Through open windows streams a scented air, fruity from near-by orchards and spiced with the breath of drying foliage.

Thump! A big apple parts its failing stem and strikes a hollow roof. The figure stirs and Sleep flies on soundless feet. Gradually

From "Sporting Sketches," The Macmillan Company.

the man gets himself dressed and then he looks the workman. The loose cord breeches closely match the broad-soled, flat-heeled knee boots; the sweater has the shade of the dried grass, and the old canvas coat admirably matches it. 'Tis a marvel, that coat—a thing of beauty and a joy forever to its owner—a horror unspeakable to his female kin. One had described it as 'A snarl of pockets held together by some remnants of filthy canvas,' and the owner had merely smiled. To him every stain upon it was a precious thing, a sign-board pointing to a dear-prized memory, and he wouldn't trade it for the mantle of Elijah. Once, a fair young thing, a frequent guest, who was clever at giving the last touch to ties and an invaluable adviser in regard to manicure sets, had declared she'd 'wash that horrid jacket!' and thus a glimmering possibility of a—a—oh! bother—it didn't come off, anyhow!

But the little woman who met him this morning was not of that sort. Once, long before, he had explained to her the difference between shooting for count and shooting as a sportsman should, and why there was no advantage in getting upon Bob White ground too early. She knew that fifteen birds was his limit so far as that particular game was concerned, and she also knew that the fifteen and perhaps some other game would load that coat at night, if all went well. So when he had nearly finished breakfast, she slipped away, to presently return amid a tumult of scratching claws and gusty breathing.

'Here—he—is—and—I—gave—him—just—three—bits!' she panted, as the strong brute strained at the chain in his eagerness.

'Down—you!' muttered the man, and as the quivering form sank promptly, he continued—'Mater mine, thou fibbest— he don't lick his chops that way after straight bread.'

'Merely an atom of gravy, dear—just a drop was kept, and the bread is so dry and he chews at it so.'

'Grease—faugh! will you never learn?' he growls, but his eyes are twinkling and he has to avert his face to keep from laughing outright, for this question of dog-fare is a rock upon which they regularly split. Right well he knows that Don has had his bread, a trifle of meat, and perhaps about a pint of soupy stuff to boot; but he wisely makes no further comment, for the mistake was lovingly made.

And so they fare forth, a varmint-looking team, both lean and hard, the long, easy stride of the man hinting of many days afoot, the corky action of the dog proving him sound and keen. 'Tis true his ribs show as though his hide covered a spiral spring, but his white coat has a satiny lustre, and he puts his feet down as though such things as thorns and burrs had never been. Behind them stands the little figure watching with moist eyes, for one is hers and the other belongs to one of hers. Though they went and returned one thousand times in safety,—still—still—it might—be. Wonderful are thy ways, O woman!

At the corner the tall figure halts and right-about-faces with military precision, the gun is whipped through the salute, and at the instant the white dog rises erect upon his hind feet. Both man and dog know that all these things must be done before rounding the turn, else the day would not be all it should. A kerchief flutters in the distance, then they pass in a few strides from town to country.

Before them spreads a huge pasture, beyond that a grove of mighty trees, and beyond that the shooting grounds—farm after farm, with here a bit of woods and there a thicket. For miles the country is the same, and through it all, in a bee-line, extends the double track of an important railway. Along either side of this runs a broad ditch, now bone-dry and bordered with low catbriers. These and the ripe weeds standing thickly in the angles of the rail-fences form rare good cover for scattered birds.

'Well, Mister,' says the man to the dog, 'guess you'd better have a pipe-opener right here.' He waves his hand and clucks softly, and the dog sails away over the short fall grass. A judge of dogs would watch this pointer with solid satisfaction. So smooth is his action and so systematic is his method of covering ground, that his tremendous speed is not at first apparent. But for all that he is a flier which few dogs can stay with, and best of all he can keep going for a week if need be.

Of course, he naturally was a fine animal, blessed with courage and brains a-plenty, but his owner's method—'keep sending 'em,' as he termed it—has done much to develop the speed. Needless to say, at the forward end of that dog is a nose—for woe unto the animal that would attempt such a clip without the very finest thing in the way of a smeller.

Half an hour later the man halts on top of a fence while the dog takes a roll. They are now on the edge of the good ground, and both feel just right after their preliminary canter. The man fills his pipe, gets it nicely going, then looks at the gun across his knees. It appears almost like a toy; but its small tubes are of the best and can throw lead with amazing power. Almost plain, but perfect of its pattern, that gun cost about three times what an unsophisticated person might guess as its price, and, as its owner declared, it was well worth the money.

'Now, Mister,' says the man, after a bit, 'there's rag-weed, standing corn, and thicket—which would you advise?' The dog sits up and stares with loving intentness, and the man continues—'When a lemon-headed fool-dog looks at me after that manner he certainly means standing corn, so here goes.' At the words he lets himself down, while the dog darts away. Soon he is into his regular stride and beating the ground with beautiful precision. The man watches and nods his head as he mutters, 'That rat-tailed rascal's going great guns to-day, he'll have 'em befo—' In the middle of a stride the dog has halted as though smitten by lightning. Some message of the air has reached that marvellous nose, and the grand brute stands as though carved in marble. There was no roading, no feeling for it, just an instantaneous propping and a breathless halt. 'That's funny,' mutters the man; 'I'd have sworn—ha!' There is an abrupt rising of a brown, hasty-winged thing which goes darting for a distant cover. At the sight the lazy man suddenly changes. The little gun leaps to the level, and before the butt has fairly touched the shoulder, the quick smokeless has hurled its leaden greeting. The bird goes down, unmistakably clean killed, while the dog slowly sinks to his haunches. As the man reloads, his face fairly shines with joy. 'Fifty yards if an inch,' he says to himself, 'and a bruising old hen at that. Who'd have expected a woodcock this time of year and away out here?' Then he goes to the dog and clucks him on.

As the dog has seen the bird fall, he merely makes a few bounds forward and again stiffens within two yards of an unusually large female woodcock—one of those choice birds only occasionally picked up at the tail-end of the season. 'Don't like that, eh?' laughs the man as he holds the bird near the dog's nose. The grand eyes are bulging with controlled excitement, but the shapely muzzle is wrinkled into an expression highly suggestive of disgust.

'Wish I understood that. It's funny, but you don't like a dead cock though you'll stop on 'em fast enough when alive—eh, old boy?' chuckles the man. 'Here, take it,' he says, and the dog obeys. 'Give it to me,' continues the man, and the dog promptly drops the bird into the hand, then wrinkles his chops as though an unpleasant flavor remained. It's a grand bird, old and fat, and the druggist's scales later prove it to weight full eight ounces, an extreme weight for even a female, which is larger than the male.

When again started, the dog sweeps away to a low-lying bit where the withered corn is taller and thicker. Here he circles, rapidly, stops for a moment, then stands looking at his master. The man moves over to him, and closely examining the ground presently detects half-a-dozen small hollows and a tiny brown feather. 'Flushed, eh?' he says to the dog, and evidently the latter agrees. Now the man's own tracks show plainly, there are no other bootmarks, nor has he seen an empty shell anywhere; so he knows the flush has been owing to natural cause. 'Mebbe hawk,' he says to himself. 'If so, where?' His eyes rove over all the surrounding cover and settle upon a clump of thicket in a corner. It is about far enough and certainly looks promising. Away goes the dog as though he could read the other's thoughts. As he nears the edge of the cover his style changes. The smooth gallop slows to a steady trot which presently alters to a majestic march. Higher and higher rises the square muzzle and up and up and up goes the tapering stern, while he steps ahead as though treading on tacks. Two yards from the cover he halts with lifted foot in the perfection of the old-fashioned stylish point. 'You beauty!' says the man, his eyes flashing with delight. Then he goes to the wonderful white form which, hard from set muscles, yet quivers with the tenseness of sudden excitement. The man, too, feels the magic of the situation. His eyes gleam and his teeth grip the pipe-stem as if they would shear it off. His heart thrills with rapturous anticipation and his strong hands grip the gun ready for instant action. Right well he knows that the pointer never draws like that or raises head and stern so high except for serious business. A dead leaf falls ticking through the tangling twigs, and at the first move of it the dog gives a convulsive twitch, while the gun flashes to the level and down again. A smile flickers in the keen eyes as the man moves a step nearer. No matter which way the game may go, he is bound to have a fair chance and he knows it. The cover is none too thick for even a straightaway drive, while all other directions mean the broad open. He clucks softly to the dog, but there is no responsive move—clearly this is a serious case. Could it possibly be a—? Ah! the roar of him, as he tore like a feathered shell through the densest growth! Oh! the beauty of him, as he curved into the mellow sunshine, his dainty crest and plumes flattened with speed. And, ho! the smashing thump of him as he hit the ground some thirty yards away. 'Twas a brave dash, Sir Ruffs, but risky withal, to dare that sunny open in defiance of trained eyes and nervously quick hands. Was it yonder mat of new clover-tips, or the red fruit of the brier-rose, which coaxed you here a fourth of a mile from your woodland stronghold?

But the dog is eager to be off. The languid air, scarce drifting in its lazy mood, is tattling something. There is some unfinished business, which the strong scent of the expected grouse had interrupted. Now, as the dog slants away, the square muzzle rises higher, and the eager stern whips frantically. Shorter and shorter grow the tacks, until the advance steadies to a straight line. Soon the gallop slows to a canter, a trot, a stately walk. With head and stern held high, on he marches until fifty yards have been covered. Then he suddenly stiffens, while the quivering nostrils search the air for positive proof. His erstwhile gusty breathing is muffled now, his jaws slowly open and close, while the marvellous nose seems to be feeling—feeling for a something rarely pleasant. Then on again, slower and slower, till he seems to fairly drift to his anchorage. Then his hind-quarters sink till he is almost on his hams.

Has he got them? Man, if you'd ever followed that dog, you'd know he had 'em. When you see that long draw and the squatting finish, bet your gun, or your wife, or whatever you prize most, that it's a bevy and a big one. Scattered birds he will pin in all sorts of fancy attitudes as he happens upon them, but when he gets right down to it, that signifies a wholesale order. The man moves up within a foot of the stiffened stern. For a moment the tenseness is dramatic—then—whur-r-r! Something like a mighty shell loaded with feathered baseballs appears to explode in a patch of dried grasses, and the air is filled with humming missiles. Even in the roar and electric rush the trained eyes mark slight

differences in coloration, and the trim tubes swing from one bird
to a second with a smooth rapidity which betokens years of practice. Two birds fall a few yards apart, and as they turn over in
the air, the man notes the flash of white and knows his lightning
choice has been correct. As he moves toward them, there is a
sudden hollow roar, and a lone bird rises from his very foot and
goes whizzing toward cover. The gun leaps to shoulder before
he can check it, but it is promptly lowered. 'Go on, you old seed-
hen, and do your best next year,' he chuckles, as the brown matron
strives to set herself afire by atmospheric friction. Her course is
wide of that taken by the brood, but he knows she'll call the
stragglers to her ere the shadows fall.

And they will be stragglers. Of the twenty strong beauties that
roared up ahead of the first point, her sweet, insistent 'Ca-loi-ee!
ca-loi-ee!' will muster but four when fence and thicket blur together in the scented dusk. Instead of doing as she had told them
time and time again—instead of lunging headlong into the convenient woods, her headstrong family has whirred across the
open and dropped here and there in the well-known resort, the
railroad ditch. Hither they have come day after day until the
awful, clattering trains have lost all terrors. In the broad ditch
are pleasant runways and much useful gravel of assorted sizes,
also cosey, sunny spots, the perfection of dust baths. Here, too,
are many unaccountable stores of grain, choicest of corn and
wheat, which seem in some miraculous manner to appear there
all ready for eating. What better place could there be?

The man looks at the dog and grins with unholy joy. The dog
looks at the man and seems to understand. Oh! they are a precious
pair of rascals, are these two.

'You old Judas,' says the man, 'we'll do things to 'em now.
It looks like fifteen straight—eh?'

And the dog cuts a couple of fool-capers, which is his method
of evincing a devilish approval. Then the pair of 'em move on
after the misguided birds.

Whur! Bing! Whur! Bing! It is almost too easy. Shooting in
that ditch where cover is barely knee-high with a high embank-
ment on one side and a stiff fence on the other, is something like
shooting into an enormous funnel—the shot has to go right. The
dog does little more than trot from point to point. Bird after bird

rises and is cut down with painless exactitude. Presently two start together, only to be dropped by a quick double-hail. Then one curves over the fence, but a rising mist of down feathers tells that he got it just in time. Then another pair, and as the second barrel sounds, a third rises. The cases leap from the gun, a hand flashes to and from a pocket—Burr!

'Here's where we quit—that makes fifteen,' says the man as the last bird is gathered. He sits down on a convenient knoll, pushes his hat back, and grins at the dog. That worthy, after a hesitating forward movement, which would indicate his belief that 'There's more,' also sits down and stares expectantly at the grimy coat. 'Yes, I'll give you half. You've done mighty well, and for once it's fifteen straight,' chuckles the man as he produces the sandwiches. The dog gets a bit more than half, for this is a red-letter day. Then the pipe comes out, and for half an hour the pair of 'em lounge in perfect peace. Little do they know or care about trouble. Twin tramps are they, heedless of the burdens of life, careless of its future. Sufficient for them that the afternoon sun is warm, the grass thick and dry. Naught care they for the five-mile homeward trudge, for neither is more than comfortably tired, and when they rise refreshed they will stride away as though they had just begun.

And the little woman will have two glorious meals all ready, for she knows what each can do in that line when thoroughly in earnest. And she will be almost sinfully happy, for the first glance will tell that things have gone well for at least one November day.

The Git Thar Stroke

By ERIC HATCH

THE MUSIC stopped. People clapped and smiled. Willie smiled too—a frozen, sickly smile. Boys and girls wandered out into the halls. One pair came and sat down in front of him on the steps which led to the indoor running track. He looked at the backs of their heads. The boy was his roommate, Bob—the girl, judging from the back of her head, was one of the pretty ones from Seattle. Bob would want to keep him up all night probably when he got in, telling him how wonderful she was. He looked away, fearful that his staring eyes would make her turn and she would know he'd been staring.

"Hello, you up there, why the crape?"

Startled, he looked down. Bob had gone. The girl was speaking to him. He gulped.

"Don't try and snoot me," she went on. "I know who *you* are."

Willie slipped down a step in astonishment. He wasn't so surprised at this girl's knowing who he was; it was her voluntarily speaking to him that made him slip.

"Who?" he said.

"You," she said, waving her hands in a carefree gesture that frightened him, "are the coxswain!"

"The *what?*"

"The coxswain; the little guy who steers the boat and makes the big boys work."

"Oh," said Willie, "the coxswain. No," he tried to laugh deprecatingly, "I'm not the coxswain."

"Why aren't you? You'd make a swell coxy. Look at you."

That was the one thing Willie Price didn't want to do. Ever

From Collier's Magazine, New York.

since he had entered Great Western his five-feet-two had made him feel ridiculous in this world of leathernecked, footballing giants.

He found himself wishing this extraordinarily beautiful girl wouldn't look at him, either. Rapidly he was getting beyond his depth. He gulped as he had at her first sally, and hoped she'd talk about something else, but she had the *idee fixe*.

"You must be the coxswain. I thought every man in this college was an athlete. Maybe you're a runner."

Willie Price had a sense of humor. For an answer he held up one short leg. "I'd have to run too much further than anybody else."

"Then why aren't you the cox?"

He thought this over. It had never occurred to him before there could be any field of sport where he could possibly fit in. It came to him that this girl wanted to believe he was the little guy who steered the boat. Suddenly he found her charming. Maybe if he let her think he was somebody she'd still want to talk to him. Why not? Certainly nobody else was the coxswain; he didn't think there was a man in the college who'd ever rowed anything except possibly a guide boat. He bent over.

"Ssh," he said. "I was just kidding you. I *am* the coxswain."

"I knew it! How did you make out last spring?"

A poser! Willie Price thought hard. For the three and a half years he'd been at Great Western no girl, except one big motherly horse of a person, had, until now, shown the slightest interest in him. He had inspiration.

"We won," he said, "every race we started in."

Then he saw his roommate coming toward them. It threw him into a panic. "Don't talk to Bob about me being coxswain," he said, "it's a sore subject with him."

"Well, I never!"

"No, please don't. You see he—he wasn't on the crew last year."

"I get you, coxy. G'-by."

She was gone as the orchestra started playing, leaving Willie feeling as though a large wave had left him washed up on a beach.

He sat listening to the music and watching the dancers and dreaming. Once the girl passed him and smiled. He got up to cut in, but someone else was there first so he went back to his step. The next time he saw her he did cut and they sat out in a car and talked.

He learned that her name was Adele Adams and that she came from New York and that she was rats about crew. Before they went in she made him promise to take her to tea when he came East with his crew for the Poughkeepsie regatta. He promised enthusiastically and then somehow he kissed her. It wasn't until he was back in his room, hours later, that he realized that he would probably never see her again. In his delirious state he had forgotten that his gleaming shell and sweating, half-naked crew were as chimerical as the galleys of Aeneas.

"Go to New York in the spring!"

He put his hand in his trouser pocket and pulled out three dollars and forty cents. The remains of his furnace-tending money for the week. Gleaming shell?

"Oh, shoot!" he said, and got into bed with his clothes on, too disgusted to bother about taking them off.

The next morning he told his roommate what he had done. Bob Ream, two-hundred-pound varsity guard, put both hands on Willie's shoulders. Willie thought he was going to kid the life out of him.

"It's all wrong," said Bob.

Willie squirmed. "I know. I shouldn't have done it."

"All wrong." Bob's mind worked slowly. "All wrong."

"I know it's all wrong, but don't keep on telling me so."

Then if it hadn't been for those great hams on his shoulders Willie would have gone through the floor.

"This here college *ought* to have a crew! You were a good kid to stick up for it. Why haven't we got a crew, anyway?"

"Ha, ha," said Willie Price, "because nobody in this dump has ever seen one and because the whole college hasn't got enough money to buy a life preserver."

"We oughta have one. Yale's got one and we play just as good football as Yale."

"Sure," said Willie, "let's get one. You can be the boat."

Ream was still thinking aloud. "We got men enough here to row the Mauretania. Look at Harrison and Jeffries. Couldn't those babies pull some though? Look at me!" He swelled up his giant muscles until they looked like oranges in an ostrich's neck.

He was serious. Suddenly Willie Price knew that what he wanted more than anything else in the world was to be coxswain of Great Western's varsity crew. He rolled the words in his head. Coxswain of the varsity! Ream was serious; maybe he could get Jeffries and Harrison interested too. Maybe . . . Not to be on the side-lines any more when the college went out to battle. To be in it, to have people cheering for *him*, too!

A picture flashed before his eyes; silver strip of ribbon, arrow-like streaks of mahogany piercing its water, trains on the bank jammed with shrieking men and women, tooting yachts along the side of the course, eight men before him bending, catching, straightening, bending, catching, straightening, panting, groaning, sweating, and somewhere on the bank, on the yachts, in the observation train, Adele Adams crying, "Great Western! Come on, Great Western! Come on, Willie Price!"

The picture faded. He became aware that Bob Ream was saying something that needed answering. He just caught the end of it . . . "—and you've got brains, Willie. I'll talk to Harrison and Jeffries. You see if you can't raise the jack somewhere and put it across with the president."

Willie Price suddenly had a feeling it might happen, but there was one thing more to be made sure of. He looked up at his roommate.

"Can I be cox, if we do it?"

Bob Ream picked him up like a feather, held him up to the light of the window and pretended to look through him. He said, "Who do you think we'd want for cox, Fat Lewis?"

The president had been difficult at first, but possibly because Price, who stood high in his classes, had never asked him for anything before, he relented and gave crew his sanction. After Willie'd been at him for six weeks he even went so far as to say he'd appropriate money for the college to buy a second-hand shell if the students would finance the rest of the expenses themselves.

Willie became a changed man. Never had the people of that college town had such warm houses as they did the rest of that winter. Never did a furnace tender save as much money as did Willie Price. Never had the library undergone such a combing for works on rowing. Then, one day in early March, the shell arrived.

The whole college went to the freight station to unload it. With their band they led it through town to the boathouse and there, with Willie Price acting as master of ceremonies, it was launched.

The coxswain of the varsity took his place at the rudder ropes. As Bob Ream, stroke, prepared to step into the dainty bobbing craft, Willie Price took a deep, deep breath of pride. It was fortunate; Bob Ream did more than step into it. Untutored, he stepped right through it and the waters of old Caluga were cold and very wet as the coxswain of the varsity sank with Aeneas' galley into the depths of them.

The shell was retrieved. So was Willie Price. Both of them suffering from submersion and the shell with a hole in its bottom just the size of Bob Ream's foot which, as feet go, was a big foot. The janitor was sent for. The janitor was official crew coach because back in the eighties he'd worked as watchman for the Harlem Boat Club in New York.

With canvas, tacks and shellac he patched the hole while the entire college watched.

After which, Aeneas' galley and her crew made their maiden voyage downstream and passed out of sight around a bend in the river. Late that afternoon they were found, still going downstream, miles away, and still later a wagon brought them back to slink like rabbits into their rooms. Without the slightest doubt it was the worst day of Willie Price's life. From then on he was known to the college as "Bubbles," and his gallant crew grew fit and hard from wiping out with blood the slurs and insults that deluged them.

It was the janitor-coach who solved the problem.

"Listen, men!" he said, standing on the boat-house steps. "The idea is for everybody to begin to row at the same time and then to keep on doing it, see?"

Bob Ream spoke up, "Why didn't you tell us that?" he said. "How were we expected to know?"

Willie Price went out and bought a life preserver, but the crew learned to row inside the boat-house, sitting on the floor with the sweeps held in rough brackets beside them. The vision of the silver ribbon and Adele Adams grew dim, but Willie Price had nerve and the miracle happened. A month later the varsity crew were actually seen on the water by an unbelieving freshman and they were rowing *upstream!*

Elated by this achievement, without thought for anything but his dream, Willie entered his crew for the great race at Poughkeepsie, where the finest eights of the country fought it out under the high span of the old bridge.

The entry was accepted by a courteous committee with wonder and private advice. It was expensive to ship a shell and eight men three thousand miles. Willie'd never thought about the money. It harrowed him.

As the weeks passed and in their rough way the crew learned to put their brute strength into their strokes and to send the slim shell skimming over the water at a speed so great hardly any of them could understand it, the money thing began to haunt Willie Price. He spoke to Bob Ream about it.

"Hell," said Bob. "We'll git across somehow. If the boat goes freight we'll go freight too."

That settled that. Willie tried to get subscriptions from the college, from the town, but all he got was ten dollars. He began to lose weight and not to sleep nights. The honor of Great Western was at stake. It was up to him to pull it off, somehow. He grew thinner and thinner, but this didn't worry him because it meant he'd be lighter in the shell and that was good.

More weeks passed and the crew grew disheartened. One or two of them wanted to call it off, but Ream and Jeffries took care of them. Price offered to put up the money himself from his own slim store of savings—they wouldn't let him. Then two weeks before the day of the race the president sent for the crew to come to his office. An anonymous donation had been received; it covered the freightage of the shell. The college went wild.

Ten dust-covered men crawled wearily from a freight car in the Poughkeepsie siding. Ten dust-covered men who had lived in a freight car for three thousand miles. Ten dust-covered men whose total wealth in all the world was four dollars and forty cents and three other dollars that the tenth man had heard was what it cost to take a girl to tea in New York.

Out of the car on their shoulders came a long shell. Ten dust-covered men carried it to a waiting wagon, rode with it to a boat-house on the bank of the broad river. Nine dust-covered men rolled out on the floor beneath it and fell asleep. The tenth took a train to New York.

Willie Price waited for his lady in the living room. At last she swept in. Willie Price thought he had never seen anything so lovely. Adele Adams thought she had never seen anything so odd. She wanted to laugh. Then she saw the way he was looking at her and she didn't want to laugh. Somehow she felt suddenly that in some way she was responsible for his being there in those awful moth-eaten clothes. She found herself wanting to cry, now, at the hopelessness of him.

"I'm Willie Price. I've come East with my crew for the regatta."

The beautiful eyes were staring at him. He had dreamed of them so much that now they made him dizzy. He felt, unaccountably, a little sick.

"You've come East!" There was an odd expression of half wonder, half pity on her face as she took in the full grotesquery of his slept-in clothes. "You've come East!"

"Yes, with my crew." They were facing each other in the middle of the room. Suddenly the months of waiting and dreaming and remembering that night in the car outside the gym overcame him. He wanted to tell her all about it; getting the shell and teaching the men to row and trying to raise the money, and about the awful furnace-like nights when the freight car had seemed like a dry, scorching prison.

"Adele—oh, Adele, ever since that night . . ."

He broke off and started toward her, his arms out.

She sat down, avoiding his arms so gracefully that her gesture seemed hardly a rebuke.

"Not now, Coxy. Don't, don't spoil things now. Please."

"But that night . . ."

"I know." She remembered that night. It had meant something to her too, but he'd seemed different. He'd looked like anybody else then and it had been so far away. He sat down beside her on the sofa and took her hand.

"You said you'd go out to tea with me."

The idea of actually being seen at the Plaza or the Ritz with him! She shivered.

"I think it would be nicer to have tea here. Just the two of us, don't you?"

He didn't think so, but then when he'd come prepared to take her in his arms and had been left standing like—like . . . He felt like a sentence without a verb and gave up.

They had tea. All through it he thought about how this afternoon should have been, the way he'd planned it. When she shook hands with him at the door, just as though there'd never been any night with a prom and a car and a gym, his cup of misery flowed over and he knew why she had wanted to have tea at home.

"Oh, shoot!" he said and walked out onto the street.

When he was gone Adele Adams locked herself in her room. That evening she told her brother about Willie Price. Tom Adams rowed number four in the Cornell boat. When she had finished he stared at her.

"You say he looked as if he'd crossed the country in a freight car?"

"He did. He said they all did."

"Three thousand miles in a freight car just for one race!" Tom Adams wondered for the first time if maybe the Eastern crews hadn't perhaps guessed wrong about "the goofy lumberjacks."

They were on the way to the starting line. Willie Price looked at the eight men in front of him and felt something hammer inside of him. As each crew pushed off from its float, a cheer rang out. His crew too had been cheered—more loudly than all the rest, for the story of their coming had got about. It rang in his ears like the trumpeting of angels. He reached over and patted Bob Ream's bony knee. He had never in all his life imagined he could feel quite as he did in that moment.

As they half drifted toward the starting line they passed close to one of the big yachts. The thing that was hammering in him now pounded. He had recognized a girl leaning over the rail. He'd show her! He shut his teeth with a snap. How was he to know that, seeing him there leading his eight half-naked giants to battle, his matted clothes of the day before had been forgotten and to the girl at the rail he seemed, miraculously not too unlike a god. Then he heard her crying out and his heart nearly stopped. She was leaning far out now:

"Come on, Great Western! Come on, Willie Price!"

His head swam. He could hardly believe it. Grinning from ear to ear he took one hand off the ropes and waved.

A girl called out as they drifted past:

"What stroke do you row, Great Western? The Oxford or the . . ."

The rest of the wise crack was lost by Jeffries' booming answer:

"Ma'am, I reckon we rows the git thar stroke!"

They were at the starting line. Somebody fired a gun and like a great bird freed of its bonds, the shell leaped out over the water. The next second its stride was broken. Harlan, up in the bow, had caught a crab!

When they got going again they were last. Willie heard the yachts tooting. They seemed to be mocking him. He saw Adele Adams as she had leaned over the rail, calling to him to win. Far ahead now, the other boats were racing. His mind snapped to a decision. To hell with this so-many-strokes-to-the-minute racket. He cried to his stroke:

"Row, Bob, row! The fastest stroke you can set—all the way!"

Ream, whose face had gone white, nodded and gave a great pull on his sweep—the shell shot forward. Faster and faster he set the stroke; the others followed him, wondering vaguely if Price had gone cuckoo.

The long sweeps bent under the strain. Now and then one of them would splash as the terrific strength of the men came into its own for the first time.

Up the line rushed the boat, gaining, gaining. Now it had come even with the last two boats. Now it had passed them and was catching up on the others.

Into the stretch of water that marked the finish it came, two lengths behind the leaders, gaining, gaining. Behind each giant stroke of its groaning crew lay three thousand miles of built-up will. Three thousand miles of prairie heat and dust and rotten food and freight-car boards to sleep on. Three thousand miles between them and home, and the only way to get back was to win.

Catching, straightening, bending, catching, straightening, bending, panting groaning, sweating. Willie Price had forgotten about crying the cadence with "Stroke!—Stroke!—Stroke!" The people on the yachts wondered. They could hear him, the pleading, the urging, the driving in his voice:

"Bob!—Pat!—Jeff!"

"Jim!—Bill!—Jack!"

"Row!—God!—Row!"

"Bob!—Pat!—Jeff!"

Eight giants lifting a pointed boat through the water—a maniac in the stern driving them till their muscles stood out like cords and their faces grew ashen under the strain: "The git thar stroke!"

Under the bridge flashed the shell, Great Western, by half a length, in the lead.

Trains on the bank jammed with shrieking men and women. . . . Sirens on the yachts blaring. . . . The river a tumult. . . .

Somewhere in Willie Price's touseled mind was a picture he'd seen of a winning crew, collapsed over their oars at the finish. He could let go now. Without ceremony he pitched forward on his face—out cold.

Bob Ream spat over the side and picked the coxswain up in his arms.

"The little cuss is done in."

Then he saw a piece of paper in the bottom of the shell. It had fallen out of Price's shirt when he keeled over. He absently picked it up. The man behind him said, "Betcha young Willie thinks he won the race!"

Ream looked at the paper and started. It was a personal receipt to William Price from the freight company that had shipped the shell. Suddenly he knew why the man in his arms was so light. He turned around.

"Yeah?" he said. "Well, he did."

A tender put out from the big yacht near the finish line. A girl in the bow was telling the sailor at the engine to hurry; her eyes were glued on the Great Western shell, nearing the landing with that figure still crumpled in the stern.

And then, as the great crew clambered out of her and laid the coxswain of the varsity on the dry hard boards of the float, Aeneas' galley, far more worn out than any of her crew, opened up her seams and with great dignity passed to the bottom of the Hudson.

DATE DUE

OC 22

FEB

EB 21

DEC 7

MAR 9

OCT 16